TYNE AND TIDE

TYNE AND TIDE

A CELEBRATION OF THE RIVER TYNE

DAVID ARCHER

Daryan Press
2003

First published in 2003 by
Daryan Press
2 Welburn Close, Ovingham, Northumberland NE42 6BD
www.daryanpress.co.uk

ISBN: 0-9544944-0-7

Printed by Kripps
The Netherlands

CONTENTS

Page

Illustrations
Acknowledgements

Preface — a glimpse of Paradise   xi

1. The waters of Tyne: river hydrology   1

2. The Tyne in flood   16

3. The changing Tyne valley and river channel   29

4. The rape of the Tyne: gravel extraction   44

5. The living Tyne: river ecology   59

6. The Tyne fishery   73

7. Fishing the Tyne   90

8. The death of the Tyne: river pollution   105

9. Regeneration of the Tyne estuary   123

10. Kielder Water: white elephant or white knight?   138

11. The sporting Tyne   157

12. The port of Tyne   172

13. Tyne industries   190

14. Getting across the Tyne   207

15. Thomas Bewick: the art of crossing the Tyne   226

16. The Tyne in music, song and verse   234

Index   265

PLATES

1. Portrait of the Tyne bridges on the wall of the remote tea house in the Bolan Pass of Balochistan. My wife, Bernice, stands by the unglazed window whilst goats shelter from the heat in the room beyond. *(Photo: David Archer)*

2. The Tyne bridges in twilight *(Photo: Graham Hancock, Robertsons of Gosforth)*

3. A typical river flow gauging station at Redebridge on the River Rede, showing the recorder house, the line of level gauges, the cableway pillar and the gauging weir. *(Photo David Archer)*
4. Manual and recording raingauges overlooking Kielder forest and moorland, high in the North Tyne catchment. *(Photo: David Archer)*

5. Haltwhistle from the air near the height of the flood on 31 January 1995. Kilfrosts is the white roofed building in mid picture and Crown Berger the larger complex beyond the old railway embankment *(Photo: Airfotos, Gosforth)*

6. Sequence showing the progressive breach of a flood embankment, from top: the flood cuts a deep channel on the downstream face: blocks of earth shear and collapse into the channel: shrubs and trees are undermined and carried off: the breach progressively widens and a turbulent turbid torrent surges through. *(Photo: Paul Elwell and Paul Davies, White Young and Green, Consulting Engineers)*

7. The sculpture marking a spring, said to be the source of the South Tyne - but perhaps raw nature is sufficient monument to itself. *(Photo: David Archer)*
8. The South Tyne looking downstream from Lambley Viaduct showing the typical natural sequence of riffles (foreground and distance) and pool (between the riffles). This sequence is repeated in natural channels and is vital to geomorphological and ecological processes. *(Photo: David Archer)*

9. The River North Tyne above Kielder showing bank erosion associated with active meander development. *(Photo: David Archer)*
10. The South Tyne at Featherstone Castle – a zone of the river that has experienced high rates of erosion and deposition during the last fifty years. *(Photo: David Archer)*

11. The River Tyne below Hexham Bridge, from an early 20th century painting. Note the absence of a fall in level through the bridge opening or downstream from the bridge and the gravel bar in the downstream channel.
12. The River Tyne below Hexham Bridge in July 2000 showing the steep drop and deep pool below the bridge induced by downstream gravel extraction from 1930s to 1970s, and the extensive structural protection measures and fish pass. *(Photo: David Archer)*

13. Alien invaders at Ovingham; the towering flower heads of giant hogweed with a lower level cover of Himalayan balsam, not yet in flower. *(Photo: David Archer)*
14. A fisherman leans his rod against a dense thicket of Japanese knotweed which overhangs the river bank at Wylam. Wylam bridge is in the background. *(Photo: David Archer)*

15. That well-known fisherman, Jack Charlton, holds a fine spring salmon caught at Broomhaugh on the Bywell Syndicate Waters. *(Photo: Aidan Pollard)*

16. A fresh-run 12 lb salmon caught at Bardon Mill on Tyneside Anglers Syndicate waters on the South Tyne on 31 May 1999. David Hetherington is photographed with his fish before returning it to the river. *(Photo: David Carrick)*

17. The Howdon treatment works, looking west. The original primary treatment works is in the rectangular block to the right (N) of the jetty, with primary settlement in the eight striped-roof buildings and four sludge holding tanks nearer the river. Secondary treatment is now carried out in the white rectangular plant in the middle distance and the process completed in the 16 circular sedimentation tanks.*(Photo: AirFotos Ltd)*

18. The 1986 Tall Ships Race – a pivotal point in the attitude of Tynesiders to their river *(Photo: Richard Pelmea, by courtesy of Graham Hancock, Robertsons of Gosforth)*

19. The straggling 'dragon' arms of Kielder Water show where the lower reaches of tributary burns have been flooded. *(Photo: Northumbrian Water)*

20. The scour valves discharging at its maximum rate of 44 cumecs from Kielder during initial testing in 1982
21. A peaceful summer's evening by the lake. *(Photo: David Archer)*

22. Sailing at Derwent Reservoir. The start at the Flying Fifteen class UK Inland Championship, May 1998. *(Photo: Robin Jefferson)*

23. Canoeing on the North Tyne. Shooting the rapids at Barrasford during The Tyne Tour, 1994. *(Photo: Barbara Pike)*

24. The picturesque and secluded bridge over the Rede, about one mile northeast of West Woodburn and known as East Woodburn bridge, lies on what was a highway leading from Hexham to Elsdon. The flattish main arch of 62 feet span, is the result of a partial rebuilding in 1832. *(Photo: David Archer)*

25. West Wylam Railway Bridge, known locally as 'The Points Bridge'. This single-span wrought-iron arch railway bridge of 1876, built for the former Scotswood, Newburn & Wylam Railway, is now part of the popular Riverside Park route for walkers and cyclists between Prudhoe and Newburn. *(Photo: David Archer)*

NOTES ON CONTRIBUTORS

Tony Champion worked for MAFF on the population dynamics of salmon before migrating north in 1974 to take up a fisheries management position with the Northumbrian River Authority. He was appointed Fisheries Manager of Northumbrian Water in 1980 and as such was accountable for the successes and failures of the region's fisheries until 1991 when he moved on into fisheries consultancy.

Tony Foster worked for over 26 years for Northumbrian Water and its predecessor, the Tyneside Joint Sewerage Board. As a young civil engineer he worked on the design of the Jarrow and Howdon works, and was involved from time to time with the scheme later in his career as a Divisional General Manager, as Operations Director of Northumbrian Water Ltd, as Group Planning Director and as Managing Director of Entec Europe, NW's international environmental and engineering consultancy business. He lives in Ovingham close to the River Tyne; too close sometimes - as the river level crept up the road where he lives in the aftermath of Hurricane Charlie in 1986, he was accused by neighbours of "...bringing his work home with him"!

Roger Inverarity is Water Quality Officer for the Environment Agency, Northeast Region with special emphasis on understanding and improving the quality of the Tyne estuary. He is also an enthusiastic Tyne fisherman.

Sam James was formerly Reader in Environmental Engineering at the University of Newcastle Upon Tyne, where he developed post graduate courses and research. He is a biologist turned mathematical modeller, with especial interest in modelling water pollution.

Anne Lewis is Conservation Officer for the Tyne catchment, Environment Agency, Northeast Region.

Stafford Linsley was born to a coal-mining family in County Durham. He completed a student apprenticeship with a Tyneside engineering company and studied Mechanical Engineering at the University of Sheffield, gaining a B.Eng. and a PhD. After four years in engineering research and development in industry, and three years as a lecturer in thermodynamics, he joined the Adult Education department (now the Centre for Lifelong Learning) of the University of Newcastle as a lecturer in Industrial Archaeology in 1971, remaining in that position until his retirement in 2002.

Malcolm Newson is Professor of Physical Geography at the University of Newcastle and has spent more than thirty years researching the hydrology and geomorphology of river systems. He is heavily involved with Research and Development projects for the Environment Agency in connection with sustainable river management.

Aidan Pollard is a Tyne salmon fisherman and member of the Management Team of Bywell Salmon Syndicate.

Paul Younger was born nearer to the River Tyne than anyone else he knows — the last house before the river in Hebburn Quay. When he's not singing Geordie songs, or disturbing his family with Northumbrian pipes, whistles or one of several stringed instruments, he works as a Professor in the School of Civil Engineering and Geosciences at the University of Newcastle, where his research specialism is the prevention of mine water pollution.

Contributors to Tyne and Tide are pleased to support the work of *WaterAid*. Conditions of pollution, disease and death such as occurred on Tyneside in the 19th century (Chapter 8) still persist amongst the world's poorest people. *WaterAid* is the only major charity dedicated exclusively to the provision of safe domestic water, sanitation and hygiene education amongst such communities.

For more information contact: wateraid@wateraid.org.uk or visit www.wateraid.org.uk

ACKNOWLEDGEMENTS

My greatest thanks must go to my friends and former colleagues who have kindly agreed to contribute chapters on their fields of special expertise. Brief notes on contributors are provided in the preceding section. I am particularly grateful to Roger Inverarity of the Environment Agency who read and commented on several chapters and provided suggestions to improve clarity and readability.

Many former colleagues at the Environment Agency helped directly or indirectly in the preparation of the book. I am grateful to Graeme Warren, the Area Manager for Northumbria for allowing me to badger his staff to bring my knowledge up to date, including:

Rachel Merrix for information on the Kielder Scheme (Chapter 10);
Viv Turner for supply of hydrological data (Chapter 1 and 2) ;
Harry Harrison for information relating to gravel extraction (Chapter 4);
Richard Robinson, Jed Lee and Tony Hardwick (now with JBAConsulting) for information on flooding (Chapter 2);
Jon Shelley for his knowledge of fisheries and fishing (Chapters 6 and 7);
Barbara Pike for a wide spectrum of information on river recreation (Chapter 11).

I am also indebted to former colleagues at Northumbrian Water, particularly Jim Prentice, John Lackenby and Bill Williamson for updated information on water resources, sewage disposal and recreation.

Research for the book brought many fascinating contacts from the world of recreation on the Tyne, including Tony Follows, Russell Kernohan and Chris Grabham(rowing), Eddie Palmer (canoeing) and Nigel Ruffle (sailing). With respect to 'the rape of the Tyne', special thanks are due to Jimmy Atkinson, Fred Stokoe, and Bob Lunn, retired workers in the gravel industry.

Contributors have also in some instances expressed thanks for specific help with their chapters.

Finally I wish to acknowledge the debt I have to Bernice, my wife, who has been the principal 'lay reader' of the text to ensure that it is within the grasp of the average reader. She suggested many ways of simplifying the text without loss of accuracy as well as shepherding my straying grammar and punctuation. Besides, Bernice has accompanied me on many enjoyable journeys along the Tyne as well as along more spectacular — though no more interesting rivers — on four continents.

David Archer
March 2003

Thanks are recorded to the following for kindly permitting the reproduction of figures and plates.

Airfotos Ltd for Plates 5 and 17 and the back cover;
Beamish, the North of England Open air Museum, for Figs. 9.1, 12.4, 13.3, 14.1 and 14.4;
Environment Agency for Fig. 6.1;
Northumbrian Water for Plate 19;
Tyne and Wear Museums for Fig. 10.2;
Jimmy Atkinson for Fig. 4.2;
David Carrick for Plate 16;
Graham Hancock (Robertson's of Gosforth) for Plates 2 and 18;
Robin Jefferson for Plate 22;
Mike Linklater (Kinghorn Davies) for Fig. 8.3;
Barbara Pike for Plate 23.

PREFACE – A GLIMPSE OF PARADISE

Do you know that those who dwell by the banks of the Tyne live in Paradise? It is common knowledge that it is only the Pennine ridge which separates the Tyne from Eden, but it was far away and a few years ago that I received unexpected confirmation of the blessed state in which we Tyneside dwellers live.

I was working in Balochistan, the western desert province of Pakistan which borders on Iran and Afghanistan. I was taken there by my hydrological profession as an adviser to the provincial government on the setting up of a Bureau of Water Resources. (The less water one has, the more important does it become.)

On a particular occasion we were travelling down the Bolan Pass from the comparatively cool plateau of Quetta to the town of Sibi on the edge of the hot and dusty Kachhi Plains. It is one of the few routes from the mountains and plateaux of Central Asia to the rich lowlands of the River Indus and one which has been followed by a succession of invaders. The pass itself is a most barren place with bare rock and scattered scrub vegetation. One of the hottest places on earth, summer temperature in the shade commonly reaches 50° C. For most of its length the Bolan River is dry; the rare summer storms in the wadis disappear under a wide sweep of boulders, in some places five kilometres wide. Near the foot of the pass the valley narrows to a canyon-like gorge and here the Bolan river appears, pure and perennial from the bed. A cluster of palms leans lazily over the river and pink oleander is reflected in clear pools; it is an oasis starkly contrasted with the bare buff sandstone of the enclosing cliffs.

We pulled in at a tea house. It was not at all like the familiar teahouse of the Tyne valley such as our favourites, Pam's Jiggery Pokery at Mickley and Barbara's Winships at Ovington, with tea in china mugs served with buttered scones and cakes. This tea house was a rough shelter, where the sweaty and coal-stained *chaiwalla* brewed up the milky tea over a smoky fire and served it in chipped enamel mugs. However, it provided shade and replenishment for lost liquid.

As we sat there enjoying the ambience, our eyes fell on a line of faded prints on the rough plastered walls. They were scenes of an Eastern paradise, cool mountain streams flowing through green meadows, tumbling waterfalls, peacocks and colourful birds flying through shady thickets. Then, at the end our startled eyes came upon a more familiar scene. Above two chai-drinking, bearded and turbaned Baloch tribesmen, was a picture of the River Tyne and its magnificent bridgescape (Plate 1). By what route the picture of the Tyne reached this remote and desolate teahouse in Balochistan and was selected to join such exalted company, one cannot imagine. But the message we received was that if

ix

you live in poverty in the midst of the scorching desert, then the banks of the River Tyne are such a place as you might hope one day to inhabit. I offer my experience as evidence that the River Tyne flows in Paradise.

However, seen from a nearer perspective, the Tyne is no paradise of eternal and unchanging perfection. This paradise has a history, always interesting but sometimes sordid. Paradise has been lost and has had to be rewon. The natural River Tyne has a robust constitution, but use, abuse and misuse have taken their toll and the river still bears the scars of its past.

It is customary for books on rivers to follow the thread of the river's course from source to mouth. However, the trouble with this approach is that, as Eric Newby[1] remarks on the difficulty of writing about railways, 'railways, like rivers, are difficult subjects for writers because they go on and on'. Instead, the chapters in this book have been arranged topically rather than topographically in order to convey more clearly the attributes of the River Tyne and to take advantage of the variety of expertise represented by the contributors. Although the chapters broadly follow a sequence from the natural environment to the river as modified by man, there are many stops and regressions on the way; man's influence intrudes right from the first chapter on hydrology.

The focus is always the river itself: its natural and manmade characteristics and those activities which use or influence the water, the channel or the river banks.

An introductory chapter on hydrology explains how flow in the river varies through the year and from place to place, and how these variations impinge on other aspects of the natural environment and use of the river. This chapter contains more graphical and numerical material than elsewhere in the book, but we would encourage non-scientific readers not to be put off. Every river user, whether engineer, canoeist or fisherman, is already an amateur hydrologist, and an understanding of the hydrology of the Tyne will help give a firmer scientific base to each of these activities. From time to time the Tyne suffers extremes of drought and flood. A comprehensive study of the history of flooding on the Tyne has already been prepared by the author in *Land of Singing Waters*[2]. However, since its publication in 1992, besides further flooding on the Tyne, there have been very damaging floods throughout the country at Easter 1998 and in November 2000; these have altered public attitudes and government policy. An update on flooding on the Tyne within the national context has therefore been provided in Chapter 2.

Chapters 3 and 4 are concerned with the origins and development of the river valley and the river channel. Malcolm Newson in Chapter 3 postulates the ancient origins of the Tyne and describes how natural fluvial (and glacial) processes over a long period of geological time have helped to shape the present landscape of the Tyne valley. Continuing fluvial processes form and modify the river channel and create habitats for river flora and fauna, whilst the processes themselves are modified by changing land use and river engineering. In particular the slowly-operating natural processes were interrupted for several decades of the twentieth century when gravel companies extracted large amounts of gravel from the river bed, thus altering the configuration and ecology of the river as well as destabilising river structures. The history and effects of gravel extraction are chronicled in Chapter 4.

Two aspects of river ecology are addressed in Chapters 5 and 6. Anne Lewis outlines the general ecology of the Tyne in Chapter 5, explaining how plant and animal communities are adapted to differing habitats and flow regime, and why the North and South Tyne differ. Although the Tyne supports a thriving biodiversity, readers will perhaps be concerned at how some significant native species have declined and at how alien invaders have usurped our river banks. In Chapter 6 Tony Champion describes the Tyne fishery. He concentrates particularly on the history of the salmon from its post-Ice Age origins through the period of natural abundance, the decline due to pollution and abuse of the river, to the recovery in recent decades. He also discusses the conflict between the commercial net fishermen and the river angler and offers an opinion on the contentious topics of predators, poachers and obstructions to the passage of migratory fish.

With improvements in the water quality of the estuary and good fisheries management the River Tyne has recently become the prime salmon fishing river in England and Wales. Aidan Pollard communicates his enthusiasm for salmon fishing in Chapter 7 and gives advice to the uninitiated and to the visiting angler on the where, when and how of fishing the Tyne. Salmon are the main interest, but reference is also made to trout and coarse fishing.

Water quality (or the lack of it) is considered in Chapters 8 and 9, commencing with a brief consideration of variations in natural water quality in the Tyne and the early impact of mineral extraction in the Pennines on the quality of the freshwater river. However, the main emphasis is on the estuary. Through the early years of the Industrial Revolution on Tyneside, before the advent of piped sewage to the river, Newcastle and other towns witnessed scenes of incredible squalor and filth, but the estuary continued to support migratory salmon and sea trout. The devastation of cholera epidemics in the mid-nineteenth century provided impetus to the development of sewerage systems which transferred the filth and the pollution problem to the estuary. The Tyne suffered from the discharge of a potent mix of untreated domestic waste and effluents from Tyneside industry and gradually became deprived of oxygen and toxic to most river life. The river became a stinking nuisance and Tyneside turned its back on the river. The growth of concern and the will to address the problem through the twentieth century are described by Tony Foster in Chapter 9. He shows how a major effort of municipal cooperation was required to fund the construction of the Tyneside Interceptor Scheme and the Howdon sewage treatment works to treat the sewage from the entire population of Tyneside. Improvements in river water quality enabled municipal planners to redevelop and regenerate the riverside corridor as a place for living, for recreation and for entertainment.

The focus of attention switches in Chapter 10 from the estuary to the upper reaches of the North Tyne where the proposal to build a massive reservoir generated heated debate through the late 1960s and the 1970s. Although the Kielder Scheme was eventually approved after two Public Inquiries and completed in 1982, criticism has continued. With the benefit of hindsight, the wisdom (or otherwise) of the Scheme is discussed in relation to the reservoir's planned and actual use and to the changes which have occurred in the North Tyne valley.

During the mid-nineteenth century rowing on the River Tyne was the favourite spectator sport of the North East with crowds of over 50,000 lining the banks for championship matches. The Tyne spawned a succession of national and world champions and made a major contribution to the design of racing boats, as described in Chapter 11. Although professional rowing declined in the late nineteenth century, the amateur sport has grown and continues to thrive. Sporting and recreational use of the river has increased dramatically over the last fifty years, driven by the increase in leisure time and encouraged by improvements in water quality, access to the river and provision of facilities. Particular reference is made to canoeing on the freshwater river and sailing on Derwent Reservoir and Kielder Water, but wide ranging sport and recreation on the estuary are also outlined.

The following two chapters by Stafford Linsley describe the interlinked growth and development of the port and industries along the river banks. The history of the port of Tyne (Chapter 12) was bound up with its major town from the twelfth century when the 'Laws of Newcastle' gave the burgesses of Newcastle monopolistic rights to trade on the Tyne. The supremacy of Newcastle conditioned the development of the port for the next 700 years and often delayed improvements. Challenges to Newcastle's hegemony did not succeed until the mid-nineteenth century when the establishment of the Tyne Improvement Commission permitted a more holistic approach to Tyne navigation and development.

The availability of coal within reach of the navigable river provided the main basis for both trade and industry (Chapter 13). For several centuries the tonnage of northeastern coal carried round Britain's coasts exceeded that of all other commodities put together, and the sea route from the Tyne to London became the busiest in the world. However, the connection between the Tyne and the growth of industry is demonstrated in many other ways, including the use of ballast from returning colliers in pottery, glass and chemical industries, the availability of water power for milling, and the development of the maritime industries, notably shipbuilding and rope-making.

The flood hydrology of the Tyne and the particular topographic features of its valley provided a real challenge to the bridge builder (Chapter 14). Response to the early failure of stone-arch bridges, especially in the great flood of 1771, led to the development of better and completely different bridge designs, notably the suspension bridge which could span much wider channels without vulnerable piers in the river. The combination of unusually steep valley sides over the tidal river at Newcastle/Gateshead and the need for navigational clearance fostered highly innovative approaches to bridge building, not least in the new Millennium bridge (Plate 2). As Stafford Linsley remarks, 'Few people fail to be impressed by the bridgescape over the tidal Tyne between Gateshead and Newcastle, essentially because of the variations in the forms of bridge built along a few hundred yards of river'.

Despite its special geography, history and hydrology, the Tyne means little without the special people who reside by its banks, whether the rural descendants of border skirmishers or the urban Geordies, now with a few exceptions a generation away from the hard labour of the mines and shipyards. In the past Tynesiders fuelled the Industrial Revolution by the labour of their hands and by the application of mental energy to formulate new ideas and invent new practical devices. For better or worse the products of Tyneside invention transformed the world through the propagation of railways, ships and armaments. There is a kind of synergy between Tynesiders and their river. They transformed the river, but the river gives them an identity and a visual focus for their fierce loyalty (some would say patriotism).

The Tyne has played and continues to play an important role in the psyche and imagination of all who live within its influence. This is shown best in the artistic and lyrical inspiration provided by the Tyne as illustrated in Chapters 15 and 16. The Tyne has inspired paintings by J.M. Turner whilst other nineteenth-century artists such as T.M. Richardson, J.W. Carmichael and B.B. Hemy[3] provide fascination illustrations of the bustle and grime of the industrial port. But Thomas Bewick was undoubtedly the most distinguished artist of Tynedale in spite of his unusual medium. His 'canvas' was the woodcut and his art was generally encompassed within a space no more than two inches in diameter. Many of Bewick's woodcuts are scenes of the river and Chapter 15 is dedicated to those which show the crossing of the river by ordinary and fanciful means.

Few rivers can have provided such an outpouring of music, song and verse as the Tyne, ranging from Northumbrian pipe and fiddle tunes, border songs and ballads, songs of the 'coaly Tyne', songs celebrating the Tyne champion oarsmen to more modern songs of Tyneside including those of Jimmy Nail and Billy Fane. The author of our last chapter is Paul Younger, professor of hydrogeochemical engineering by day, but equally entertaining and knowledgeable as a Geordie folk singer.

Although the attributes of the river have been treated individually, the Tyne is clearly more than the sum of its parts. Indeed, the river is like a living breathing organism. Whilst the organism has an anatomy and physiology, properties and processes, it also has individuality and personality. Within the text there are frequent cross references between chapters. There is inevitably some overlap and even some disagreement.

Sustainability is the new environmental buzz word. It is a useful concept. It means essentially that use of the river (or other features of the natural environment) should not be at the expense of depriving others of the same benefits in present or future generations. But, if the river is to be used at all, sustainability cannot mean that the river is left in or restored to a completely natural state — however that may now be interpreted. Every use of the water or control of the river involves a change from its natural or current state. Such uses are essential to our modern life. We expect a continual supply of clean water to flow from our taps. We expect our wastes to be carried away. We expect industrial products for our everyday use. All such uses have some impact on the quantity and quality of water in the river. Similarly, if we expect to be protected from floods then - unless we vacate the floodplain - the floodbanks and diversions used for protection may impair amenity and our view of the river. No, the task is not to prevent use of the river. First we must understand the interrelated traits of the river's personality – between its climate, flow, its channel and bed, and the life of the river, between what happens on the catchment and in the river and between past use and abuse and present condition. Then we must use this understanding to ensure that the impact of any proposed developments are fully investigated, and the best environmental option chosen to maximise benefit and to minimise damage.

This is a task which will continue indefinitely. We, the authors, have had the privilege of working in the paradise of Tyne, of trying to unravel its natural and unnatural mysteries, of interpreting the past in order to understand the present river within its landscape, and of applying the knowledge to sustainable development. We hope we have conveyed our interest, fascination and enthusiasm for our respective professions, and that we have managed to bridge the gap between the specialist and general readership. We can assure the younger generation that science, engineering and history can even be fun, particularly when the subject is paradise; a day spent working by the river is worth a thousand in the pursuit of wealth, position or thrills.

REFERENCES

1. Newby, E. (1995) *A Merry Dance around the World. The Best of Eric Newby*, Harper Collins Publishers, (originally in *The Big Red Train Ride*, Picador)
2. Archer, D.R. (1992) *Land of Singing Waters; Rivers and Great Floods of Northumbria*, Spredden Press, Stocksfield.
3. Port of Tyne (2000) *Port of Tyne The first two thousand years*. Port of Tyne Authority, South Shields.

1. THE WATERS OF TYNE: RIVER HYDROLOGY

INTRODUCTION

The focus of our study is the River Tyne and all its attributes and uses. The science and art of hydrology is at the core of all river studies and their application to river management. Hydrology is concerned with the movement and storage of water in the environment, and with how the amount of water and the rates of movement vary from time to time and from place to place.

The movement of water as river flow is of interest for its own sake in the development of water resources (Chapters 10) and flood defence (Chapter 2), but the moving river also shapes its channel (Chapter 3) and provides the medium in which river life thrives, survives or dies (Chapters 5 and 6). The river is the recipient and conveyor of pollutants and sediments; the effect of pollutants on river ecology and fisheries depends on the magnitude of the river flow which acts to dilute polluting substances (Chapters 8 and 9). The nature of the river flow and the hydrological regime has also influenced the innovative design of bridges over the River Tyne (Chapter 14) and the growth and development of the port (Chapter 12) and industries (Chapter 13).

The amount of water in the river varies from year to year, from season to season and even from moment to moment. The sum total of these variations defines the *hydrological regime* or *flow regime* of the river.

Of course there are also changes from one reach of a river to another and from source to mouth as tributaries contribute their flow to the main channel. The ultimate source of river flow is rain and melting snow, but the response of the river depends also on the moderating effects of the catchment – its vegetation, soils and underlying rocks, in which water may be stored, and from which water is lost as evaporation and transpiration. The river channel itself further influences the way in which water is transmitted from one reach to another. Together the mosaic of variations in space and in time creates what may be called the river's unique 'hydrological personality', which provides the basis not only for use but for our aesthetic appreciation (Chapters 15 and 16).

THE IMPORTANCE OF DATA

Whilst aesthetic appreciation requires no data except for the signals from sense to mind and heart, all our material uses of the river require data. The most important data are of river flow (or *discharge*) which is the volume of water passing a given point in a specified time. Discharge in rivers is usually measured in cubic metres per second (*cumecs*).

With limited exceptions, discharge cannot be measured directly and continuously, so the information must be obtained indirectly. Data acquisition requires the establishment of a gauging station which typically consists of a recorder house, a set of staff gauges, a cableway for measuring high flows and sometimes a downstream weir. Plate 3 shows the picturesque station on the River Rede at Redebridge. The process of measurement consists of the following steps:

1. River level (or *stage*) is measured continuously or at 15-minute intervals.
2. A graphical or mathematical relationship between level and discharge, known as the *rating curve,* is obtained by repeatedly measuring the discharge for given levels using a current meter. Such measurements are done by wading at low flows, but in high flows measurement is made using a fixed cableway or boat.
3. The rating curve is then applied to convert all the 15-minute values of level to discharge. These data form the basis of all subsequent analysis, planning, design and operation of water-based schemes.

This is a simplified description of a process which involves many variations of instrumentation and method as well as considerable application of time and skill to ensure the reliability of the data. Data collection and management is not a glamorous activity; there are no votes in data. Around the world, networks previously established were neglected for several decades and the data curtailed or fabricated. In the author's experience some data are as corrupt as the bureaucrats who managed them. International funding agencies now recognise that investment was misplaced on many multi-million dollar schemes which failed because they were based on dubious data. One outcome of the Earth Summit in Rio de Janeiro in 1992 and the subsequent Agenda 21[1] was an added emphasis on improvement of data networks as a basis for decision-making and design. The author was involved in schemes to strengthen water data management in India and Pakistan.

Even in the UK and Northumbria, periodic battles have had to be fought between management and more environmentally-oriented staff. For example, in the late 1980s after wholesale cuts had already been made to the measurement network, the author who was then responsible for managing the Northumbria network struggled to avoid a further 50 percent reduction proposed by a privatisation-directed management. Most of the stations closed in the 1980s have since been reopened by the National Rivers Authority/Environment Agency to meet specific requirements for environmental management. However, I am told that the battle continues even today in the Environment Agency with data acquisition still considered by some to be the Cinderella of water management.

The current gauging network on the River Tyne is shown in Fig. 1.1. Most of the stations are used for flood forecasting and warning, and data can be obtained remotely by telephone from the data logger and modem at the station to a computer at home or office. However, virtually all the stations have multiple uses including: operation of the Kielder scheme, ensuring compliance with statutory minimum flows, assessing and issuing abstraction licences and consents for effluent discharges, planning and designing flood alleviation, and assessing and monitoring the impact of accidental spills of pollutants.

THE INFLUENCE OF CLIMATE

Precipitation, both rain and snow, is the primary influence on river flow in the Tyne and is measured at numerous sites in the Tyne catchment (Fig. 1.2). Rainfall is measured by a *raingauge* in which a cylindrical gauge of standard diameter funnels the falling rain into a glass jar or volumetric measuring device. Manual gauges are read once daily by pouring the contents of the jar into a graduated measuring cylinder and reading the total in millimetres. Recording gauges typically catch the rainfall in a tipping bucket which tips and records every 0.2 mm of rainfall. Plate 4 shows a pair of raingauges high in Kielder forest in the North Tyne catchment. Digital recording and telemetric transmission operates in much the same way as for river level.

Ordinary raingauges, though used, are not very satisfactory for measuring snowfall owing to the setting up of wind eddies around the gauge, which cause snow to fall elsewhere than the gauge. Special wind-calming devices on snow gauges have been used in other countries but not in Britain. Recently an unusual instrument called a *snow pillow* was set up at a few sites in the neighbourhood of the Tyne catchment (the nearest being Cow Green) to measure the water equivalent of snow on the ground. It is used principally as a basis for forecasting runoff when the snow melts[2].

The amount of precipitation received at a particular location is influenced both by altitude and by the rain shadow effect of the Pennines which lie across the track of the prevailing southwesterly and westerly winds. Precipitation therefore declines rapidly from high values over the Pennine ridges to a minimum at the coast near the mouth of the Tyne (Fig. 1.2). Highest average annual totals of over 2000 mm occur in the headwaters of the South Tyne around Cross Fell, but lower annual totals of around 1500 mm occur in the North Tyne headwaters. The lower Tyne valley from Hexham seaward has annual totals below 650 mm and the coastal fringe receives as much of its annual rainfall from the east as from the west[3].

On average there is little difference between the summer-half (April to September) rainfall and the winter-half with a tendency for a slight summer maximum in the east and winter maximum in the uplands. On average August is the wettest month in the lower part of the Tyne catchment but November or December in the Pennines. However, one of the delights of British or northeastern weather is its variability from year to year, providing a perpetual topic of conversation. Raingauge sites with long records may have experienced each month in turn as the wettest and driest in the year.

Snowmelt is a significant contributor to runoff in the River Tyne and especially to flood runoff. Although snow lies for an average of only eight days at the coast (Tynemouth), it increases to 20 days at Haydon Bridge, 39 days at Catcleugh in the upper Rede catchment and over 100 days at the source of the South Tyne on Cross Fell[4]. Snow is reported to have remained in patches on Cross Fell in 1979, sufficient for local skiing on Midsummer's Day.

The snow cover does not persist continuously for the durations noted but may accumulate and melt completely several times during the course of a winter. The intermittent character of the snow is illustrated by the average number of

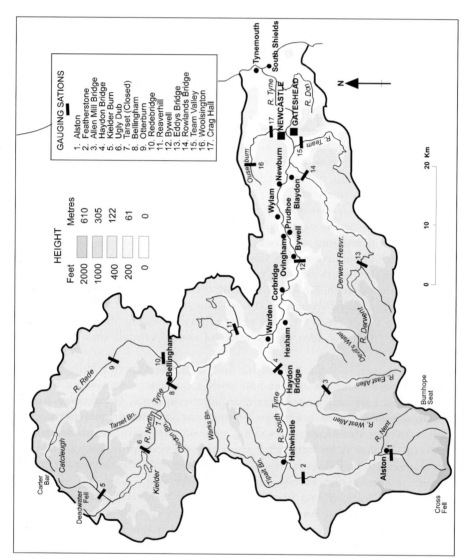

Fig 1.1 The river gauging network on the River Tyne.

4

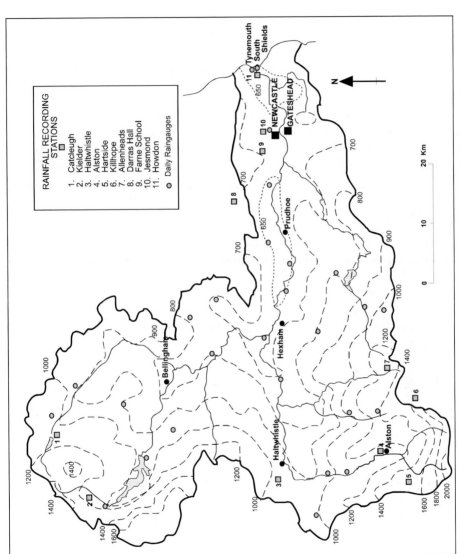

Fig 1.2 Rainfall (millimetres) over the Tyne catchment showing daily and recording raingauge sites.

snow spells (from accumulation to melt) per winter and the average duration. Thus at Catcleugh, the 39 days of snow cover occurs in 6.5 spells each lasting an average of only 6 days[5]. Nevertheless in severe winters such as 1947, 1963 and 1979 snow may persist for several months with over 200 mm of snow water equivalent accumulated on the ground before melt occurs[6]. During such winters uncharacteristically low winter river flows occur whilst snow persists. Severe flooding may ensue upon melting of such a volume of snow when the cold spell is terminated by a vigorous warm front with a rapid rise in temperature accompanied by rainfall.

The other climatic variable which is of significance for river flow is evaporation. Potential evaporation (PE) is defined as the theoretical rate of water loss to the atmosphere, assuming an uninterrupted supply of water to be evaporated. It is usually calculated from climatic data using a formula derived by Penman from theoretical considerations. The average annual PE is closely related to altitude and declines from 500 mm at the mouth of the Tyne to about 350 mm in the higher Pennines. More significantly, most of the evaporative loss occurs during the summer months. Thus the fairly even seasonal distribution of rainfall is transformed to a distinct summer minimum of river flow, as described below.

ROUND AND ROUND AND UP AND DOWN

In principle the movement of water in the environment is cyclic (*the hydrological cycle*); water ultimately returns to the same point in the cycle but with a time delay which varies enormously from hours to thousands of years. If we start arbitrarily with the point at which rainfall reaches the ground, water may flow off over the surface into streams and rivers, infiltrate to the soil or groundwater or evaporate back into the atmosphere. Water entering the soil may further percolate to groundwater, or be returned to the atmosphere after storage, by transpiration through plants or by direct evaporation from the soil. Part of the water moves laterally by sub-surface routes to streams and rivers but with a longer delay than water moving over the surface. Water reaching permanently saturated rocks below the water table may be stored for a very long time but is again released slowly and steadily to the rivers. Rivers flow to the sea and from here again evaporation occurs to the atmosphere, where it condenses in clouds and falls as rain or snow.

In contrast to this cyclic behaviour an observer standing on the river bank can see the rising and falling of the river in response to rainfall or melting snow over the catchment. If one plots these changes over a period of time or measures them with a level recorder, the pattern of change is wave-like. The changing level is not usually visible to the observer as a wave on the sea because of its long wavelength, but it unmistakably behaves as a wave and thus provides a scientific basis for hydraulic modelling, which is essential for engineering studies of the river. The plot of river level over time is referred to as a *hydrograph*.

The characteristic shape of the hydrograph, including the rate of rise and fall at a particular location, is an important element in the river's hydrological regime. It is not at all arbitrary but depends upon the properties of the catchment and of the river channel. However, since rainfall amount and distribution as well as the state of the catchment varies from event to event, it is no easy matter to forecast downstream levels and discharges and such forecasting is the subject of an extensive scientific literature on rainfall runoff modelling[7].

Where the River Tyne stands out in comparison with other English rivers of comparable size and discharge is in the rapid rate of its rise and fall, right down to the estuary, and the rate at which rain falling in the headwaters is evacuated from the river to the sea. Fig. 1.3 shows the progress of the flood wave of November 2000 from the upper reaches of the South Tyne at Alston, through Haydon Bridge to the lowest measuring point on the river at Bywell. In this particular example there is only two hours from the peak at Alston to the peak at Haydon Bridge and a further three and three-quarter hours to Bywell, a total of five and three-quarter hours. Notice also that although the rise in river level starts first at Alston, the rise to the peak there is quite gradual. As the flood

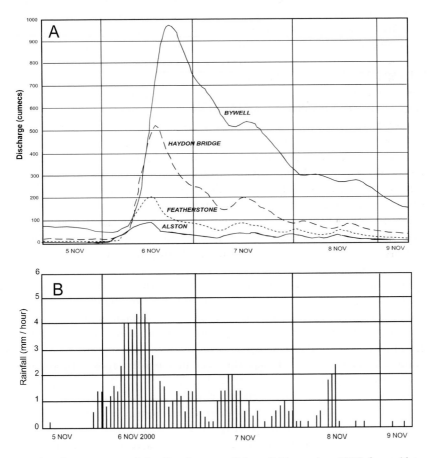

Fig 1.3   A. The progress of the flood wave of 5 to 8 November 2000 from Alston on the upper South Tyne to Bywell. B. Concurrent hourly rainfall at Alston.

wave progresses downstream it becomes progressively steeper with a very rapid rate of rise at Haydon Bridge and Bywell. Rainfall at Alston is also shown with the total time from the occurrence of rainfall at Alston to the peak river flow at Bywell of approximately 8 hours. Such a short response time compares with a period of several days for rivers like the Severn and Yorkshire Ouse. The short lag creates a problem for flood forecasting and warning as it leaves much less time to ponder over the calculations and get the message to the public (Chapter 2).

The speed of response is largely due to the slope of the catchment and river channel and to the very limited extent and storage capacity of floodplains which can delay and reduce the magnitude of the flood.

Occasionally, the interaction of intense rainfall in the headwaters and the steep slope of the main river and tributaries creates a dynamic wave with a near vertical and distinctly visible wave front which can persist to the lower reaches. Wading fishermen have been washed away or have had to scamper up the bank to safety, leaving their tackle to the elements. They sometimes attribute such waves to releases from Kielder, but serious incidents are invariably 'acts of God' rather than of Northumbrian Water.

In one particularly severe event on 17 July 1983, a young man enjoying a summer dip in the River West Allen was swept away by a 'wall of water' more than 1.5 metres high and barely survived by clinging onto overhead branches which had suddenly come within reach.

SEASONAL AND SPATIAL VARIATION

Whilst day by day changes are crucial for river activities, many attributes and patterns of river behaviour only emerge when averaged over a long period of time. In the short term, such patterns are obscured by the variability of rainfall.

Fig. 1.4a shows the monthly mean discharge in cumecs for selected stations along the Tyne. This figure illustrates the regularity of seasonal flow from the headwaters to the lower reaches of the river; the differences between stations mainly reflect the contributing catchment areas. The lowest station Bywell has, of course, the highest flow with a mean January flow of 76 cumecs, nearly double the annual average, whilst the mean June and July flows are less than half the annual figure. Reaverhill on the North Tyne with a large catchment area has higher monthly flows than Haydon Bridge on the South Tyne. There are progressively lower mean discharges as we proceed to smaller catchments.

The uniformity in the pattern of seasonal variation amongst the stations is further confirmed if we examine the monthly totals as a percentage of the annual average (Fig. 1.4b). This transformation removes the effect of the overall magnitude and it is observed that the seasonal percentages through the year now fall within a comparatively narrow band.

An alternative way of transforming the data is to remove the effects of catchment area by converting the mean river discharge in cumecs to runoff in millimetres over the catchment (Fig. 1.4c). The units are then directly comparable to rainfall. This graph now shows the much higher runoff rates from the wetter upland catchments of Alston and Featherstone on the South Tyne and Kielder Burn at the head of the North Tyne. Haydon Bridge (South

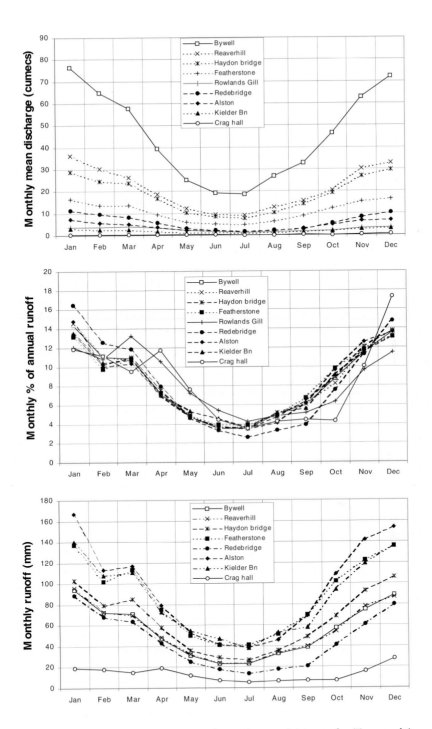

Fig 1.4 Monthly mean discharge at several gauging stations on the Tyne and its tributaries: (a) cumecs; (b) as monthly percentage of the annual total; (c) as runoff (equivalent millimetres over the catchment).

Tyne) has a higher runoff than Reaverhill (North Tyne), which almost exactly coincides with Bywell. The lowland catchments of Ouseburn and Team have much lower runoff because of the lower incident rainfall and higher evapotranspiration.

NO DAM GOOD?

Dams around the world have received an increasingly bad press partly because their performance has not lived up to expectation (bad data again?) and partly because of the collateral damage to the environment and local society. Every new dam which is proposed, whether in the UK or elsewhere, meets with a barrage of opposition. Engineers on the other hand have argued that the provision of clean water supplies and hydropower, made possible through the building of dams, has done more to improve global health and well-being than all the medical prescriptions and interventions combined.

Few would deny that dams in the Tyne basin have been critical for the life and growth of Tyneside, but the most recent and biggest of the Tyne dams above Falstone, which holds back 200 million cubic metres, has continued to suffer sniping from various quarters since its first filling in 1982. Although the impact of Kielder Water is considered in more detail in Chapter 10, it is worthwhile to show here how it has modified the amount and seasonal distribution of river flow in the downstream river, and to make a comparison with Derwent Reservoir on the River Derwent.

Kielder is a regulating rather than a direct supply reservoir. That is, it regulates the flow in the North Tyne so that abstraction can be made at a point nearer to the Tyneside demand. It does not change the overall volume of water released into the North Tyne, but it does change the seasonal distribution. Comparison is made in Fig. 1.5 between the monthly runoff and monthly discharge before and after the construction of Kielder. The early record was measured at Tarset eight kilometres below the dam and with a catchment area of 285 km^2, some 19% greater than the reservoired catchment. The post-dam record is from Ugly Dub, immediately below the dam.

Fig. 1.5a shows that there is not a great deal of difference overall in the annual flow before and after Kielder though there is some seasonal shift. More water is now being released from January to March and during the summer. In July, when the natural flow is near its minimum, the average discharge has increased by 30% and the percentage of annual flow occurring in that month has increased from 4.5 % to 6%. The regulated flow reaches a minimum in May and June and thereafter increases through the summer. Since the summer months of a drought year are naturally the time when most stress can be placed on ecology and fisheries, the change has clearly been beneficial if considered purely on the basis of monthly flow. However, there are more subtle effects of river regulation and these will be discussed in Chapter 10.

Unlike Kielder, Derwent Reservoir is a direct supply reservoir. Water is abstracted directly from the reservoir to Mosswood treatment works, and from there the treated water is piped to Wearside. The abstracted water is completely lost to the river. The change in the flow regime is shown by a long flow record

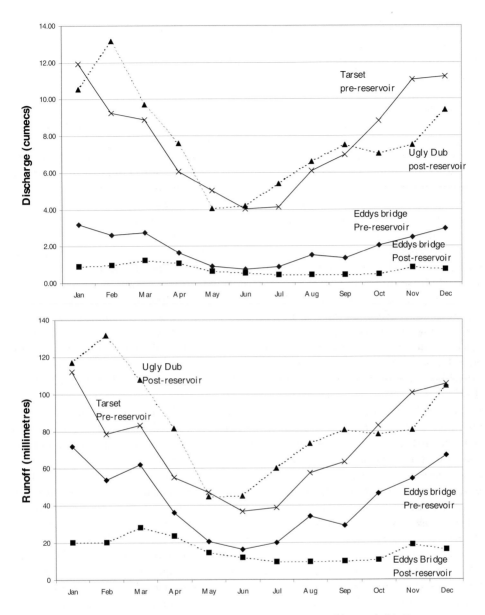

Fig 1.5 The effect of reservoirs on river flow (a) Kielder and (b) Derwent.

from the gauging station at Eddy's Bridge, just below the dam, before and after dam construction. Fig. 1.5b tells a sorry tale for the river. Due to the abstraction the mean annual flow has declined from 1.86 cumecs to 0.73 cumecs, a reduction of 61%. The flow is uniformly low through the year since the reservoir is full and spilling for only brief periods of time, and the only water reaching the downstream water channel is the statutory minimum release. Even at Rowlands Gill much further downstream, after intervening tributaries have made their contribution, the percentage decrease in mean annual flow resulting from Derwent Reservoir is over 30%. For most of the last century the River Derwent additionally suffered from noxious effluents released to the river from the Consett steel complex and from Derwenthaugh coke works. The closure of these industries has enormously improved the water quality of the river, but the decreased water quantity remains.

Whether or not the reader is convinced that Kielder has improved flow conditions in the North Tyne, there can be little argument that the impact of Derwent Reservoir on river flow conditions has been predominantly negative. But perhaps that is an acceptable price to pay for an adequate water supply through Wearside taps.

HOW LOW CAN YOU GET?

The occurrence of low flows is critical for the ecology of a river (Chapter 5). In very low flows the river margins dry up, water temperatures rise, dissolved oxygen is depleted, and food sources diminish. The river becomes more vulnerable to pollution incidents. Although organisms adopt strategies for survival, very low flows lead to wholesale mortality of individuals and even of species. River life, including fish, must survive such extremes of flow as well as the mean condition.

Rivers naturally fall to a low level after a period of prolonged summer drought as storage of water in soils and underlying rocks of the catchment is depleted. However, one period of heavy rainfall after a drought will not top up these storages and often the underlying condition of low groundwater-fed flow can persist for more than a year. The lowest flows often occur when there is a succession of dry years. It is believed that changes in land use such as moorland drainage and afforestation can alter the rate of restoration of groundwater storage and hence the drought flow in the river. The extent of these influences is still subject to debate. In addition, reservoirs are often seen to be releasing insufficient water in drought conditions to satisfy downstream ecological needs, in spite of the fact that there is a statutory requirement to release a continuous minimum flow – called the *compensation flow*.

Some river users strongly contend that river flow in the Tyne is now lower than it used to be. It is not always clear for what period of time the claim is made, but frequent reference is made to the influence of Kielder. Fortunately there are flow records in the River Tyne extending back several decades with which it is possible to check the changes in low flow.

One method of investigating and comparing low flows is to prepare a graph known as a flow duration curve. This graph shows the percentage of time that the flow exceeds a given discharge (Fig. 1.6). From the graph one can read off directly the 50% (or median) flow. The lower end of the graph shows a widely-used measure of low flow, known as *'the 95% exceedence flow'*. This is the level of flow which is exceeded an average of 347 days in the year; conversely the flow is less for an average of 18 days a year. The example shown in Fig. 1.6 is for the River Tyne at Bywell and it should be noted that special scales have been used. The horizontal axis uses a probability scale which stretches out the

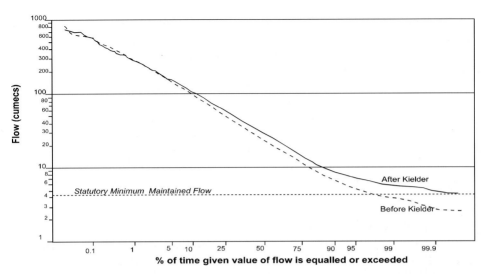

Fig 1.6 The flow regime of the Tyne at Bywell before and after river regulation by Kielder as shown by flow duration curve.

extreme values to give better definition; the vertical axis uses a logarithmic scale. Flow durations compare the pre-Kielder period 1956 to 1980 with the period 1982 to 2000; it is immediately clear that low flows are significantly higher in the later post-Kielder period. The 95% exceedence flow has increased from 5.1 cumecs to 7.2 cumecs (an increase of nearly 40%). Similar changes have occurred on the North Tyne at Reaverhill but not on the River South Tyne, which has been unaffected by reservoirs.

The reason for the changes in the North Tyne and Tyne is not hard to find. As part of the conditions laid down in the Kielder Inquiries, Northumbrian River Authority (the organisation then responsible for river management), accepted minimum flow conditions both for the reach immediately below the dam and for the lower reaches of the Tyne below the Riding Mill abstraction. For Riding Mill the flow is required to be maintained by Kielder releases at a minimum of 4.21 cumecs (or in round figures in the old units of 80 million gallons a day). This figure was derived as 10% of the average flow or, as can be seen in Fig. 1.6, at the 97% exceedence level on the pre-Kielder flow duration curve. In reality, in order to avoid penalties arising from violating the statutory condition, Northumbrian Water release a little more than this requirement. In addition, at Kielder itself a minimum compensation flow of 1.31 cumecs (25 million gallons a day) was set. Previously flow had fallen below 0.50 cumecs in drought years.

The difference between personal perception of low flows and the evidence of data can be put down mainly to the fickleness of memory. It is also possible that observers are comparing water levels at some fixed rock on the riverside where levels now appear to be lower than in the past. As illustrated in Chapters 3 and 4 there may have been natural and artificial changes in the river channel and the bed level so that the same flow is now associated with a significantly lower river level.

THE FISHERMAN'S MANTRA

Another aspect of change in the hydrological regime of the River Tyne can be related in terms of a statement so frequently made by fishermen that I have come to think of it as the 'fisherman's mantra'. It goes like this:

> "When I was a lad the river used to come up and stay up for a week. Now it is up and down in just a few hours. It has ruined the fishing. It's all because of (*variously*) the moorland drainage, afforestation, too many sheep, or simply Kielder!"

Statements like this have been applied not only to the main Tyne and its upland tributaries but also to rivers all over the north of England including the Yorkshire Ouse. The mantra highlights concern about flow variability and more specifically the frequency and duration of spates. In spite of the perception of river users it has been extraordinarily difficult to validate the assertion.

To tackle this problem I recently I devised a simple method to define flow variability in the terms described by the fisherman – the frequency and duration of spates or pulses[8,9]. The method looks at the annual hydrograph of flow and counts the number of times the flow rises above a particular threshold and the time duration till it falls below the same threshold. The analysis can be repeated for many different thresholds but requires a digital record of flow at 15-minute intervals. The data are analysed year by year and the impact of the rainfall for a given year can be assessed and deducted, leaving only the effect of land use (if any).

In one study of a very small catchment at Coalburn (1.5 km²) in Kielder forest it was found that a distinct sequence of changes occurred over the period from 1967 to 1999[10]. This period represented a change from natural moorland, through ditch drainage in preparation for planting, to nearly mature forest growth. In summary the study shows that from pre- to post-drainage the number of pulses and the total duration increased substantially. The average pulse duration decreased sharply at higher flows. Forest growth has brought about even more radical changes in the opposite direction, with a marked and continuing reduction in pulse numbers and an increase in the average pulse duration.

The results appear to give some support to the mantra on a small catchment with respect to the impact of ditching. For the first ten years or so after planting, the river had a much more flashy response with shorter pulses. However, as the forest matured the flashy response was reversed (fewer and longer pulses), and the Coalburn is now much less flashy than it was under its natural moorland cover.

There is some uncertainty whether such changes occur on larger catchments. The method has not yet been tried on tributaries, unaffected by reservoirs, within the Tyne catchment. However, on the neighbouring Irthing catchment (330 km²) which is a tributary of the River Eden and is nearly 20% afforested, the influence of ditching and forest growth can be detected. The pattern of hydrological change from moorland through ditching and forest growth is the same as at Coalburn but the amount of change is very small and would hardly be noticeable to the casual observer. On the upper Wear (at Stanhope) where similar changes have been alleged as the result of moorland drainage, no evidence whatever was found for change either in pulse duration or pulse number during the period from 1959. Pending further analysis, the jury remains out on the hydrological impact of moorland drainage, with or without afforestation on large catchments, and consequent effects on river ecology and fisheries.

CONCLUDING REMARKS

The above examples illustrate some of the ways in which hydrology can be applied to elucidate the hydrological regime of the River Tyne catchment, to solve problems, and to aid decision-making in river management. Many other problems, whether concerned with ecology, fisheries, control of pollution, or river engineering and management, need specific hydrological studies to be effectively applied. Some of these applications are apparent in subsequent chapters, but often the work of hydrologists is hidden behind the final visible structures of concrete, earth and steel or in the softer landscapes of industrial rivers restored to natural peace and harmony.

REFERENCES

1. UNCED (United Nations Conference on Environment and Development) (1992) *Agenda 21: Programme of Action for Sustainable Development* (Rio de Janeiro), UNCED.
2. Archer, D.R. and Stewart, D. (1995) The installation and use of a snow pillow to monitor snow water equivalent. *Jour. Chartered Inst of Water and Environmental Management*, **9**, 221–230.
3. Wheeler, D. (1997) North-east England and Yorkshire in D Wheeler and J Mayes (Eds) *Regional Climates of the British Isles*, 158–180, Routledge, London and New York.
4. Manley, G. (1971) The mountain snows of Britain, *Weather*, **26**, 192–200.
5. Archer, D.R., Bailey, J.O., Barrett, E.C. and Greenhill, D (1994) The potential of satellite remote sensing of snow over Great Britain in relation to cloud cover, *Nordic Hydrology*, **25**, 39–52
6. Archer, D.R. (1981) Severe snowmelt runoff in northeast England and its implications, *Proc. Instn. Civil Engrs.* Pt 2, **71**, 1047–1060.
7. Beven, K.J. (2001) *Rainfall-runoff modelling: the primer*, 360pp, Wiley
8. Archer, D.R. and Williams, G. (1995) Resolving conflicts between sustainable energy and water resources in the regulation of the River Tyne, England, In: *Modelling and Management of Sustainable Basin-scale Water Resources Systems*. IAHS Publ. 234, 3–14.
9. Archer, D.R. (2000) Indices of flow variability and their use in identifying the impact of land use changes, Seventh National Hydrology Symposium, British Hydrological Society, 2.67–2.73.
10. Archer, D.R. and Newson, M.D. (2002) Indices of flow variability and their use in assessing the hydro-ecological impacts of afforestation and drainage, *Journal of Hydrology*, **268**, 244–258

2. THE TYNE IN FLOOD

INTRODUCTION

We are told by the Environment Agency that five million people in England and Wales are at risk of flooding from rivers or the sea. This is an enormous number and a figure that was little appreciated until the severe floods of Easter 1998 struck the Midlands and the November 2000 floods affected a much wider area. In some places, subsequent investigation has shown that the floods in 2000 were the largest that had occurred for several hundred years. In the 1998 floods, the financial losses, insured and uninsured, were close to £500 million and in the later floods around £1.2 billion, with more than 10,000 properties flooded at over 700 locations. Losses are not just financial; the trauma of losing home and possessions can be devastating. Homes may not be habitable for months after a flood. Recent experience has served to alter the perspective on flooding of the Government and the Environment Agency, the organisation primarily responsible for flood defence. Although these floods were not particularly severe on the River Tyne, the change in perception and policy warrants a further review, ten years on from the account of historical flooding in *Land of Singing Waters*[1]. Moreover, the Tyne, and particularly the South Tyne, did have an unusually severe flood in 1995, as described below.

The Environment Agency and its predecessors (National Rivers Authority: 1989–1996, Northumbrian Water: 1974–1989, and Northumbrian River Authority: 1963–1974) did not give the same sustained effort to flood defence as that given to pollution control. European legislation as well as public perception has ensured that river pollution has made steady progress. In contrast, there are no EU directives specifically relating to flood defence, although the EU Water Framework Directive, in force since December 2000, requires member countries to introduce integrated sustainable river basin management in which flood management would play an integral part. Activity has been motivated largely by public fears driven by the severity of recent flooding. The last sustained and serious nationwide flooding in the 1960s provided the basis for a period of intense research and the introduction of legislation to improve the safety of reservoirs in relation to flooding. The Reservoirs Act 1975 replaced the outdated legislation of 1930. However, many other aspects of flood risk suffered from weak legislation including planning control on flood plains and certain aspects of flood warning.

By the late 1980s, after two decades without serious floods in the North East, a senior manager at Northumbrian Water insisted that the Tyne and neighbouring rivers 'did not suffer serious floods'. A flood control room, which had been specifically designed in the mid-1970s to enable a flood warning team to monitor rainfall and river levels and to communicate warnings to the police, was commandeered for the use of training. As then the responsible officer at

Northumbrian Water, I can recall more than one occasion in the late 1980s when I was obliged to monitor floods alone and to provide emergency flood response from a portable computer on the corner of a desk. Fortunately none of these events turned out to be serious, but I would hate to imagine what would have happened if a flood of the severity of the January 1995 flood on the Tyne had occurred. My interest in historic flooding from the Tweed to the Tees as described in *Land of Singing Waters*[1] was motivated in part as an antidote to this official complacency. The cycle of flooding, investment and complacency until the next flooding event is not unique to the North East[2]; it is widespread and not just in Britain. The Institution of Civil Engineers report on *Learning to live with Rivers*[3] remarks that "It is easy to imagine the difficulties confronting funders and flood management professionals to maintain funding and alertness through a period of longer than a generation when other pressures on the public purse are relentlessly present".

The separation in 1989 of the privatised functions of water supply and sewage disposal at Northumbrian Water from environmental regulation at the National River Authority (now the Environment Agency) helped to secure a more realistic focus on flood protection. However, it was the nationally widespread floods of 1998 and 2000 which generated public concern and the main changes in policy and practice.

RABBITS AND THE FLOOD OF JANUARY 1995

The reader may well wonder what rabbits have to do with river flooding. Indeed a management expert called in by the Environment Agency to ensure 'value for taxpayer's money' might well get an unexpected answer when he quizzes the engineer about the heavy expenditure on flood defence. The flood defence engineer explains that there is considerable professional activity in planning flood defence works, such as embankments, and in the development and operation of flood warning schemes. The engineer continues, "Then, of course, there are a good number of staff engaged in grass cutting and maintenance of flood banks". The manager's eyes light up. He senses an opportunity to reduce staff costs by eliminating a cosmetic activity which seems inappropriate for a river bank. Surely there can be no justification for cutting grass and weeds on flood embankments so the manager asks the engineer who replies, "Well, it's so we can better see the rabbits".

We can only imagine this conversation leading in one direction. So, to explain the flood engineer's curious interest in rabbits, let us move the scene to a cold winter's night on the River Tyne. It is 31 January 1995, and rain has been falling heavily since early morning. With rising temperatures the snow, which has lain since 17 January, has been melting and adding to the flow in the headwaters. All the rivers of the northeast are in flood including the Tyne, the Wear and the Tees. The River South Tyne has reached the highest level ever recorded at the gauging stations at Featherstone and Haydon Bridge. At Haltwhistle, the flood bank upstream from Kilfrost's factory has been overtopped, flooding the administration block and warehouse, together with an adjacent builder's yard, a saw mill and the nearby Crown-Berger paint works. Plate 5 shows an air photograph of the extent of the flooding in Haltwhistle. There is no record of such an occurrence in the memory of local inhabitants, including comparisons even with the floods of 1954 and 1955.

The flood warning response team of the National Rivers Authority (as it then was) has long since sprung into action. The Duty Officer has been alerted to the possibility of heavy rainfall by weather forecasts on 30 January and has been tracking the progress of the storm. From his home computer he has called up raingauges which record and transmit the amount of recent rainfall, river level recording gauges, and rainfall radar maps which show the location and intensity of the storm. The Flood Warning operations room at the National Rivers Authority has been open since 08.45, when the first signs of a major event was on the cards. Stand-by staff have been called in for monitoring, forecasting and communication with the public and emergency services. Field staff have been in action checking vulnerable areas, delivering sandbags and sending flood information back to the office, to aid forecasting and warning and to transmit directly to emergency services.

The main area of concern after mid-afternoon is the lower Tyne, where locations at Corbridge and Prudhoe are vulnerable in the most extreme events. There is some relief when the forecast level at Corbridge is shown to be well below the crest of the flood bank, and houses should thus be safe. In fact, due of the flood-holding capacity of Kielder Water, the contributing flow from the North Tyne is not nearly as serious as that in the South Tyne, and the forecast level at Corbridge is considerably below that in 1955.

Then at 18.12 a message is received from a resident in Station Road in Corbridge to say that the water level at her house has risen six inches in 15 minutes. The Duty Officer is taken aback. The information can mean one of two things — that his forecast is wrong and the water has risen over the flood bank, or, that the bank has been breached without being overtopped. In either case, there is now nothing to stop the full force of the Tyne spreading out over the floodplain and over the roads and houses south of the river at Corbridge. In such conditions the flood level behind the flood bank rises at a much greater rate than the natural rate of rise of the river, with consequent dangers to residents and those unwise enough to still be out on the roads.

All hell breaks out in the Flood Operations Room for the next few minutes. (Did someone say that hydrology is not an exciting career?) A flurry of messages is sent off to the police and through them to the Emergency Services, to alert them to the dangers to local inhabitants and to advise evacuation or retreat to upstairs rooms.

The Field Supervisor for the National Rivers Authority Peter Angus, who has been patrolling the affected areas all day and directing his staff, is alerted and requested to go immediately to Corbridge to inspect and report. He is in Corbridge within 15 minutes and drives over the Tyne bridge. The road dips steeply on the south side of the bridge and he comes to an abrupt halt with his engine stalled, as he runs into a pool of water nearly a metre deep on the roundabout.

Undaunted and equipped with a heavy-duty torch, he leaves the car and sets out with a colleague upstream along the flood bank to assess the damage and to determine if emergency remedial work is possible. It is a dangerous business, with the rain still beating down and the river surging by only a little below the top of the flood bank where they are walking. About 500 metres upstream from the bridge the torch suddenly reveals the breach 20 metres ahead with the muddy waters spilling through and the bank sides still crumbling away. It is dangerous to proceed further. What they can see suggests there is nothing that can be done to mend the breach until the flood subsides. Soon the Police helicopter is at the scene, providing a floodlit view of the breached embankment and continuing further upriver to inspect for further damage.

The flood had indeed broken through the embankment when the water level was still well below the crest level. The strongly suspected culprit was – the rabbit.

In all, 14 properties were flooded in Station Road and Stanners Lane. Operations staff from National Rivers Authority, together with emergency services and the army provided sandbags, but there was little that could be done to save ground floor carpets and furniture in many houses as the rate of rise was too rapid. At the Dyvells Public House a sandbag barrier placed across the entrance to the courtyard gave way due to the wash from an army lorry. Pumps were brought in to pump water from houses and from underfloor cavities after the flood had receded. It was the worst flooding in Corbridge since 1955.

Here we return to our earlier conversation in the Agency office. Rabbits are indeed a serious menace to earth flood embankments. If undetected and 'untreated' they can burrow right through the embankment, thus providing a route for flood waters even while the water level is still well below the crest, with disastrous results as at Corbridge. As their activity is concealed by long grass, the only way to ensure that rabbits and other vermin are not burrowing is to cut the grass regularly. Inspection and cutting must continue without a break from year to year since, even if the rabbits are removed after the damage is done, the only way of ensuring the bank's integrity is to reconstruct it. Superficial evidence of burrowing may disappear after a few years, but the cavities may remain below the surface. The damage at Corbridge may have been done decades earlier.

The breach of the flood bank at Corbridge occurred in darkness, so there are no photographs of its occurrence. However, to illustrate the rapidity with which an earth embankment can disintegrate on overtopping or seepage, Plate 6 shows a unique sequence of photographs taken on the neighbouring River Tees following a flood in 1992. A farmer cut a shallow trench across the top of a flood bank to allow the water accumulated on his floodplain fields to drain back into the river when the flood had receded. To his horror and the surprise of passing engineers (with camera), the trickle of flow became a roaring torrent, carrying with it shrubs and trees and widening to a breach of 20 metres over a period of no more than twenty minutes.

Here ends the defence of the flood engineer against the cost-cutting axe of the efficiency expert. If the integrity of flood defences is to be maintained, then grass cutting with associated costs simply must be continued. Grass and weeds on flood banks along the Tyne, as in other parts of Northumbria, are now cut twice a year and some vulnerable sites like Corbridge are inspected monthly. In some places the cuttings are swept up to improve visibility of the ground underneath; this also tends to reduce the vigour of weed growth in subsequent years.

A balance must be struck between the need for flood protection and the potential loss of plant life and habitat for birds and other animals that are not degrading the flood bank. The time of cutting must be carefully chosen to avoid disturbing nesting and brooding birds. Generally a strip of natural vegetation is left adjacent to the water's edge.

THE PROBLEM WITH CARAVANS

There is no better place to spend a relaxing day than on a river bank, whether engaged in fishing, observing birds or other wildlife, or just letting the world go by to the music of rippling and murmuring water. And how better to prolong your pleasure than to park your tent or caravan by the water's edge and to be lulled to sleep at night by the sound of running water and the soughing of the wind in the willows? You could be dead wrong! Such idyllic holidays may well go undisturbed, but there is also nothing more vulnerable than tents and caravans caught on the riverbank in a rising flood. Mobility becomes a hazard rather than an asset. There are no fire escapes nor an upstairs to which to retreat.

After the 1998 Easter floods which struck the Midlands with such devastating force, the Environment Agency commissioned an independent report on its performance with respect to flood defence. One of the principal conclusions of the resulting the Bye Report[4] concern the vulnerability of camp and caravan sites and the planning law associated with them.

The problem is a well-known one in Northumbria and one which planning authorities over the years have been obliged to confront. A landowner applies for planning permission to locate a new caravan site or extend an existing one adjacent to the river. The planning authority (the District Council) passes a copy of the application to the Environment Agency as a statutory consultee. The Agency inspects its records and carries out analysis of the likely flood levels at the site and makes a recommendation to the Council, which then takes this recommendation into consideration along with other planning matters, in deciding to issue or refuse permission.

The problem is this: how do you balance the enjoyment of a generation of holiday-makers with the risk of a flood at intervals of 10, 20 or even 50 years? The planning authority has an obligation to err on the side of safety and, in spite of their sympathy with the views of the site owner, should not issue a permission where there is an avoidable risk to life and property. The site owner is naturally unhappy with a refusal and will often come back with arguments for special consideration including the following:

1. All the caravans can be moved from the affected part of the site in 30 minutes, allowing sufficient time after the first alarm is raised. This may well be true on a fine afternoon in summer, but it is questionable on a

stormy night with the ground rain-soaked and soft and the flood water creeping up around the wheels of the caravans. There is also the question of what happens when the experienced site owner is absent or if the site is sold on to someone less competent.

2. The caravans will only be occupied in summer and floods occur only during the winter months. It is true that summer floods are less frequent than winter ones[5], but nevertheless floods do occur in summer. The flood on the South Tyne following Hurricane Charlie in August 1986 was second only to the 1995 flood in a 40-year gauged record. On that occasion floods reached about a metre in depth at caravans in the Tyne valley.

3. The Agency's flood warning service always issues sufficient warning for remedial action to be taken. This is the most difficult argument to counter for the Agency is damned if it agrees and damned if it doesn't. However, it must be said that flood hydrology is not an exact science and failures have been known to occur. Reliable and timely warnings on the South Tyne are particularly difficult as illustrated below. Besides, it requires someone to be at home to receive and act on the message for the warning to be effective!

The risks to riverside caravan sites was clearly demonstrated in the 1998 Easter floods in the Midlands. On the Warwickshire Avon alone, 1300 caravans were flooded. Holidaymakers, unaware of or ignoring the dangers, waded to their caravans with the waters still rising. A number of caravans were washed away, some with residents still inside. Hazardous rescue operations were later featured in BBC1's '999' programme. The Bye Report noted that:

> Although development on floodplains is now better controlled, caravan sites are exceptionally vulnerable and licensing must include arrangements for defence against and response to inundation, and,

> Past disregard for the advice of the Agency's predecessors against caravan park developments and extensions had serious consequences at Easter. These large sites, situated by rivers with minimal warning and evacuation arrangements, provided the most serious risk of loss of life. More stringent licensing conditions with requirements for flood risk advice with warning and evacuation instructions are essential.

The danger of flooding to riverside caravan sites raised sufficient public concern that a Private Member's Bill was introduced in the House of Commons in July 1998 by Sally Keeble MP. This recommended that there should be a legal obligation on property owners, (including owners of caravan parks and camping sites) to ascertain from the Agency what the risk of flooding is for the property and then to pass this information on to prospective purchasers or tenants. It also recommended that the proprietors of sites should have a legal obligation to draw up a plan of action in case of flooding. As is often the case with bills introduced under the ten-minute rule, the bill failed at the first hurdle. However the Agency supported the principle of the Bill and continued discussions with the Department of the Environment which has introduced tighter regulation within existing legislation.

Meanwhile the Agency will continue to advise against the siting of any new caravan sites within floodplain areas or the expansion of existing sites. Nevertheless, it is recognised that it is unlikely that well-established sites will be closed and the need for regulation remains.

MANAGING FLOODS

Householders whose property has been flooded must cope with the trauma and expense of the flood and are unlikely to succeed in suing for damages against the government or any official body. Recent policy guidance from the government[6] reiterates that the primary responsibility for safeguarding property from natural hazards such as flooding remains with the owner and that there is no statutory duty on the government. The operating authorities, the Environment Agency and local authorities, have permissive powers but not a duty (except the general 'duty of care') to respond to flood risk and take whatever action is appropriate to minimise such risks. There are essentially four ways in which flood risk and flood damage can be reduced:

❍ Avoiding the flood – planning control on floodplains
❍ Controlling the flood – provision of flood storage
❍ Protecting from the flood – embankments and diversions
❍ Warning and responding to the flood – provision of flood warning services.

National policy and practice have undergone significant changes since the recent widespread floods in 1998 and 2000. Planning controls and flood warning services have been particularly affected. Aspects of relevance to the Tyne are outlined below.

Avoiding the flood

Flood-risk management requires the identification of flood risk areas so that effective controls are exercised on development within such areas. Flood risk in the past was assessed on a reach-by-reach basis but the need for a more holistic approach has now been recognised through catchment flood-management plans. An important contribution to this has been the preparation of 'indicative floodplain maps' for the whole of England and Wales at a scale of 1:10,000, based on a compilation of previous studies[7]. These maps (more than 8000 of them) show the extent of the 100-year return period flood (the flood which occurs on average once in 100 years, or has a 100 to 1 chance of occurrence in the current year). The maps provide the basis for initial evaluation of proposed developments by the local authority in consultation with the Environment Agency.

There are two important considerations. Firstly the development should not itself occur where there is a significant risk of flooding, and secondly the development should not exacerbate flooding elsewhere by restricting natural floodplain storage. Guidance issued by the government to local authorities[7] allows much less local flexibility than was previously available and, although a more rigorous approach was clearly necessary, the new rules may seem unfair and over-restrictive in certain instances.

Developers who wish to contest a refusal by the planning authority on the basis of the indicative maps are obliged to arrange for their own specific hydrological and hydraulic study. It must be recognised that the floodplain maps are 'indicative' rather than definitive and their reliability depends on the availability and quality of previous studies. Locations with no known history of flooding may be included within the mapped boundary. This could be the result of the inadequacy of the indicative maps, but it is also possible that the 100-year flood boundary will enclose some locations which have not been affected for over a century. Most of the people who were affected in the Midlands in the 1998 flood were in locations not previously known to the occupants or to the Environment Agency to be vulnerable to flooding.

Following the recent floods, discussion of development control has centred on what control procedures to adopt for new development. Inadequate consideration appears to be given to existing properties within flood risk areas. There is a danger that occupants who have suffered the trauma of flood eviction may suffer the further harassment of being unable to insure or sell their property.

Stricter controls are now being exercised on floodplains which are defended by flood embankments. It is impractical to build flood banks which will protect against the biggest flood that could ever occur. Flood banks may provide security against the floods of 50- or 100-year return period for which they were designed. However, as recent events have shown, extreme events may overtop, bypass or breach defences, creating more dangerous flooding (through rapid rise in water level) than would have occurred on the undefended floodplain. If there is a loophole in the defences, water will surely find it.

Controlling the flood
The severity of flooding can be ameliorated by the construction of reservoirs specifically designed for the storage of flood water in the headwaters, to be released more slowly after flood conditions downstream have eased. Whilst headwater flood storage reservoirs are widely used to control floods on large catchments in countries such as the U.S., they are not common in Britain and are generally restricted to small urban watercourses.

One alternative is to use reservoirs built for other purposes and adapt the operating rules to include flood control amongst their multifunctional uses. The most important reservoir on the River Tyne in this respect is, of course, Kielder Water which makes a significant contribution to flood alleviation on the North Tyne and Tyne. The operating policy at Kielder ensures that the reservoir is rarely full and spilling, and that there is reserve storage capacity to capture at least the initial flood inflow into the reservoir. Even when Kielder is full, the reservoir storage reduces the peak downstream flow to less than half of what would naturally have occurred. Thus gauged records show that flows of over 300 cumecs were experienced on a number of occasions on the upper North Tyne before Kielder was built, but the highest recorded flow since construction has been 122 cumecs in February 2002.

A reduction of up to 200 cumecs in flood flow from the Kielder catchment reduces flood risk downstream but does not eliminate flood risk entirely even on the North Tyne. The catchment area of 240 km^2 is only one quarter of the whole North Tyne and one tenth of the catchment area to the Tyne estuary. In other words, 75% of the North Tyne and 90% of the main Tyne is uninfluenced by Kielder and remains subject to the natural vagaries of storm rainfall and melting snow. The flood of January 1995 demonstrates the continued potential for flooding from the Tyne, and especially the influence of the South Tyne which is without means of control.

Flood storage may also take the form of 'washlands' which are essentially parts of floodplains to which the entry and exit of water is controlled. In modest floods the floodplain is protected, but in higher floods, gates in the embankment are opened and the flood water allowed access. In this way the flood volume downstream is reduced and vulnerable sites protected. Such washlands are common on the Yorkshire Ouse. There are none on the Tyne and no prospect of using such a device. The extent of active natural floodplain along the Tyne is limited and it has been restricted even further by the dredging of the bed for gravel extraction (Chapter 4). Many reaches such as the South Tyne at Fourstones and the Tyne between Bywell and Ovingham have floodplains which were historically active but now, even in the most severe floods experienced, the flood level has fallen well short of the banktop.

Protecting from the flood
Historically the primary focus of flood defence in England and Wales has been the building of engineering structures, mainly flood defence embankments. After the floods of 1998 and 2000 such structures have been more widely recognised as incomplete solutions.

For a river of its length, the River Tyne has only a small proportion of its length along which land and property are protected by floodbanks. Compared with rivers further south, the number of vulnerable properties on the floodplain or adjacent to the river are fortunately small. Most riparian towns and villages such as Hexham, Corbridge (at least the north bank) and Ovingham are located on post-glacial terraces well above current flood levels.

Reaches protected by flood banks include parts of Haltwhistle, Haydon Bridge, Warden, Corbridge and Prudhoe. There are no flood embankments on the North Tyne and only limited reaches are protected on the River Rede at West Woodburn and Otterburn. Most of the present structures on the Tyne were designed in response to the occurrence of a particular severe flood, for example, those at Warden and Corbridge which were constructed following the January 1955 flood with the banktop at one foot above that flood level. More recently, statistical risk assessment has been used in design flood estimation, and the original design embankment levels and channel capacity have been checked against the new standards. Nevertheless, embankments have been constructed to finite design standards; it is impractical to build defences which will protect against the most extreme flood possible. When a more extreme event than the design flood occurs (as it ultimately will — though hopefully not in our lifetime), the embankment will be overtopped and may be breached, leading to severe and rapid flooding of property thought to be protected. Also, the structural integrity of embankments several decades old also cannot be completely assured. Such was the case at Corbridge in 1995.

It is unlikely that many more embankments will be built on the River Tyne though, no doubt, greater impetus will be given to ensuring that present structures are structurally sound and of an adequate height.

Flood warning

Flood warning is the last line of defence against damage and loss in flood incidents. On the River Tyne the first rudimentary flood warning service was established in the early 1960s with the setting up of river level recording stations at Bellingham and Haltwhistle to send alarm signals to Hexham Police Station. Technological advances in monitoring and communication, as well as public expectation, have ensured that a more robust system is now in place. However, floods are such variable natural phenomena that, even with the best scientific expertise, flooding cannot always be predicted with complete reliability.

The prediction of flood levels at vulnerable locations can enable householders and industry to take action to mitigate the damage. However, there are many links in the chain of warning and response; if one of these is weak or broken, then no action is taken and damage is done which could have been avoided. The Environment Agency now has the lead role in the flood-warning service which comprises several interlinked elements as exemplified in the flood of January 1995, described above.

O Monitoring of weather and catchment conditions through a network of river level and rainfall gauges whose locations are shown in Figs. 1.1 and 1.2. Rainfall radar systems accessible by computer also show the current areal distribution and intensity of rainfall. Prior warning of such events is given by the Met. Office through its severe weather warning service.

O Prediction of future water levels. In its simplest form this involves comparison of levels between upstream and downstream stations. Computer models are now more widely used to predict river levels from rainfall and to track the progress of the flood wave down the river channel.

O Preparation of warnings for locations vulnerable to flooding, usually by establishing threshold levels at which particular sites will flood.

O Dissemination of warnings to those at risk and to operational organisations including the police and emergency authorities. Warnings were issued to the public through the intermediary of the police until the mid-1990s when they relinquished the responsibility as possibly conflicting with their front-line duty of crime prevention. The Environment Agency has now taken on the role directly and have concentrated efforts on technological solutions of automatic voice messaging by telephone and media coverage.

❍ Emergency response by operational organisations and the public.

The River Tyne provides the most challenging conditions for the operation of a flood-warning service. This is mainly due to the extraordinary speed with which the flood wave moves down the channel but there are other complicating factors. Fig. 1.3 shows the progress of a flood wave on the South Tyne and Tyne in November 2000 whilst Fig. 2.1 shows equivalent data for the severe flood of January 1995. These figures provide a simplified picture because there are data from many more gauges to consider including those on the North Tyne. In Table 2.1 the travel time of the peak flow from Alston down to Bywell is shown for the two events.

Table 2.1   Travel time of peak flow from Alston to Bywell

Event date	ALSTON Peak time	FEATHERSTONE Peak time	Time from Alston (hrs)	HAYDON BRIDGE Peak time	Time from Alston (hrs)	BYWELL Peak time	Time from Alston (hrs)
Jan 1995	13.30	13.15	−0.25	14.45	1.25	18.45	5.25
Nov 2000	12.15	13.15	1.0	14.15	2.0	18.00	5.75

1. Travel time of the peak from the headwater station at Alston to Bywell, a distance of 72 km, is less than 6 hours in these two floods. Just another couple of hours can be added for the time from the occurrence of rainfall and a further hour for the peak to pass to the estuary – a total of less than 10 hours. This compares with approximately 2 days for the Yorkshire Ouse and 4 days for the rivers Severn and Trent.

2. In the January 1995 event the downstream station at Featherstone reached a peak earlier than the upstream one at Alston. This earlier occurrence may have been due to the areal distribution of rainfall or the effects of melting snow – which is always a complicating factor with Tyne winter floods.

3. Industrial properties at Haltwhistle (which were flooded in 1995) between Featherstone and Haydon Bridge have little more than one hour's notice from the highest gauging station at Alston. Given the time for monitoring, preparing the forecast and communicating the message, there will inevitably be little time left for mitigating action.

4. The flood wave front becomes steeper as it moves downstream. At Alston the maximum rate of rise was only 0.25 metres per hour, but this increased to over one metre per hour at Haydon Bridge and 1.5 metres per hour at Bywell. If occupants wait until the flood approaches their

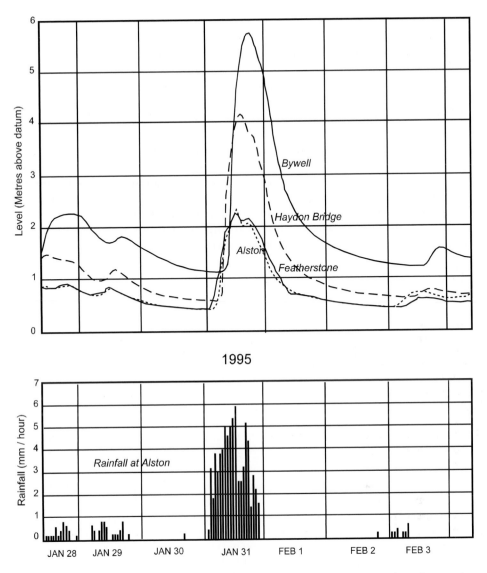

Fig 2.1 The destructive flood wave of 31 January 1995 (shown as level at the gauging station) on the Tyne from Alston to Bywell, with Alston rainfall.

property (or the top of the flood bank) before taking mitigating action, they are likely to be too late.

Amongst the recent changes in EA approach has been the creation of a National Flood Warning Centre (NFWC) which is attempting to improve the quality of the service to the public. Based on experience in recent floods the NFWC stated that 'the provision of accurate forecasts is of no benefit if a warning is not received or acted upon or if actions taken are ineffective'[8]. The first efforts have not therefore been on technological improvements but on simply getting the message across. Firstly NFWC has introduced a more understandable set of flood warning codes. Secondly they have set up a programme to raise public awareness of flood risks and to motivate people at risk to take action to protect themselves and their properties. If readers wish to know more or require information during a flood, they can contact the EA FLOODLINE at 0845 9881188.

Nevertheless, it is now recognised that in some locations, including parts of the Tyne catchment, it is not yet possible to provide accurate, reliable and timely warnings in every set of circumstances. It would seem appropriate that the Environment Agency, as part of its new emphasis on integrated flood management, should accord a higher level of protection by embankments to existing developments where flood warning is difficult or impossible, and secondly should discourage further inappropriate development in such locations.

REFERENCES

1. Archer, D.R. (1992) *Land of Singing Waters: Rivers and Great Floods of Northumbria.* Spredden Press.
2. RIBAMOD (1999) RIBAMOD River basin modelling, management and flood mitigation – concerted action: the impact of climatic change on flooding and sustainable river management. In: (Eds) Balbanis, P., Bronstert, A. Casale, R. and Samuels, P.G. *Proceedings of the Final Workshop.* European Commission, EUR 18287 EN, 1-404.
3. Institution of Civil Engineers (2001) *Learning to Live with Rivers,* Final Report of the ICE Presidential Commission to review the technical aspects of flood risk management in England and Wales, ICE, London.
4. Bye, P. and Horner, M.W. (1998*) Floods; Report by the Independent Review Team to the Board of the Environment Agency.*
5. Archer, D.R. (1981) Seasonality of flooding and the assessment of seasonal flood risk. *Proceedings Institution of Civil Engineers,* Part 2, 1023–1035.
6. Department for Transport, Local Government and the Regions (2001) *Planning Policy Guidance Note 25: Development and Flood Risk* (PPG25).
7. Jeremy Benn Associates Ltd. (2000) *The Environment Agency national Section 105 framework agreement – NATCON 257: Extreme flood outline. Final Report.* JBA, Skipton.
8. Haywood, J. (2001) Flood forecasting and warning theme: introductory notes, in *Proceedings of the 36th DEFRA Conference of River and Coastal Engineers.* Paper 10.6.

3. THE CHANGING TYNE VALLEY AND RIVER CHANNEL

MALCOLM NEWSON

INTRODUCTION

Although our study of the River Tyne starts with the flowing water in the river, it is also concerned with the changing channel in which the water flows, the valley which holds the channel and the catchment or basin which contributes water to the river. Flowing water plays a key role in the creation and form of the channel and adjoining floodplain, valley and catchment. Geomorphology is the science of landforms whilst fluvial geomorphology is concerned with river *forms* and the *processes* of erosion, transport and deposition by which rivers sculpt their channels, floodplains and valley floors.

Whilst hydrology is often concerned with changes in river flow over very short timescales, for example in floods, geomorphology deals with a much wider range of timescales. Where it is concerned with river *processes* the geomorphological timescale of interest is often the same as for hydrology since sediment moves with the water in the channel, given of course that sediment is available. However, in studying the evolution of river basins like that of the Tyne, a very long timescale is required; the journey of a rock particle through weathering, to soil, to landslide, to floodplain storage and thence via the channel to the ocean may take tens of thousands of years. Over such a long period the climate changes and the balance of natural and man-made influence also changes. Disentangling these influences brings a considerable element of forensics to the work done by fluvial geomorphologists.

Different elements of river landforms adjust at different timescales. A gravel bar at a meander bend may fluctuate in size and shape on an annual basis, but the overall gradient of the channel from source to mouth may take thousands of years to adjust to geological and climatic changes. Long timescales of change have obvious relevance for modern sustainable approaches to river management that implicitly cover centuries and are represented in the slogan 'our children's children's children'. Fluvial geomorphology is in a good position to think in these timescales and therefore to provide a counterbalance to the river manager's tendency to adopt the political timescales of 'action now, here'.

TRADITIONAL GEOMORPHOLOGY AND THE TYNE

Fashion changes in science. Many readers will have used school textbooks which described the landscape in terms of 'the cycle of erosion' based on the work of an eminent American geomorphologist, William Morris Davis[1]. His basic idea was that rivers worked on a pristine rock surface that had emerged from beneath the ocean, and by stages wore it down to a nearly flat plain (peneplain) adjusted to the current level of the sea – called base level. Such wearing down operated over very long geological timescales (millions of years). Although within Davis' scheme, landform development was also influenced by geological structure and physical processes, the main determinant of landforms was the stage of development. Both rivers and landscapes were described as *youthful, mature* or *old age,* with characteristic features of each stage. In its simplest form the scheme indicated that there was a progressive change in rivers from youthful, steep, upland channels hemmed in by narrow valleys to old age river channels meandering over wide flood plains.

Whilst such a scheme worked well for some parts of the United States, far from the sea and uninfluenced by glacial activity during the Ice Age, it could not be so easily applied to Britain, where rivers were clearly influenced by fluctuations in relative sea level and by glacial disruption of river courses. Nevertheless this framework was also used in Britain by some geomorphologists who set up a grand theory of the origins of all our landscapes and major river systems, while recognising that landscapes and rivers are the result of more than a single cycle of erosion. Landscapes and rivers were said to be polycyclic and to retain the evidence of former cycles in their catchment areas and in their long profiles. Thus upland surfaces of low relief, such as the moorlands of Hexhamshire, were identified - and dated - as remnants of ancient flood plains, elevated by earth crustal movements. This interplay of land and sea level creates the context for our description of the Tyne and its tributaries in terms of their relationship with landscape.

Hikers often trek to "where the Tyne begins" – a point on Alston Moor now marked with a sculpture (Plate 7) – but few ask "**when** did the Tyne begin?" The Tyne and other 'proto-rivers' such as the Tweed, Trent and Thames started to cut their courses approximately 30 million years ago in the early Tertiary era. The land mass of Britain was rising from the sea in which Chalk rocks had been laid down during the previous Cretaceous period, providing the eastward-tilting 'proto-landscape', upon which these rivers began to carve their valleys. In the Tyne area the Tertiary rivers entirely removed the softer cover of Chalk rocks and, in accordance with the principles of the cycle of erosion cut a nearly flat peneplain surface on harder, more ancient rocks. This surface was subsequently elevated to create the plateaus we see forming moorlands today. Thus the Pennine moorlands appear to be primarily the inheritance of the Tertiary period. Quaternary ice-sheets and valley glaciers then further etched the pre-glacial surface and diverted and blocked the river systems to create the origins of today's river landscape.

Whilst geomorphologists today would argue little with this broad outline of historical river development, they would be much more cautious in their interpretation of the origins of comparatively flat moorland surfaces as the end-products of the cycle of erosion. At this stage there was very little knowledge of how rivers 'worked' in terms of moving sediments, and so the interpretation of such ancient surfaces was highly speculative.

Interpretation of the cycle of erosion with respect to rivers and neighbouring seas depended to a great extent on an examination of the river's longitudinal

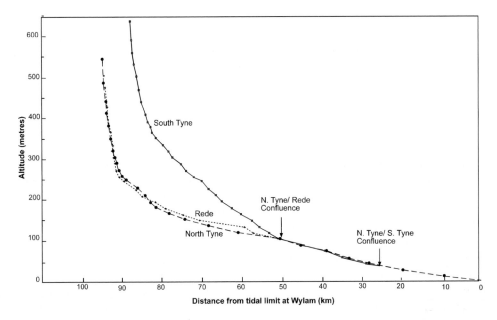

Fig 3.1 The longitudinal profiles of the Tyne, South Tyne, North Tyne and Rede

profile, that is the pattern of gradient from source to mouth (Fig 3.1). The ideal or 'graded' river profile, cut to a stable base level, is a smooth progression from the steep channel in the headwaters to a low gradient as the river approaches the sea. In the River Tyne headwater tributaries have gradients of between 1% and 10% whilst at the tidal limit the channel gradient is around 0.1%. The South Tyne has clearly a much steeper gradient than the North Tyne. However, the River Tyne shows several deviations from the smooth decline of river gradients, an example being the steep section of the North Tyne at Warden gorge compared with much flatter sections upstream on the North Tyne and Rede.

Such changes in river gradient have been interpreted as the result of changes in base level. When base level falls, rivers adjust by cutting down into their bed, initially near the coast, and then enhanced downcutting progressively works its way upstream. Such polycyclic longitudinal river profiles show a levelling off towards a historic base level with a break or 'knick-point' in the river's longitudinal profile, for example at the confluence of the Rede and North Tyne (Fig 3.1). Whilst the profile of the Tyne may well be influenced by such base level changes, the changes in gradient may equally be the result of glacial erosion, deposition or river diversion.

The influence of base level is also recorded in the lower reaches of the Tyne where excavations/drilling (e.g. for the A1M motorway bridge foundations) have revealed a buried bedrock valley some 35m below current sea-level on the south side of the river.

Whatever their origin, these changes in base level and river gradient are critical for the way the river now works. Because gravity is the principal physical driver of river development, the steeper knick-point sections deliver very high stream power for erosion, including the erosion of bedrock, and the flatter gradients and wider valley floors offer an opportunity for storing and sorting sediment.

The Tyne was completely within the limits of the most recent major glaciation of Britain — the Devensian. Ice sheets flowing in a southeasterly direction originated from the Lake District and Solway area, but there were also local ice caps in the upper reaches of both the South Tyne and North Tyne. The direction of ice movement resulted in considerable erosional and depositional development of the pre-glacial river valleys but also in modification of the intervening watershed lines, for example through meltwater drainage beneath the ice[2]. Such drainage channels were not conditioned by the underlying topography, rather their flow depended on hydraulic pressure in the sub-glacial tunnels. Thus they often cut across the existing topography and even across interfleuves between valleys and can be recognised as steeply-cut channels, now with very small streams or none at all. Examples can be seen on Hexhamshire Common on the upper Rowley Burn and Devils Water and at Whittonstall and East Dipton[3].

The deglaciation process is not now interpreted as being in the form of 'withdrawal' of ice but rather as stagnation and melting in-situ. During the summer months glacial melt released large flows from the glaciers, containing a heavy load of readily-available sediment; we know this from observations of contemporary 'wasting' glaciers and ice sheets. These sediments were then deposited to create a variety of glacio-fluvial features – eskers, kames and deltas such as those between Whittonstall and Ebchester and at Ryton. Typically these glacio-fluvial sediments are less well sorted and rounded than river gravels but in the North East they provide the basis for some of the largest sources for economic extraction of gravel.

Between them the Tertiary and Quaternary eras (of fluvial and glacio-fluvial activity, respectively) have profoundly influenced the courses of rivers and their valleys. The process called 'river capture' is often invoked to explain anomalies in the direction which rivers take. The suggestion is that a more vigorous component of the drainage network 'lures' a neighbour to draw its flow and divert its valley. The Tyne has benefitted from a number of suggested captures. For example, it has been suggested that rivers like the Wansbeck and Blyth would, like the Tyne, have originally arisen on the Pennine watershed, but the more active erosion of the North Tyne valley has captured their headwaters. Thus, according to this theory[4] the Rivers Rede and North Tyne were once headwaters of the Wansbeck, and the Warks Burn a headwater of the Blyth (1, 2 and 3 in Fig. 3.2). In support of this theory it is pointed out that the Rede at West Woodburn and the North Tyne below Redesmouth make abrupt changes of direction, which are interpreted as 'elbows of capture'.

Rivers may also have been captured by blockage of the valley by ice or by glacial and glacio-fluvial deposits. The Tyne has lost a major tributary as a result of glacial diversion. The pre-glacial River Wear joined the lower reaches of the Tyne via a channel along the course of the lower Team (4 in Fig. 3.2). Its original valley, cut in bedrock and identified in boreholes, was blocked by glacial deposits, forcing the Wear to find an alternative route to the North Sea.

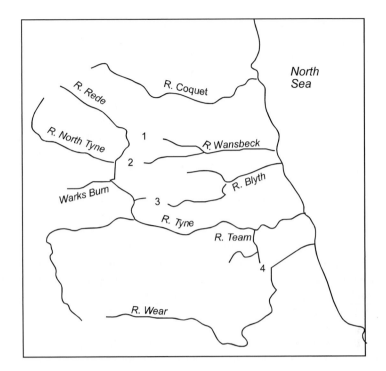

Fig 3.2 Possible river captures in the Tyne catchment

A MODERN VIEW OF RIVER SYSTEMS: THE TYNE AS A CONVEYOR OF SEDIMENTS

There has been a trend in the study of geomorphology over the past two decades away from such explanatory and descriptive studies of the landscape to the investigation of contemporary geomorphological *processes*. In the case of river systems the main focus of attention has been on the dynamics of sediment movement. In particular there is a practical interest in how and why rivers, which in the past have been stable, begin to erode their banks and to either cut down or build up their bed.

The study of river dynamics is shared between geomorphologists and civil or hydraulic engineers; both have an important role to play in river management. Engineers in the past have been required to solve such practical problems as overbank flooding and bank erosion. They have done so by attempts to 'control' the behaviour of the river by dredging the channel, protecting or stabilising the bank or, in the extreme case, confining the river in a straightened channel between earth embankments or even encasing it in concrete as in the Team valley. Experience has shown that such attempts at control have sometimes been misplaced.

The natural River Tyne (insofar as it is natural after several millennia of human occupation of its basin) is in a state of *dynamic equilibrium*. What this means is that the river adjusts its form and gradient to transport the sediment load provided to it from the basin upstream. If engineering causes a change in channel slope, cross section or sediment load, there is a displacement of the equilibrium in a direction that will tend to absorb the effect of the change. Thus engineered solutions in one reach have sometimes exacerbated problems upstream or downstream, requiring the repeated and costly application of control measures. Recognising these difficulties, river managers have sought solutions which would be more in sympathy with the natural behaviour of the river — to work with the river rather than attempt to control it. This approach is the basis for the work of 'river restoration' — now being applied to rivers which have previously received harsh control measures, such as the Team. River restoration also has significant benefits for river ecology.

Such an approach requires an understanding of relationships between the hydrological regime (and especially flood flows), sediment transport and river geometry or form. Given the variability of each of the elements in the equation, the task is far from simple. Engineers have tended to address the problem by studying the physics of sediment movement and by laboratory modelling studies. This approach has the advantage of limiting the variability of the elements being considered. Geomorphologists on the other hand have concentrated on field studies, attempting to measure each of the controlling variables in the natural state and to assess the changes which are occurring or have occurred as the result of some natural or man-made disturbance to the equilibrium. Practically, this means that geomorphologists measure sediment sizes and structures in the active river channel, trace sediment movements and link these to hydrological regime and local hydraulic conditions.

Thus geomorphological studies link very closely to engineering studies of river mechanics and consequently have a considerable applied value in river management. Typical problems that are addressed by geomorphological research and for which management advice can be provided include:

○ Flooding out-of-bank from the channel (Chapter 2),
○· Loss of land to erosion or flood hazards resulting from erosion/ deposition,
○ River and riparian habitats - the river is not just a channel! (Chapter 5),
○ Impacts of development, urban and rural, on the river's flow and its sources of sediments.

Studies of river processes also have a historical perspective, though the emphasis now is on the timescale of decades to perhaps a few millennia rather than on the geological timescale of descriptive geomorphology. Such studies centre on the survey and interpretation of valley-floor landforms and deposits of river sediments in terms of the effect of changing climate and land use. Archaeological evidence and datable objects such as buried trees that can be sampled for radio-carbon dates assist in the interpretation. However, river process studies must also have regard to the pre-glacial inheritance and the influence of glacial activity on valley morphology and the availability of sediment for working by the river.

The ultimate 'drivers' of channel form or morphology are the flow regime and the input of sediment to the river channel. The balance between water and sediment inputs controls the tendency of the channel either to erode or to build up its bed. Intensity and frequency of flooding are the most important characteristics of the hydrological regime with respect to sediment because coarser sediment is only eroded and transported when the flow and associated velocity exceed given thresholds. Over time, the intensity and frequency of flooding change in response to changing climate and land use. Land use also influences the amount of sediment available for transport. Some of the ways in which changes in climate and land use have influenced the changing river channel of the Tyne, through the intermediary of the flow regime and available sediment, are explored below.

In bringing together both the 'pure' and 'applied' worlds of science and the historical and contemporary impacts of the Tyne catchment upon the river, geomorphologists have learned to be much more flexible. Rather than the rigidity of the W.M.Davis 'universal' model of river basin development, we have evolved a much more site-specific analysis that focuses on the way in which processes work at particular sites, in suites of sites and — tentatively — for whole systems.

THE WINDING RIVER: A TENDENCY TO WANDER

Rivers have a natural tendency to *meander* wherever they have sufficient power to erode their banks and bed. If we set up an experiment in the laboratory with an initially straight channel in erodable material, the channel quickly develops asymmetrical deeper pools and shallower riffles (Plate 8), which divert the flow against the banks, causing erosion. It is not long before the straight channel develops a sinuous course (Plate 9). Examination of both laboratory experiments and natural rivers in alluvium suggests that the wavelength of such meanders (the distance from the crest of one meander to the next) is about 12 times the width of the river.

The Tyne has meanders, but only in limited reaches is the width of the valley sufficient for full meander development. The valley topography is still strongly influenced by the heritage of the glacial period, and the river does not have to swing far across its narrow valley floor before it is confined by steep banks of glacial deposits or even by rock. Analysis of historical Ordnance Survey maps shows that the North Tyne has occupied essentially the same course for at least 140 years[6]. The Tyne is confined right down to the estuary; the steep valley sides between Newcastle and Gateshead are hardly characteristic of the Davisian model of the river in old age.

Even when the meanders are confined or when the river is nearly straight, as it is between Bywell and Ovington, sequences of pools and riffles alternate along the channel. These are also natural features of gravel bed rivers and it is generally observed that riffles are spaced at about five to seven times the channel width — or about half the spacing of meanders. This pattern has been found to be true of the North Tyne which has a system of well-defined diagonally alternating riffles and pools[7]. In spite of the river's ability to move sediment in floods, the riffles tend to remain in the same location. Riffle sites on the North Tyne appear not to have changed position since at least 1867, as suggested by the position of fording sites, which were established on the shallower riffle sites.

Whilst a single thread channel is typical, locally the South Tyne has developed a quite different channel form – the *braided river* (Plate 10). Braided reaches are characterised by having a number of alluvial channels in which bars and islands separate the channels, presenting from the air the intertwining effect of a braid. The overall width tends to be much higher than for single-thread channels. Braided reaches occur on the South Tyne at The Islands, Williamston, Knarsdale, Eals, Lambley, Featherstone and Broomhouse[8].

Braided rivers are the most dynamic and unstable of fluvial patterns. During floods there are rapid changes in channel position; bars and islands migrate and river banks are rapidly eroded. There is no clear-cut set of conditions which determines whether a channel reach will be of a single-thread or a braided pattern but it is evident that two important conditions are, a very high load of sediment and erodable banks. Braiding often occurs where tributaries join and contribute a heavy sediment load, e.g. the Islands (Black Burn) and at Knarsdale (Knar Burn). Divided channel zones are separated by laterally-stable, entrenched, single-thread reaches that vary in length from 14km (between The Islands and Williamston) to 0.5km (between Lambley and Featherstone).

THE ROLE OF CLIMATE CHANGE

We are in the midst of a period of significant climate change. Global warming appears to be driven by the rapid and continuing increase in emission of greenhouse gases to the atmosphere. The Inter-Governmental Panel on Climate Change predicts that if no action is taken to further limit greenhouse gases, average global temperatures could rise by up to 3.5°C by the end of this century. Some readers might consider this a welcome improvement to Britain's weather, whether or not the change will spell disaster for countries further south. However, there are other predicted effects which will hardly be favourable to Britain, including the effects of rising sea level and the changing hydrological regime of rivers with associated effects on river stability. It is predicted that Britain's climate will become more subject to extremes of droughts and floods. The severe droughts and floods of the last decade seem to indicate that such a climatic change has already occurred, though due allowance must be made for natural variability.

Global and local climate change is not new. Over the last 1.6 million years the climate has fluctuated between glacial and interglacial states, and the last glacial period, the Devensian, came to an end only 11,500 years ago. There seems little doubt that the present period is interglacial rather than marking a definitive end to glacial activity. Such broad climatic changes are generated by cyclic variations in solar activity but can be accentuated by feedback mechanisms in global climate and oceanic circulation. The changes can also be extremely rapid. Analysis of Greenland ice cores shows that at the end of the cold Younger Dryas period (which marks the beginning of the present climatic era) the temperature rose abruptly by 7°C over a period of only a decade or so[9].

Nor has climate been static since the end of the Ice Age nor even over the last millennium; there have been fluctuations both in temperature and in precipitation. The Little Ice Age from about 1600 to 1800 was a period of notably low temperatures, both preceded and followed by milder conditions. Wetter and drier periods are characterised by changes in the frequency and strength of depressions moving into Britain from the Atlantic and by the consequent frequency of large floods that can erode and move sediment. Periods of high and low frequency of depressions last for a decade or more and are related to variations in atmospheric pressure gradients over the North Atlantic.

Rumsby and Macklin[10] have compared such periods of 'meridional' and 'zonal' circulation with the changing behaviour of the Tyne with respect to the cutting down (incision) and building up (aggradation) of the channel. Meridional circulation produces storms with widespread, heavy rain and leads to long-duration, high-level flood flows capable of moving tributary-derived sediments down the main-stem of the river. Zonal circulation produces a preponderance of convectional local storms of high intensity that tend to have more effect on tributaries. The periods of meridional circulation are identified as 1760–1799, 1875–1894 and 1955–1969 and appear to be associated with rapid incision of the river bed at investigation sites on the Thinhope Burn (tributary to the South Tyne) and at Hexham and Low Prudhoe. Periods of zonal circulation, 1820–1874 and 1920–1954, tend to be associated either with a stable bed or aggradation of the channel. It must be noted however that gravel extraction (see below) has also had an effect on vertical changes in the bed level through the mid-twentieth century, though the precise impacts of such 'damage' to the river bed remain to be evaluated by geomorphological surveys.

The intensity of river braiding processes also appears to vary with broad changes in climate. Historical studies[11] shows that river braiding was more active in the late Roman period, in the thirteenth and fourteenth centuries and in the eighteenth and nineteenth century.

These historic fluctuations in fluvial personality of the Tyne provide a model for the kind of changes which may be in store with future climatic change.

THE HUMAN INFLUENCE: THE TYNE FROM THE 'DAWN OF CIVILISATION'

Human development pressures can influence the hydrological and geomorphological character of river basins but our knowledge of these impacts is recent and partial. There is continual debate about the magnitude of human influences on river landforms and processes, and whether the small research areas chosen for study because they are geomorphologically 'interesting' are really representative of broader patterns of river behaviour. Are land use influences ever as significant as direct river management options like damming? It has also been difficult to unravel the comparative influence of human activities and those of climate. Lewin and Macklin[12], for example, have described the current fluvial signature of the Tyne as being "climatically driven but culturally blurred".

Deforestation

Much attention has been drawn to the fluvial impacts of rapid deforestation in the developing world. Sediment yields tend to be increased, for example, by increased landslides in headwater catchments and by the direct mechanical impacts of extraction procedures. Prehistoric and historical deforestation has also been linked with increased sediment production and deposition in Britain. However, the manual transformation of the landscape was by comparison very slow and is unlikely to have generated anything like the changes that have occurred with modern forest extraction or destruction. The first evidence we have of forest disturbance in the Tyne basin does not occur until the second millennium BC when trees were cleared for farming. Expansion of settlement in the Iron Age and Romano-British periods led to widespread and permanent clearance; the construction and use of Hadrian's Wall formed a focus for the settlement of the northern parts of the catchment and this expansion lasted until depopulation set in (for a couple of centuries) in the fourteenth century.

Lead/heavy metal mining

Metal mining activity increased the quantity of both fine (sand and smaller) and coarse (gravel and larger) sediments delivered to river channels. Additions of coarse material occurred mainly from the spoil heaps of ore-processing but also through the process of 'hushing'. 'Hushing' involved clearing the soil from the valley floors of upland tributaries by breaching temporary dams (constructed from earth) and allowing the resulting flood wave to do the geomorphological task of exposing bedrock. Fine-grained sediments originated from the use of water for separating the ore in 'buddles'. (Lead, silver and zinc are 'heavy metals' and settle preferentially to the barren rock).

The legacy of lead mining has been profound, both positively and negatively. Whilst botanists can now invoke national-level protection for some of the rare metal-tolerant plants colonising the South Tyne gravels (Chapter 5), farmers utilising floodplain soils for livestock or cereals are faced with very high metal contents which either stunt or pollute the pasture or crop. Generally, in the South Tyne the lack of plant colonisation of channel forms such as bars and islands, because of metal pollution, has created a less 'stable' river channel — although vegetation growth is not the only factor in channel stability.

Documentary evidence for lead mining in the South Tyne valley dates from the twelfth century and probably earlier; peak production occurred in the mid-nineteenth century. Production virtually ceased by the beginning of the twentieth century but the valley floor and valley sides are littered with hushes, adits and spoil heaps, that form sources of both fine and coarse river sediments to this day, especially during flood conditions.

However, from the academic viewpoint of fluvial geomorphology, a positive outcome is that where heavy metal content is related to production figures from the mines, it is possible to estimate dates of river features. Use has also been made of metal-tolerant lichens whose size correlates with age. Together with analysis of historic maps, these techniques have allowed a forensic compilation of the dynamic switches of fluvial adjustment, as exemplified by the South Tyne

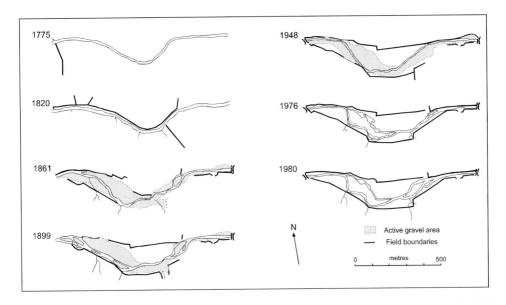

Fig 3.3   A sequence of channel changes on the River Nent at Blagill illustrating the
change from a single thread channel to a complex braided channel
(After Macklin, 1986)

during the last century and a half. Sites of detailed investigations have included
the valley of the West Allen[12], and of the River Nent at Blagill[13]. On these valley
floors are both palaeo-channels (former courses of the river etched as sinuous
depressions in the floodplain) and terraces. The terraces of the Tyne, especially
those of the South Tyne, are not only prominent elements of the landscape but
they can also be dated. The lower ones can be dated according to their heavy
metal content and the higher ones from artefacts or carbonaceous material, whose
radioactivity can be analysed.

Fig. 3.3 shows a sequence of channel changes on the River Nent at Blagill[13]
illustrating the change in channel form from a single-thread channel in the early
nineteenth century to a complex braided channel by mid-century. The active
gravel area has been decreasing again since the mid-twentieth century.

Gravel extraction

Most of Britain's gravel-bed rivers are exploited for building materials, road
materials and fill for drainage schemes - most frequently by riparian farmers
who remove a few hundred tons of material annually by driving a digger and
trailer on to exposed bars at low flow. However, on the Tyne at least fifteen
commercially-worked sites have been identified[14] (Chapter 4). Two-thirds of
these are on the main stem of the river and the remaining sites on the South
Tyne; the total worked reach was almost 20 km but the influence extended
upstream and downstream from each reach for a further considerable distance.
The total extraction from 1891 to 1972 is estimated to be 4.6 million tonnes,

whilst estimated bed material transport rates for the affected reaches range from 10,000 to 15,000 tonnes per annum. Archer[15] suggests a potentially major influence for gravel removal on morphological adjustment; in some of the affected reaches (e.g. Fourstones) recent channel change has been spectacular, with the South Tyne moving away from bank works (installed after the 1947 floods) by up to 20 m and incising below their level by almost 2 m.

River regulation: dams on the North Tyne

The headwaters of the North Tyne were impounded during 1981-82 in the final stages of construction of Kielder Dam; since then the hydrological regime of the reaches immediately below the dam has been dominated by releases through the turbines for hydro-electric power generation (Chapter 10). Whilst flow variability can be quite rapid (e.g. from 1.3 to 16.0 cumecs in two hours) the overall flow range is heavily constrained by storage of flood waters. The main impact stems from the lack of 'big' floods at points downstream until the contributions of unregulated tributaries help to make up the flood discharge deficit. This regime has many geomorphological and ecological implications which may be progressive through time.

The main geomorphological impact of the reservoir has been the 'de-coupling of the sediment conveyor belt'[7]. Coarse sediment and sand from upstream tributaries is trapped in the reservoir and the released water contains only fine sediment in suspension or solution. The combination of reduced flood flows and the cessation of sediment from upstream has resulted not only in a progressive coarsening of gravel on the riffle surfaces but also in an increase in the infiltration of fine sediment (<1 mm) into the gravel bed[16]. The 'normal' sediment transport regime during flood conditions empties pool accumulations on to the next riffle downstream - thus diversifying the riffle's sediment size range, loosening the sediment, and creating ideal ecological conditions for invertebrates and for salmon spawning (Chapter 5). The constrained flow range below Kielder causes the finer gravel/sand material to be transported from riffles to pools, coarsening and hardening (armouring) the riffles, so that they can become unsuitable for salmon spawning. The effect is most marked above the confluence of North Tyne with the Tarset and Chirdon Burn confluences, but is also evident further downstream.

The geomorphological influence of unregulated tributaries has also been demonstrated on the North Tyne, particularly in the form of the troublesome bar that regularly forms below the entry of the Tarset Burn[17]. The Tarset is an energetic upland stream with plentiful sediment supplies, able to deliver an abundant load to the North Tyne which, due to lack of flood power, cannot move the material downstream. The resulting accumulation has promoted erosion of the opposite bank, threatening the minor road.

Afforestation: North Tyne

One of Europe's largest plantation forests, Kielder Forest, is located predominantly in the headwaters of the North Tyne. Influences of afforestation on the hydrological regime are outlined in Chapters 1 and 6; afforestation has also potential for significant geomorphological changes both in influencing the sediment supply and in altering the flows to carry the sediment. The main information on the effects of afforestation are from the Coalburn experimental catchment set up in 1973[18]. Although it was situated in the Irthing catchment (anticipating reservoir construction there) rather than the North Tyne, results are widely relevant to upland afforested catchments in Britain.

In summary, the Coalburn study has shown that:

○ Ground preparation (ploughing/draining) to establish trees on wet moorland peaty sites leads to increased 'flashiness' of flood response and to a 'haemorrhage' of peat-bog water, boosting low flows for a decade or more.

○ As conifers grow and close their canopy across the entire land surface, interception of rainfall adds to transpiration losses, dries the soil beneath the trees, and reduces the runoff from the catchment.

○ Ground preparation releases from the catchment large amounts of sediment which are removed by the increased floods.

○ Conifers are efficient scourers of atmospheric pollution, notably dry deposition of the acid components of combustion. Biodiversity suffers from the resulting episodes of acid streamflow.

River restoration and riparian management schemes
Some may feel that our present attitude to the human influence on the natural environment is unduly tinged with guilt, provoking an over-reaction to unproven 'damage'. Communities and their livelihoods do indeed need to be protected against flooding, and infrastructure does require access to and crossings of river channels. However, it is now recognised that at the national level more than 60% of our river channels have had their ecosystems disturbed by human intervention, and the European Union (in its Water Framework Directive) is forcing us to turn our attention to the promotion of ecosystem goods and services *as well as* human well-being. Unlike other Northumbrian rivers like the Till, the Tyne has no overall conservation status at the international level but formal status is not relevant in the case of community-driven 'grassroots' schemes of rehabilitation, for example the promotion of fisheries. There are now active schemes for improvement in the case of Tyne tributaries like the Ouseburn and the Team, not just in terms of the river channel and its requirement for a diverse set of features, but in terms of the riparian corridor on both banks, where neglect or intensive development can threaten the channel's stability and ecology.

CONCLUSIONS
The Tyne has been a focus of study for geomorphologists for decades, possibly because of its size and grandeur, but also because of what T. Dan Smith once called 'Education upon Tyne' - the involvement of the universities of the region in research and development across a wide range of river studies. Rivers represent a truly interdisciplinary challenge if sustainable management is to be based upon good scientific information, proper democratic procedures (including the

knowledge and views of local people), and sound economic appraisal. Having been a primarily academic discipline, geomorphology is a recent arrival in the interdisciplinary contribution to river management. The author considers that the inputs of geomorphology to river management are as vital as the scientific understanding of the pipe network and flows in pipes to the distribution of clean water and the collection of sewage; there is catching up to be done!

REFERENCES

1. Davis, W.M. (1899) The geographical cycle, In: *Geographical Essays,* Ginn and Co, New York.
2. Allen, P. and Rose, J. (1986) A glacial meltwater drainage system between Whittonstall and Ebchester, Northumberland, In: *Quaternary river landforms and sediments in the Northern Pennines* (Eds. M.G. Macklin and J. Rose). Field Guide, British Geomorphological Research Group.
3. Peel. R.F. (1949) A study of two Northumbrian spillways, *Trans. Inst. British Geographers,* **15,** 73–89
4. Robinson, H. (1969) *Morphology and Landscape,* University Tutorial Press, London.
5. Archer, D.R. (1992) *Land of Singing Waters: rivers and great floods of Northumbria,* Spredden Press, Stocksfield
6. Haile, S.M., James, A. and Sear, D. (1989) *The effects of Kielder reservoir on the ecology of the River North Tyne.* Northumbrian Water Authority
7. Sear, D.A. (1992) Impact of hydroelectric power releases on sediment transport processes in pool-riffle sequences, In: *Dynamics of Gravel Bed Rivers* (Eds. P. Billi, R.D. Hey, C.R. Thorne and P. Tacconi), Wiley.
8. Macklin, M.G. and Lewin, J. (1989) Sediment transfer and transformation of an alluvial valley floor: the River South Tyne, Northumbria, UK. *Earth Surface Processes and Landforms,* **14,** 233–246.
9. Alley R.B. (2000) *The Two Mile Time Machine – Ice cores, abrupt climate change and our future,* Princeton Univ. Press.
10. Rumsby, B.T. and Macklin, M.G. (1994) Channel and floodplain response to recent abrupt climate change: the Tyne basin, Northern England. *Earth Surface Processes and Landforms,* **19,** 419–515.
11. Passmore, D.G., Macklin, M.G., Brewer, P.A., Lewin, J., Rumsby, B.T. and Newson, M.D. (1993) Variability of late Holocene braiding in Britain. In: *Braided Rivers* (Eds. J.L.Best and C.S.Bristow) Geological Society, Special Publication 75, 205–229.
12. Macklin, M.G. and Lewin, J. (1993) Holcene river alluviation in Britain. *Zeitschrift fur Geomorphologie* (supplement) **88,** 109–122.
13. Macklin, M.G. and Aspinall, R.J. (1986) Historic floodplain sedimentation in the River West Allen, Northumberland: a case study of channel change in an upland, gravel-bed river in the Northern Pennines. In: *Quaternary River Landforms and Sediments in the Northern Pennines, England* (Eds. M.G. Macklin and J. Rose). Field Guide, British Geomorphological Research Group/Quaternary Research Association, 7–17.
14. Macklin, M.G. (1986) Channel and floodplain metamorphosis in the River Nent, Cumberland. In: *Quaternary River Landforms and Sediments in the Northern Pennines, England* (Eds. M.G. Macklin and J. Rose). Field Guide, British Geomorphological Research Group/Quaternary Research Association, 19–33.
15. Archer, D. (2000) The influence of river bed gravel extraction on the sediment regime and morphology of the River Tyne. British Hydrological Society, 7th National Hydrology Symposium, Newcastle upon Tyne. 5.9–5.10.

16. Sear, D.A. (1993) Fine sediment infiltration into gravel spawning beds within a regulated river experiencing floods and the ecological implications for salmonids. *Regulated Rivers*, **8**, 373–390.
17. Petts, G.E. and Thoms, M.C. (1987) Morphology and sedimentology of a tributary confluence bar in a regulated river. *Earth Surface Processes and Landforms*, **12**, 433–440.
18. Robinson, M., Moore, R.E., Nisbet, T.R. and Blackie, J.R. (1998) From moorland to forest: the Coalburn catchment experiment. *Report 133*, Institute of Hydrology, Wallingford, Oxon.

4. THE RAPE OF THE TYNE: GRAVEL EXTRACTION

BACKGROUND

In Chapter 3 Malcolm Newson has shown how the natural river channel undergoes slow and gradual change as a result of the erosion, transport and deposition of sediment. Gross changes by the hand of man were superimposed on these natural adjustments and devastated much of the South Tyne and the main Tyne below the confluence during the twentieth century. Within the space of a few decades, gravel was taken from the bed which will not be replaced for several hundred years. Gravel working in the river bed destabilised the river, undermined bridges and other river structures and destroyed salmon redds and other fish spawning habitats.

And yet – the direct evidence of the workings is now hard to see; time and the growth of vegetation have been great healers. Even experienced geomorphologists who worked for ten years on the river asserted (mistakenly) in 1994[1] that , "direct channel modifications have been relatively limited in extent". Little has been written about river gravel extraction; it is neither a glamorous nor a photogenic industry. However, there are still many older residents of the riverside as well as former gravel workers who can provide evidence of its extent and corroborate its impact.

Gravel extraction from river beds is a world-wide phenomenon. In the United Kingdom river beds were for centuries a traditional source of gravel for building and for track and road making but amounts were generally small and impacts localised. For example, in neighbouring Cumbria in the late nineteenth century, male inmates at the workhouse in Cockermouth were required to deliver a barrow-load of gravel from the confluence of the Rivers Derwent and Cocker in exchange for a night's accommodation.

Demand increased rapidly in the 1930s with the increasingly widespread use of concrete in construction. There was an increase in commercial gravel production in the U.K. from 2.2 million tonnes in 1922 to 106 million tonnes in 1968[2], thereafter remaining fairly steady. A significant proportion of extraction was from river beds. The Tyne was a particularly attractive source being a gravel-bed river virtually from source to tidal limit and in proximity to the urban area of Tyneside. Its bed was used for commercial gravel extraction from the 1890s to 1972. Fifteen worked sites have been identified. The combined worked reach length of 8.75 km is 34% of the total river length from the tidal limit to the confluence of North and South Tyne. On the South Tyne the total worked reach is 10.5 km — 37% of the total reach length.

REGULATION?

Before World War II there was a major expansion in the demand for aggregate for building and road works. New extraction sites were opened and sites previously worked manually were converted to large scale commercial operations. Such works were eventually granted permissions under the Town and Country Planning Act of 1947. The County Council was responsible for issuing consents but rarely monitored the operation of the sites.

In the first instance the land drainage authority, then the Northumberland and Tyneside River Board, supported such works as they were seen to reduce flood levels. They did, however, impose a time limit in most cases and required that gravel only be removed 'down to the general bed grade of the river'. Prior to 1960 the Board opposed developments in a single case only.

The first indication of the Board's concern for the consequences of these works was given in their Annual Report for 1962[3].

> "The excavation of gravel from river sites in the Board's area is increasing year by year. There are more than 20 sites in the Board's area and of these 13 are in the Tyne valley. Each site produces its own problems, e.g. discoloration of the water, loosening of the bed of the river upstream of the workings and greater mobility of the bed generally. The latter feature results in the replenishment of the gravel deposits at some sites after every big flood and is accompanied by a greater liability to erosion of the river banks. There are of course, other river and riparian interests which must be considered, in particular fishing interests, where the loss of spawning gravel beds and destruction of insect life in the river tend to diminish the fish population and size of the fish.."

In spite of these reservations, however, the Board approved commercial extraction of gravels from river beds in 9 out of 11 proposals in 1962 and balanced the losses with perceived benefits in flood level reduction. By 1964, however, in the light of growing problems resulting from gravel removal, the balance had shifted and 4 out of 5 proposals were opposed, with accompanying strongly expressed views on effects on erosion and channel stability[3].

> "Removal of the gravel inevitably alters the river bed, and changes in depth and width take place which progress upstream, undermining bank protection works and bridge inverts and, whatever conditions are framed it is impossible to safeguard all interests."

Even in the case of flood protection, the deepening of the channel was no longer considered entirely beneficial as "washlands which form valuable flood reservoir areas are no longer effective so that flood water is passed downstream in greater concentrations to areas where it may do greater harm".

By 1965 the River Authority had agreed with Northumberland County Planning Officer that "in future, proposals to remove gravel from the river channel should be opposed unless there were special reasons for not doing so".

Nevertheless a number of existing consents remained in force, some without time limits, and workings on the River Tyne continued until the early 1970s when they were discouraged by the imposition of conditions which made extraction uneconomic. At present, County Councils retain broad powers with respect to gravel and other mineral extraction under the Town and Country Planning Act 1990, whilst the Environment Agency, under the Environment Act (1995), can recommend conditions under which consented extraction can operate.

The reversal in attitude to river bed gravel extraction in the early 1960s was prompted by the evidence of impact on channel stability. The effects on the River Tyne were particularly marked as gravel extraction had occurred intermittently at numerous sites on the South Tyne and Tyne since the end of the nineteenth century. An attempt has been made to identify gravel working sites, their periods of operation, and the volume or tonnage of extraction.

INFORMATION SOURCES

Official sources of information on the extraction of gravel from the River Tyne are quite limited. Northumberland County Council was responsible for issuing consents for gravel workings under the Town and Country Planning Act of 1947. It keeps archive records of consented gravel workings with maps showing the limits of the licensed reach. However, neither the County Council nor the Water Board maintained a routine record of rates of extraction. Nor did they monitor the operation. A single county map record was prepared at the time of implementation of the Town and Country Planning Act in 1947 showing annual output volumes by site for that year. There were then four in-river sites on the Tyne.

The principal evidence for the extent and impact of gravel extraction comes from conversations with retired workers in the sand and gravel industry, whose recollections date back to the late 1920s. These include a machine operator, a foreman and the owner of a haulage company. For example, Jimmy Atkinson of Stocksfield started work as a labourer in gravel extraction at Mickley in the early 1930s and spent his entire working life (apart from a short time in the services during World War II) in extracting gravel from the River Tyne. After the war he owned a transport company carrying gravel from the workings to the place of use. Recollections of the quarrymen enable estimates of extracted volume to be made from the number of lorries per day from the site, tonnage per lorry and days per year. More approximate estimates were made from information on the available plant and equipment on site or the number of employees where the workings were manual. They also indicated that not all consented sites were operated and some sites were worked which were not consented.

GRAVEL EXTRACTION SITES

The location of gravel extraction sites on the River Tyne is shown in Figure 4.1 and estimates of extracted tonnages are shown by reach and by period in Table 4.1.

Plate 1. Portrait of the Tyne bridges on the wall of the remote tea house in the Bolan Pass of Balochistan. My wife, Bernice, stands by the unglazed window whilst goats shelter from the heat in the room beyond.

(Photo D. Archer)

Plate 2. The Tyne bridges in twilight (*Photo Graham Hancock, Robertsons of Gosforth*)

Plate 3. A typical river flow gauging station at Redebridge on the River Rede, showing the recorder house, the line of level gauges, the cableway pillar and the gauging weir. *(Photo D. Archer)*

Plate 4 Manual and recording raingauges overlooking Kielder forest and moorland, high in the North Tyne catchment. *(Photo: David Archer)*

Plate 5. Haltwhistle from the air near the height of the flood on 31 January 1995. Kilfrosts is the white roofed building in mid picture and Crown Berger the larger complex beyond the old railway embankment *(Photo: Airfotos, Gosforth)*

Plate 6. Sequence showing the progressive breach of a flood embankment, from top: the flood cuts a deep channel on the downstream face: blocks of earth shear and collapse into the channel: shrubs and trees are undermined and carried off: the breach progressively widens and a turbulent turbid torrent surges through. *(Photo: Paul Elwell and Paul Davies, White Young and Green, Consulting Engineers)*

Plate 7. The sculpture marking a spring, said to be the source of the South Tyne - but perhaps raw nature is sufficient monument to itself. (*Photo: David Archer*)

Plate 8. The South Tyne looking downstream from Lambley Viaduct showing the typical natural sequence of riffles (foreground and distance) and pool (between the riffles). This sequence is repeated in natural channels and is vital to geomorphological and ecological processes. (*Photo: David Archer*)

Plate 9. The River North Tyne above Kielder showing bank erosion associated with active meander development. *(Photo: David Archer)*

Plate 10. The South Tyne at Featherstone Castle — a zone of the river that has experienced high rates of erosion and deposition during the last fifty years. *(Photo: David Archer)*

Plate 11. The River Tyne below Hexham Bridge, from an early 20th century painting. Note the absence of a fall in level through the bridge opening or downstream from the bridge and the gravel bar in the downstream channel.

Plate 12. The River Tyne below Hexham Bridge in July 2000 showing the steep drop and deep pool below the bridge induced by downstream gravel extraction from 1930s to 1970s, and the extensive structural protection measures and fish pass. *(Photo: David Archer)*

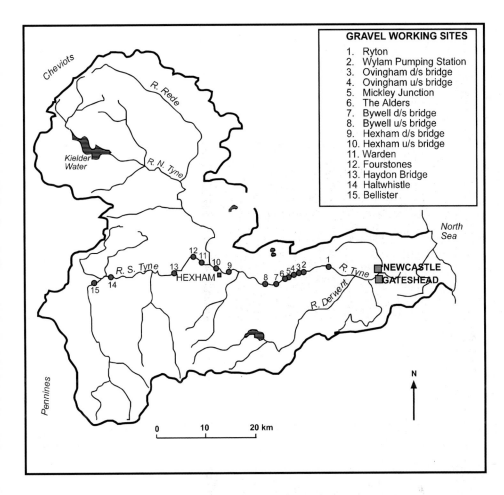

Fig 4.1 Gravel working sites on the River Tyne and South Tyne

Wylam Pumping Station

The earliest record of gravel extraction in the non-tidal River Tyne was at Wylam adjacent to the old pumping station. Gravel and sand required for the construction of filters at Whittle Dene (1891 to 1897) was extracted from the river bed, washed and graded and transported by a specially constructed narrow gauge railway[4]. The requirement for the filters was 46,000 cubic yards. Operations continued until about 1906 to supply construction materials for the tunnel and aqueducts between Hallington and Whittle Dene reservoirs.

Work recommenced in the early 1920s as Stephen Eastons Tyne Wash. Working was by hand, and graded gravel was loaded directly to side-loading rail wagons at a siding from the Newcastle to Carlisle Railway, extending to the river bank. The gravel was used in part for rail track ballast. In the late 1930s the plant was taken over by Ryton Sand and Gravel Company and rail transport was discontinued. The plant closed around 1940. Annual extraction is estimated at 12,000 tonnes on the basis of the number of employees (> 25).

Table 4.1.   Estimated gravel extraction from the River Tyne (1000 tonnes) by reach and by period 1891 to 1975

Channel Reach	Reach No.	Reach length	1891–1900	1901–1910	1911–1920	1921–1925	1926–1930	1931–1935	1936–1940	1941–1945	1946–1950	1951–1955	1956–1960	1961–1965	1966–1970	1971–1975	Reach total
Wylam	2	0.3	60	40		50	60	60	54								324
d/s Ovingham Br.	3	0.5									50	350					400
u/s Ovingham Br.	4	0.2												15			15
Mickley Jct.	5	0.2				25	25	50	90	55	48						243
u/s Mickley	6	0.6							72								72
d/s Bywell Br	7	2.2										40	10				50
Bywell	8	0.75											70	30			100
d/s Hexham Br.	9	2.8							100	160	203	370	400	100	25	25	1383
u/s Hexham Br.	10	1.2							10	100	168	410	560	50	50	20	1368
TOTAL Main Tyne		8.75	60	40	Nil	75	85	110	326	315	469	1170	1040	195	75	45	4005
Warden	11	0.3													30		30
Fourstones	12	2.1										70	250	30	150		500
Haydon Br.	13	0.3										40					40
Haltwhistle	14	6.8															?
Bellister	15	1.0							15								15
TOTAL South Tyne		10.5										110	250	30	180		585
TOTAL South and Main Tyne		19.25	60	40	Nil	75	85	110	341	315	469	1280	1290	225	255	45	4590

Ovingham – downstream from bridge
The reach stretching from about 100 metres to 500 metres below the bridge was worked mechanically from about 1950 to 1955, first by McAlpine and later by Ryton Gravel. During the latter period the gravel was washed and graded at Ryton, with 35 to 40 ten-tonne loads taken per day, suggesting an annual output reaching a peak of 90,000 tonnes per annum. A longer reach extending downstream as far as Wylam pumping station was licensed for extraction in 1948, but the lower part of this reach is not believed to have been worked.

Ovingham - upstream from bridge
Extraction was licensed in the short (200 metre) reach, 90 metres upstream from Ovingham bridge to the confluence with the Whittle Burn, for a four-year period from 1961 to 1964. However, extraction occurred for approximately 6 months only in 1961 and was terminated when a dragline operator lost his life in an accident.

Mickley Junction
Work started around 1925 at Mickley Junction where the firm of Christers employed 12 to 14 men who hand-filled skips running on a 2-foot rail from the river to the grading machine. In 1936 a Rushton dragline was acquired (Fig. 4.2) and production increased from 10 to 20 lorry loads (of 5 tons each) by the beginning of the war. Typically the gravel was taken for building in Newcastle, including Spillers Flour Mill and the Power Station at Dunston, and from 1938 onward was used for the building of air-raid shelters. Work continued through the war but closed down in 1948/49.

The Alders
Just upstream Wimpey worked a site intensively from 1937 until the beginning of the war. With 24-hour working they supplied 30 to 40 lorries per day, mainly for the construction of the Team Valley Trading Estate. The site was licensed for use in 1948 but is not believed to have been worked after that date.

Bywell - downstream from bridge
After World War II, large scale land-based sand and gravel workings were established by Ryton Sand and Gravel Company at Merryshield on the river terrace south of the river, with mechanised washing and grading not only for this site but also for several river extraction sites upstream. Gravel extraction was not confined to the river terrace gravels but was periodically extended in the early 1950s to the river downstream from Bywell bridge, although such operations were unlicensed. Old access routes can still be identified on the north bank. Sites were worked to exhaustion (extraction down to bedrock or to blue clay) and then working moved on to a new site in the reach.

Bywell - upstream from bridge
In the 1950s and early 1960s Ryton Sand and Gravel worked the reach for a distance of 750 metres upstream from the medieval weir. The site was adjacent

Fig 4.2 Gravel extraction using a 10RB Rushton dragline at Mickley Junction (Site 5) in 1937. The gravel company widened the river and created a shallow lagoon where work could continue in high flow *(Photo: J. Atkinson).*

to the ancient churchyard of St. Peters, which became more vulnerable to flood erosion as a result of the works. The flood of January 1955 eroded and damaged the churchyard and some coffins were displaced. Work was finally brought to a halt around 1961 at the insistence of the Water Board, when it was realised that extraction had lowered the bed level at Bywell gauging station 700 metres upstream and made flow measurement unreliable.

Hexham - downstream from bridge
Work commenced around 1938 in a reach stretching from 100 metres downstream from Hexham bridge almost to the confluence of the Devil's Water and continued uninterrupted until 1961. For most of that period, washing and grading was done on site but when the rights transferred from West Tyne Gravel Company to Ryton Sand and Gravel in the late 1950s, processing at the site was discontinued and gravel was hauled to Ryton's Merryshield plant. The Northumberland County Council survey notes an annual extraction of 38,500 tonnes in 1947 but production probably increased substantially through the 1950s.

Hexham/Acomb - upstream from bridge
The reach from the confluence of the Red Burn to the Border Counties railway bridge (demolished 1956) was worked by Wrights of Benwell from about 1940 and subsequently by Hexham Sand and Gravel Company, to whom the site was licensed in 1948. It was again acquired by Ryton Sand and Gravel around 1953. Local plant processing was discontinued and gravel was transported to Merryshields for crushing and grading, at a peak rate of 500 tonnes per day (150,000 tonnes per year). These works caused major changes to the configuration of the channel. Continuous works terminated in 1959 but sporadic working continued for approximately 2 months each summer until 1972.

South Tyne - Warden
In the late 1960s there was a brief period of gravel working by Ryton Sand and Gravel in the reach downstream from the paper mill, with access along the south bank from Warden bridge. Works lasted about one year only.

South Tyne - Fourstones
Gravel was extracted in the reach from Crossgate Ford to the paper mill, first by Wrights from the early 1950s, then by Ryton Sand and Gravel from 1959 to 1961. Gravel was loaded onto lorries on the south bank and brought across the river on a temporary bridge situated at the Crossgate Ford. The works were very extensive and caused serious bank erosion and changes in channel morphology. Work recommenced in the late 1960s for a period of two to three years with an alternative access route further downstream. It is probable that the works extended beyond the licensed geographical boundaries and time limits.

South Tyne - Haydon Bridge
In the early 1950s McAlpines operated in the reach extending 300 metres downstream from the A69 bridge, with intensive working for two periods of three months.

South Tyne - Haltwhistle
There were gravel workings in the reach downstream from the railway viaduct but the precise location and duration are not known.

South Tyne -Bellister
Gravel extraction at this site was in the late 1930s for a period of about 18 months with a total extraction of about 15000 tonnes. The gravel was used in the construction of the airfield at Longtown.
    Other sites may have been worked briefly in the South Tyne but were discontinued due to the poor quality (coal particles) or the excessively large gravel.

North Tyne
The only known workings on the North Tyne are those carried out by the Forestry Commission for the building of forestry roads. Extraction was mainly

in the area now flooded by Kielder Water but in the early 1960s small amounts were also taken out in the reach downstream from the dam site to Falstone.

IMPACTS OF GRAVEL EXTRACTION

Gravel extraction had a major visible impact on the river at the time of its occurrence as illustrated by contemporary photographs and by descriptions of working practice by gravel workers. An average depth of excavation of 2.6 metres over the worked reach can be estimated from the total tonnage extracted and the length and typical width of the affected reach. It is clear from descriptions by gravel workers and riverside observers that excavation depths of this magnitude and greater were locally achieved. However, both natural and enhanced sediment movement from immediate upstream reaches reduced the maximum 'scour' depths and spread it over a much greater channel length. The bed level in many worked reaches remains deeply incised below the pre-worked level. It is estimated that it will take several hundred years for natural gravel movement to replenish the river gravels lost by extraction.

Upstream and downstream adjustments which occurred during extraction have also continued long after cessation. Impacts are described in the categories below, with examples denoted as numbered in Fig. 4.1. Effects on river structures are provided as evidence of the severity of morphological changes.

- Channel deepening at the worked site
- Continuing upstream erosion
- Depriving the downstream reach of gravel
- Channel widening
- Hydrological impacts
- Ecological impacts

Channel deepening in the worked reach

Gravel workers indicated that it was the general practice until the last few years of extraction to dredge large hollows ('bloody great holes') in the bed to the maximum practical depth of three metres using the dragline. This was in anticipation that gravel and boulders moved in flood from the upstream reach would be captured in the hollows. Retired water engineer, Harry Storey, recalls how during his youth in Hexham (10) in the 1950s his adventurous schoolmates on weekends climbed the cables of the dragline and dived from the bucket into these deep pools. Deep excavation exposed for the first time the foundations of Gott's bridge completed in 1770 and washed away in the great flood of 1771[5]. The timber platform on which the piers were built and the supporting timber piles were exposed; the platform had been set one metre below bed level at the time of construction[6]. A deep channel, dredged by the gravel company, removed one pier; the lowest bed level remains (1992 survey) more than two metres below the level of the platform. The works thus damaged a structure of considerable historical interest.

Upstream erosion

Excavation results in increased channel slope on the upstream margins of these hollows and enhances movement of gravel on the bed, with resulting upstream incision. Although planning consents in the River Tyne generally imposed a separation distance from bridges and other structures (e.g., 140 metres below Hexham road bridge (9)), the distances were quite inadequate and serious damage resulted both at the time of working and afterwards.

Scour in the major flood in January 1955 seriously damaged several bridges upstream from worked reaches. At Hexham (10) the Border Counties Railway bridge was undermined and the piles exposed. Fears concerning the safety of the bridge precipitated the closure of the line in 1956 and the bridge superstructure was demolished. Incision continued long after working ceased. As shown in Fig 4.3, the bridge platform, which at construction in the early 1850s would have been set at bed level, now stands at more than three metres above the bed. The dual-carriageway Hexham by-pass bridge a further 400 metres upstream has experienced repeated scour and subsidence since its construction in 1975 and has required costly remedial works.

In a Public Inquiry in 1969 relating to gravel workings in north Northumberland, the Northumberland County Council, in opposing a development, detailed the cost of remedial works carried out by the highway

Fig 4.3 The foundations of the Border Counties Railway bridge demolished after damage by flood in 1955. The piles are now exposed to a depth of 3 metres above the bed. Photographed in October 1997 *(Photo: David Archer).*

authority and the river authority. These included downstream protection works for the main road bridge at Hexham (9) and a bridge at Haltwhistle (14).

The effects of extraction at the main road bridge at Hexham (9) are further described by Bob Robson, foreman for the Northumberland County Council bridges section[7].

"The local gravel extraction firm working some 200 yards downstream was warned that its activities were drawing gravel from underneath the apron with each successive flood. In 1948 the apron and stream bed had been level; by 1955 there was a three-foot waterfall off the downstream end of the apron and a void extended almost to the bridge piers. I found that I could crawl into a hole six to seven feet deep right under two of the pier bases."

Repairs were carried out at that time but the downstream channel has continued to adjust and repeated strengthening of the foundations has been required. The drop below the bridge became an impediment for the passage of fish and required the installation of a fish pass (Chapter 6). Plates 11 and 12 show the change in the bridge from the early twentieth century to 2000.

Large blocks of rough-cut stone below the bridge at Ovingham (3,4) have the appearance of an ancient weir but the explanation is more mundane. Headward erosion from downstream workings undermined the bridge foundations during the flood of January 1955 and left the bridge piles visible. To protect the structure the gravel company was required to place very large stone penning in the reach below the bridge.

Depriving the downstream reach of gravel
The trapping of moving gravel in the worked reach allows clear water to pass downstream, with excess energy for setting the gravel in motion and transporting it. Prior to the workings above Hexham bridge (10), for example, the upstream channel had lateral gravel bars and a pool and riffle sequence. This gravel has now been evacuated and there is a single deep pool extending 1000 metres upstream from the bridge, having the positive effect of creating a much improved reach for rowing (Chapter 11).

Channel widening
Channel widening was sometimes a deliberate working policy, as at Mickley Junction (5) and Bellister (15), with a lateral higher working area to enable work to continue when the river was in flood. However, a consequence which was often more significant and extended beyond the limits of the worked reach was that channel incision induced bank instability and collapse. At Fourstones (12) the River Board was obliged to build a series of groynes on the north bank in the early 1950s to deflect flow and protect banks and adjacent agricultural land from erosion. These groynes did encourage deposition and are now silted up and separated from the main channel. However, active undercutting and collapse has shifted to the reach immediately downstream.

Hydrological impacts

Channel incision and widening created a channel with greater capacity for carrying floods (conveyance) and hence less frequent floodplain inundation. In principle this reduction in flood water storage would pass the flood problem downstream and increase downstream flow. There are examples of such increases in flow from arterial drainage on Irish rivers[8]. However, as the natural flood plain on the River Tyne is of limited extent, the effect of the change is likely to be much less severe than in the Irish examples.

Of greater practical significance is the impact of lower bed levels and increased channel capacity on flood levels for given discharge. This is a positive impact which the early River Board considered would adequately balance the negative impacts. For example, at Fourstones (12) a major flood in February 1995 (estimated at 100 year return period) resulted in a peak flood level nearly three metres lower than the less severe floods in 1881 and 1926 (whose levels are shown by engraved marks from on a riverside building at Crossgate).

Such changes have practical implications for planning control. The Environment Agency is required under the Environment Act (1995) to draw flood plain maps showing the extent of the 100 year return period flood. It is normal to use surveyed levels and measured discharges in historical floods to calibrate a hydraulic model for reapplication to the discharge of required return period. Where the channel conveyance has altered over time, a quite different level may now be achieved for a given discharge than occurred in a past flood. Continuing channel adjustments from gravel extraction may make assessment even more difficult.

Ecological impacts

The most obvious ecological effect was that during the period of extraction, gravel spawning beds for salmon and sea trout were rendered unusable over long reaches of the river, as indicated in the River Board report quoted above. A River Board map of 1967 shows a total of 10.7 km of spawning grounds spoiled on the South Tyne.

A more persistent effect is the disruption of pool/riffle sequences and the substitution of long pools extending beyond the margins of the original workings.. This reduction in morphological diversity has resulted in less varied flow types[9] and a weakening of ecological diversity, with effects through the food chain to migratory fish (Chapter 5).

THE TIDE SWEEPS IN

In the tidal reach the river has been dredged for quite a different purpose (Chapter 12) – to improve navigation in the estuary. But even here the effects have extended well beyond the bounds of the original workings and caused an upstream shift of three kilometres in the tidal limit. The transformation of the estuary was described in *Land of Singing Waters*[10] with nearly 220 million tons of mud dredged from the bed of the river from the mid-eighteenth century to the present day. Guthrie[11] provides a graphic account of the development of the estuary up to 1880 and provides survey data for comparative levels of the river bed before and after dredging (Fig 4.4). By 1880 the main deepening of the estuary extended up to Elswick and Kings Meadows Island (which divided the channel at that point) but some dredging had been done as far up as Blaydon.

One interesting feature of the survey section in Figure 4.4 is the dotted line showing the proposed extension of dredging to full navigational depth right up to the tidal limit, which was the limit of authority of the Tyne Improvement Commission. The tidal limit marked by the tide stone had from medieval times remained at Hedwin Streams above Newburn. Strict application of these proposals would have created a drop in the bed at that point of eight metres. This step would have been covered at high tide but could have left a waterfall at low tide of nearly four metres.

But the river had other ideas. With the dredging of the bed from Newburn to Ryton from 1880 to 1900, the channel was steepened in the reach upstream and gave the river new energy to erode. The bed of the river was ripped out from the old tidal limit right up to Wylam, which by 1900 had become the new tidal limit. Houses in Wylam, including Stephenson's birthplace cottage and the miner's cottages of East Water Row which had flooded in 1881 and many times previously, now found themselves well above any flood danger. The erosion of the river reach below Wylam, which was rapid at first, continued at a slower pace through the twentieth century; the bridge was undermined and required repeated strengthening of the bridge footings. By the end of the twentieth century, the fall at the lower side of the bridge had become an impediment to salmon migration. The Environment Agency alleviated the problem first by placing large boulders in the downstream channel, thus raising the level of the downstream pool, and then by constructing a fish pass in 1997.

Dredging in the upper estuary provides further strong evidence of the way in which the effects of gravel extraction can migrate far from the site of extraction and continue long after the extraction has stopped.

CONCLUSIONS
1. At the time and place of occurrence, gravel extraction has led to major changes in the channel of the Rivers Tyne and South Tyne. Further major changes continue to occur over a broader time span and along a wider reach by cutting upstream and depriving the reach downstream of sediment.

2. Rates of extraction were much greater than natural rates of erosion and transport of the gravel bedload. Analysis suggests a recovery time for the sediment removed, of the order of 300 years. In many places the lowering of the bed level is likely to have swamped natural variations in sediment erosion and deposition due to changes in climate and land use, described in Chapter 3.

3. Gravel extraction has had serious practical consequences, especially in undermining of bridges and bank erosion. In addition, the replacement of natural pool/riffle sequences by long pools has resulted in loss of ecological diversity

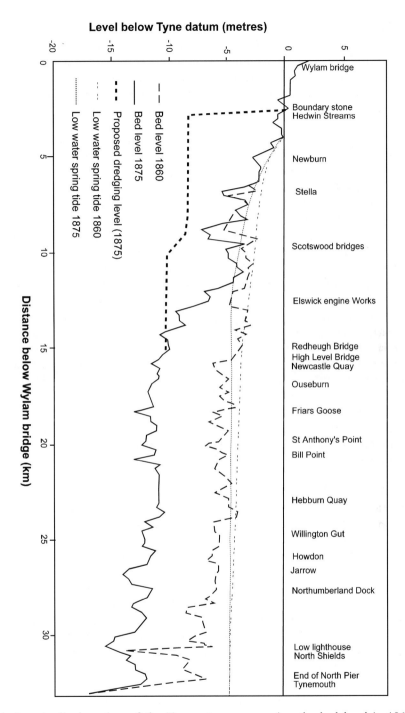

Fig 4.4 Longitudinal section of the Tyne estuary comparing the bed level in 1860 and in 1875, indicating the extent of dredging and the proposed upstream extension which was essentially complete by 1900.

4. Whilst no gravel extraction from river channels is currently taking place on the River Tyne, a number of consents remain in force. The responsible authorities must not be tempted to permit reactivation of such consents or to issue new licences to achieve cost savings in the provision of channel conveyance for drainage and flood protection. Past experience, now almost forgotten, shows that such a liaison is misconceived.

REFERENCES

1. Rumsby, B.T. and Macklin, M.G. (1994) Channel and floodplain response to recent climate change: the Tyne basin, northern England, *Earth Surface Processes and Landforms*, **19**, 499–515.
2. Newton, M. (1971) *The sand and gravel industry in N. E. England.* University of Newcastle upon Tyne, Department of Geography Research Series, No 7.
3. Northumberland and Tyneside River Board, 1962 and 1964 *Annual Reports*
4. Rennison, R.W. (1979) *Water to Tyneside: A History of the Newcastle and Gateshead Water Company*, Newcastle and Gateshead Water Company. 361 pp.
5. Archer, N. (1993) Discharge estimate for Britain's greatest flood: River Tyne 17th November 1771, in *Fourth National Hydrology Symposium*, British Hydrological Society, 4.1–4.6.
6. Ruddock, E.C. (1979) The foundations of Hexham Bridge, *Geotechnique*, **27**, 385-404.
7. Robson, R. 1998. *Bob's Bridges: Jottings from a Northumbrian Foreman's diaries.* Northumberaland County Council, 148 pp.
8. Bailey, A.D. and Bree, T (1981) Effects of improved land drainage on river flood flows, In: *ICE Flood Studies - Five Years On*, Thomas Telford , London 131–142.
9. Padmore, C.L. (1997) Biotopes and their hydraulics: A method of defining the physical component of freshwater quality, in Boon, P.J. and Howell, D.L.(Eds), *Freshwater Quality: Defining the Indefinable?*, Scottish National Heritage, Edinburgh, 251–257.
10. Archer, D.R. (1992) *Land of Singing Waters: Rivers and Great Floods of Northumbria*, Spredden Press, Stocksfield, Northumberland, 217 pp.
11. Guthrie, J. (1880) *The River Tyne, its History and Resources*, London.

5. THE LIVING TYNE: RIVER ECOLOGY

ANNE LEWIS

INTRODUCTION

River plants and animals, like humans, tend to live in a place in the first instance because they were born there. Their parents and ancestors lived there because they found space, security, food and shelter — a suitable habitat. They did not make a conscious choice to live there, but survived because they found such a place, whilst those which did not died. River plants and animals share their living space with other species that can survive and thrive in the same habitat. They are all dependent on or influenced by the flow regime of the river (Chapter 1). However, there is clearly a variation in habitats across the river channel, ranging from those that are always inundated, to those on the channel margins and lower banks which are frequently covered and uncovered, to those on the upper banks and floodplain that are only sporadically flooded.

Habitats and flow regime also vary downriver from the typically shallow, swift-flowing, flashy headwater tributaries with rock and boulder beds to the deeper flow of the lower reaches. Typically rivers also vary in the amount of nutrient available to sustain river life. The low nutrient levels (oligotrophic) of the headwaters are dependent mainly on decay of organic matter falling in from the banks whereas the medium to high levels of nutrients (mesotrophic and eutrophic) in lower reaches are sustained by biological activity driven by photosynthesis within the channel. However, within these broad patterns there is great local variability, dependent primarily on the size and stability of sediments and flow patterns within the channel.

In this chapter we look at ways in which the habitats and flow regime of the River Tyne have influenced the ecology. A particular comparison is made between the North Tyne and the South Tyne; in the latter the ecology of some tributaries is affected by enriched heavy metals in water and sediments . Some species native to the Tyne are considered in detail either because they are characteristic of the river or are in danger of extinction. Similarly the influence of some alien invaders to the bed and banks are described. Fish are omitted from this chapter and reserved for Chapters 6 and 7.

HABITATS AND BIODIVERSITY

Although chemical water quality can affect biological response in rivers, it is the physical characteristics of the river that mainly determine the assemblage of species to be found there. The ecological characteristics and diversity of a river depend primarily on the flow regime and the range of physical habitats which the river offers for colonisation and occupation.

Flow regime and habitat are closely interlinked. River flow creates or influences habitats through:

○ its capacity to erode, transport and deposit sediment on the bed and banks, thus creating microhabitats for animal and plant communities,
○ the direct effect of velocity at the bed on the ability of species to remain in place and to survive through their life stages,
○ the expansion and contraction of the river channel in floods and droughts and the associated changes in velocity which animal and plant communities experience in different habitats.

Where there are sediment sources available, steep fast-flowing rivers such as the Tyne tend to have beds of coarse material whilst slower flows are associated with fine material. The Tyne and main tributaries are 'gravel bed rivers' for the greater part of their courses. This does not mean that rivers of a certain hydrological regime have a uniform channel with a uniform size of material on the bed. On the contrary, there is a natural tendency for the sediment to be distributed in an undulating bed as an alternating sequence of pools and riffles or bars with local variations in sediment size and stability. The particle size on the bed tends to be larger on the riffles or on lateral bars than in the pools. Variations in the size of material on the bed and its distribution in the river create quite diverse microhabitats. In one reach there may be a patchwork of microhabitats of bare rock, boulders, cobbles, gravel, sand and fine organic drift material, with living plants either growing in or hanging into the river. The greater the variation in microhabitats the greater the biodiversity of the river. The special importance of the woody debris, wrack thrown up by floods, as a microhabitat is described in the following section.

Microhabitats based on bed material tend to be reinforced by the local variations in velocity of the current. Velocity near the bed is generally lower over the finer sediment in pools than it is over the larger gravel on riffles. Some species can tolerate a wide range of current speed, but others are only able to live within a narrow range. Nevertheless, the invertebrate community relies on the current to bring food and to maintain the oxygen supply.

The spatial variation of microhabitats is supplemented by variation in time. A suitable habitat in normal flow may become untenable at higher flows. In floods and droughts there may be high mortality of individuals. However species survive by a variety of means.

In a rising flood, animals and plants on the river bed are bombarded with material carried by the increasing flow. Some animals may be shaken loose to 'drift' with the flow. Some of these may find a new home, but many must be killed among the tumbling rocks. Even animals that continue to cling to their rocks may find that their home is on the move.

Animals adopt a variety of survival strategies in increasing flow and velocity. Many move down through the river gravels to greater safety. The smallest animals (the early larval stages or 'instars') are able to penetrate the gravels to the greatest depth, and are therefore more likely to survive in larger numbers than older and bigger animals. Other animals may survive because they move or drift to a backwater area where they are out of the fierce flow. Plants of course have no escape mechanisms but must take what the river throws at them. Some break off at the root and can swiftly recolonise at the same site; the broken pieces carried down river may find a new location to colonise.

As a big flood recedes, surviving animals move back to new and different territories. Smaller instars that have been hiding deep in the gravel may find that life is possible on the surface of the river bed with the predation pressure reduced.

In a drought not only does the shrinking river have less space for all the animals but it becomes warmer with a consequent loss of oxygen-holding capacity. Pollutants tend to become more concentrated as there is less clean dilution water. Animals migrate with the shrinking channel where competition for territory can become fierce. Plants can be left high and dry. Plants adapted to aquatic conditions rapidly wilt and die when exposed. Mosses are an exception. An aquatic moss such as *Fontinalis antipyretica* can spend days apparently dead and dry but when the flow returns the moss rehydrates, apparently no worse for the experience.

At the end of an extended period of drought, animals are able to spread out and recolonise the river bed as it is inundated whereas plants take longer to recover.

Woody debris
Woody debris (also called wrack) is a major feature of riparian habitats along both the main stem of the Tyne and along small tributary channels. It originates from riverside woodland throughout the catchment. The debris is deposited mainly at the highest level of a flood, and builds up around obstructions on the bank such as living and fallen trees but also at bridges and weirs. It can be viewed as unsightly, a nuisance or even a danger. Small tributary channels may be blocked by debris dams which subsequently break and add to erosion and downstream flooding. Even on the estuary a huge mat of floating woody debris processes up and down on the tide when the wind and water conditions are right. This can be a significant hazard to river users.

However, wrack is an important part of the natural system. While some fragments may make it from tree to sea in a single flood, others take years and most never leave the river at all but are recycled within the system. It is this recycled wood that has the greatest importance to the ecosystem. The breakdown of vegetable material provides a rich supply of nutrients. Micro-organisms like fungi, bacteria and protozoans live on the rotting material and on each other at the base of the food web that eventually supports fish, otters and birds.

Wood that becomes incorporated in the bank releases its nutrients to enrich the river bank soils and support riparian vegetation which in its turn provides a new generation of woody debris. The wrack itself also provides an important physical habitat. Waterlogged trunks and branches can naturally create the varied bed pattern important to fish ecology. Sunken wood can also provide refuge areas to protect fish during floods and even a spawning medium for some coarse fish.

Wrack on the bankside constitutes an important habitat type with a rich invertebrate fauna. This in turn supports birds and small mammals. Larger animals such as otters and aquatic birds can use wrack dams left in high floods as refuges and even breeding areas.

Large tree trunks can even influence the shape of the channel. A large trunk can form the nucleus of an island as other materials are deposited around it. Conversely a trunk wedged on or near the bank can cause bankside erosion as the water is forced to flow around the new obstacle. Although sadly not completely free of man-made litter, the Tyne is blessed with a rich source of woody debris that is a vital attribute of the river.

COMPARISON OF THE ECOLOGY OF NORTH TYNE AND SOUTH TYNE

With perhaps the exception of the pearl mussel, prominent species that are found on the North Tyne are also found within some microhabitats on the South Tyne and vice versa. However, there are differences in the abundance and distribution of certain species between the two river that result from differences in their characteristic habitats. Certain tributaries of the South Tyne, affected by high concentrations of heavy metals in their sediments, have a more restricted and specialised flora and fauna, as discussed later.

The North Tyne has a more stable channel with less bank erosion and a near absence of bare gravel haughs. It tends to have stable vegetated islands. Whilst the main channel has a gravel and cobble bed, the edge sediments are often sands and silts. The main channel vegetation can include reeds (as at Hesleyside) and aquatic plants, including mosses (particularly *Fontinalis antipyretica*), and water crowfoot (*Ranunculus* sp.), which can only really develop on stable gravels. Together the sediments and the plants provide a variety of habitats for a wide range of aquatic animals.

The South Tyne in contrast has extensive bare gravel bars throughout the river system. The gravel bed and bars are much more active and mobile than on the North Tyne. Typically the active gravels are honey-coloured sandstones. Some higher bars are comparatively stable and are darker in colour due to the development of crustose lichens (e.g. *Huilia tuberculosa*). Since lichens increase in diameter regularly with age it is possible to estimate the date when the lichen was established and thus when the gravel became stable. Some gravel bars upstream from Lambley Viaduct have remained stable for over 80 years even though they are flooded nearly every year. Nevertheless, there are surprisingly few flowering plants or grasses established on these bars, probably because the finer sediments are rich in heavy metals (derived from former zinc and lead mining) which inhibit root growth. Shallow flow over the surface in floods scours the rock and prevents the build up of surface humus that would help plants get a foothold. The retreating flood tops up the metal rich sediments. The South Tyne also has very few flowering plants in the channel due to the constant attrition of the shifting gravel.

Some 'generalist' species are able to exploit a variety of habitats and are common in both North and South Tyne. An example is the river limpet (*Ancylus fluviatilis*), a gastropod mollusc that looks like a miniature version of its familiar marine cousin. It grazes algae from surfaces of stones or plants. Similarly flat-bodied mayfly nymphs (Family Echdynuridae) are perfectly adapted to life on bare rock surfaces with strong clinging feet and a streamlined shape which tends to be pushed down onto the rock surface by increasing water velocity. Some caddises (*Hydropsyche* sp.) which live under a stone can tolerate high velocities. Members of the mayfly family Baetidae are generalists and can cope with still or fast water. They are found in a wide range of habitats from fast-flowing rivers to ponds.

Slow flows and finer sediments associated with them, create the conditions required by the mayfly *Ephemera danica*. This rather large nymph likes to bury itself in silt with just the gills on its back above the surface. It is more common on the North Tyne than on the South, simply because of the presence of suitable habitat. The shrimp *Gammarus pulex* more often finds the conditions it prefers on the North Tyne. It is not a strong swimmer and so prefers life under a stone or rotting wood to being in the main flow.

In contrast, some of the biggest stonefly nymphs (*Isoperla grammatica*) require fast-flowing cold and well-aerated water. These nymphs are active predators, prowling around and beneath the stones of riffles in search of prey. They find a more ideal habitat in the South Tyne than in the North.

Metallophytes

The concentration of certain 'heavy' metals (especially lead, zinc and cadmium) in the waters and sediments of the upper South Tyne, the East and West Allen, is elevated to well above the background levels found, for example, in the North Tyne. The metals are derived from the veins of the North Pennine Orefield and are accompanied by high concentrations of fluoride. Even under natural conditions the concentration of metals would have been elevated in this area, but past mining and processing has vastly increased the supply of metal-rich water and sediment to the river system (Chapter 8). With the abandonment of mining activity, metals enter the system in solution from abandoned adits and from the re-working by the river of metal-rich sediments in the banks and bed.

The metals are ecologically important because they are toxic to animals and plants. However, the effect is moderated to some extent because the mineralised veins occur in Carboniferous Limestone; the calcium of the limestone increases the pH and thus reduces the solubility of the metals and their toxic effects.

Though lead is more toxic to most animals, it is zinc which has the greatest impact on the ecosystem. One reason for this is that zinc is extremely toxic to fungi. This disrupts the food chain as insect herbivores grazing on the algae in the river rely on their fungal gut flora to digest cellulose. With a severely inhibited gut flora, insects are malnourished no matter how much they eat. The importance of algal grazing — or its absence — is immediately obvious to the observer of the Nent in early summer. The whole river bed is a waving mass of hair-like green algae. This can even be seen from aerial photographs! In the absence of invertebrate grazers, algal growth is only checked by breaking apart in the flow or by attrition during storms. The algae looks like the common

Cladophora of nutrient-rich waters but it is in fact mostly *Mougeotia,* a metal-tolerant species.

The disruption of the food chain can be observed in samples from the invertebrate fauna. Instead of a range of animals including herbivorous grazers, shredders and detritovores, samples from the Nent are dominated by carnivorous animals (e.g. the caddis fly *Rhyacophila*). The carnivores must supplement their diet of instream fauna with other animals that fall in from the river banks. The samples are also very low in abundance with perhaps only one tenth to one twentieth of the number of animals found in comparable samples from the North Tyne catchment. Higher in the food chain the dipper, a bird which lives on aquatic invertebrates, is less frequent than elsewhere.

Zinc also impairs the breeding success of fish. Water circulating in the spawning gravels of the river bed has a high concentration in solution and zinc is absorbed at the early stages of fish egg development. The Nent and the West Allen show particular evidence of these impacts; the fish population of the River Nent is less than one fiftieth of what would be expected in a similar river unaffected by metal pollution.

Metal-rich shingles on the South Tyne, Nent, Allens and upper Derwent are inimical to the growth of most plants. They are quite bare but have a characteristic flora of metallophytic plants including thrift, narrow-lipped helliborine and alpine penny-cress which binds zinc such that its leaves may contain up to 5% pure zinc. Several metallophytic shingle sites of the Nent Allen and South Tyne have been designated Sites of Special Scientific Interest (SSSIs) including Blagill, Alston, Lambley, Ninebanks, Wharmley and Williamston. These sites collectively make up the two European-designated Special Areas of Conservation (SACs), the Tyne and Nent, and the Tyne and Allen river shingles.

SPECIAL CREATURES OF THE TYNE
The pearl mussel
Although the pearl mussel (*Margaritifera margaritifera*)(Fig 5.1), a bivalve mollusc, was once abundant in rivers throughout northern Europe and Siberia,

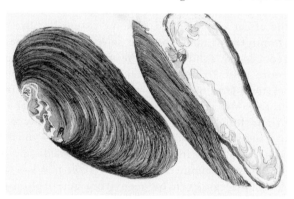

Fig 5.1 The pearl mussel (*Margaritifera margaritifera*) a bivalve mollusc.

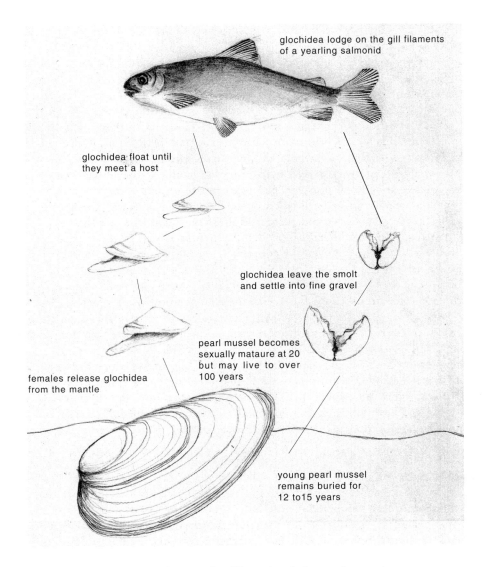

glochidea lodge on the gill filaments
of a yearling salmonid

glochidea float until
they meet a host

glochidea leave the smolt
and settle into fine gravel

pearl mussel becomes
sexually mataure at 20
but may live to over
100 years

females release glochidea
from the mantle

young pearl mussel
remains buried for
12 to15 years

Fig 5.2 The complex life cycle of the pearl mussel

it is now threatened and declining throughout its range. It has disappeared from
many river systems, and the total population of about 12,000 in the Rede and
North Tyne is one of the few remaining populations in England. It occurs
sporadically on the main stem of the River Rede downstream from the Elsdon
Burn confluence to Redesmouth. In the North Tyne it is found singly, in groups
or beds from the Rede confluence to Watermeet. The Rede populations are
generally small but there are some bigger beds in the North Tyne.

The pearl mussel has a complex life cycle (Fig 5.2). The males release sperm
into the water and this is filtered out by the females which retain their fertilised

eggs until late summer when they are all released into the water column. The tiny larvae (glochidia) have only a day or so to find a host. In this time they are swept down river. The lucky few are 'breathed' by a salmonid parr – only a salmonid will do and only a young one at that. The larvae get a grip as they are swept through the filaments of the gills and lodge there for some six months leaving the host unharmed when it is about to smolt. Fish that acquire a heavy load of larvae seem able to shed most of them and it is only in some Scottish salmon farms that heavy infestations cause problems to the fish. Once the tiny mussels drop off, they must land in clean well-aerated sand where they must spend about fifteen years buried before joining adults at the gravel surface.

Why such a complex life cycle? The pearl mussel is not a very mobile animal. In floods animals tend to be washed downstream. The only way the species can move back upstream in a river system is to hitch a ride with a fish host.

It is often said that the salmon is the creature which is most sensitive to pollution within a river. I would contend that the young pearl mussel is even more sensitive.

The species is very long lived with individuals over 100 years old being not uncommon. Unfortunately in the North Tyne population there seem to be more pearl mussels aged over 80 years than aged under 20. Clearly the population is not viable. There is little repopulation (recruitment); there are simply not enough young to replace the aging adults. Even the improvement in salmon populations as host for the glochidia life stage of the mussel does not appear as yet to have improved recruitment. It seems likely that this fascinating creature will be lost from the North Tyne catchments in the next few decades. If the reason for the decline could be identified, then effective remedial measures might be put in place.

The White Clawed crayfish (Austropotamobius pallipes)
There is only one native British crayfish species – the White Clawed Crayfish (Fig 5.3 top). It was at one time found in suitable rivers throughout England and Wales but Northumberland now holds one of the last remnant populations of this species. It was lost from many rivers in southern England from 1981 onward, a victim not of pollution - although the crayfish is only found in relatively clean rivers - but of a fungal disease (*Aphanomyces astaci*) known as crayfish plague which is endemic in populations of the American Signal Crayfish (*Pacifastacus leniusculus*) (Fig 5.3 bottom).

The Signal Crayfish, bigger and faster growing than its cousin, was brought into the country for growing in fish farms as a source of fish food. The crayfish plague fungus which came with it is harmless to the Signal but invariably fatal to the White Clawed. Once the infection is introduced into a river, it spreads quickly and stretches of river of over 50 km have been known to lose all their crayfish within three weeks. Because the fungus spreads by water-borne spores, whole catchments have lost their native crayfish populations wherever the Signal was introduced. Now, the unlicensed keeping of Signal Crayfish is prohibited in the north of England.

The disease has then spread further by other means – on fishing tackle, the

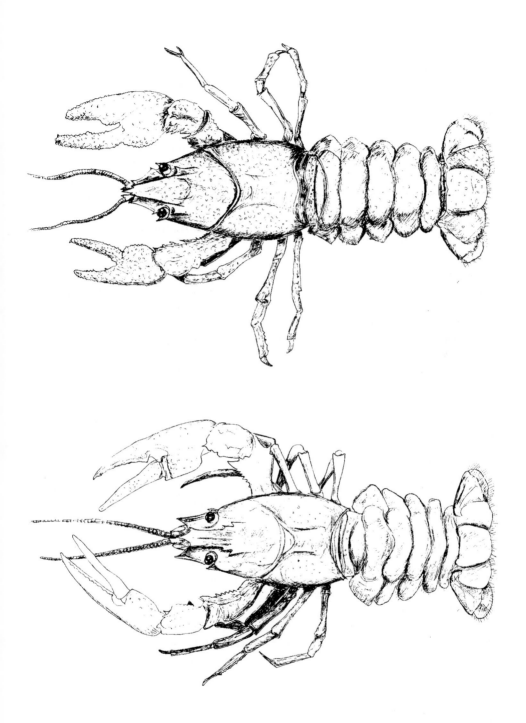

Fig 5.3 The White Clawed crayfish (*Austropotamobius pallipes*) - above:
the American Signal crayfish (*Pacifastacus leniusculus*) - below.

legs of water birds and possibly on the equipment of the investigating biologists! Only in rivers in the north where no one tried to farm Signals, did the White Clawed remain.

In the Tyne catchment only a few small tributaries such as the Erring Burn ever had crayfish populations. In the mid-nineties the species was lost from most of these streams at the same time as a crayfish mortality in the rivers Pont and Blyth. The presence of plague was never proven nor were Signal Crayfish found. Nonetheless, there has not yet been a return of white clawed crayfish to these catchments, suggesting that plague was indeed the problem.

The species has not quite disappeared from the Tyne catchment. The only remaining small populations are in the isolated Roman Wall loughs and streams running into them and in the Warks Burn. Recently, crayfish remains have been found in the droppings of otters on the Warks Burn, although living crayfish have not yet been seen.

Midges

Much as one would like to omit reference to the midge and its distinctly unpleasant habits, it is only fair to warn visitors to the upper Tyne. Like their Scottish sisters of the same species, they bite! They can wreak havoc with a camping holiday and can have a significant impact on the productivity of forest workers or the enjoyment of ramblers and fishermen.

Biting midges belong to the Insect Order Diptera, the true flies (only one pair of wings, unlike most other insects which have two pairs). There are about 37 species of biting midge in Britain and about five that bite humans, but the real villain of the uplands is *Culicoides impunctatus* which inflicts most of the damage. The midge does not breed in the river but the midge larvae thrive in the top five centimetres of damp, acidic peaty soil or wet vegetation, and their distribution is related to such wet breeding areas. The pupae and larvae must remain moist or they die; occasionally a dry spring will kill large numbers.

Young midges over-winter as larvae and then pupae, these stages lasting about ten months before they turn into adult flies. *C. impunctatus* has two generations per season. The first adults emerge in mid- to late May, triggered by an increase in day length and temperature. Male midges emerge a few days before the females. Males form mating swarms, and females fly into these swarms and pairs fall to the ground. The females of *C. impunctatus* do not require a blood meal to lay the first batch of eggs but they require one for subsequent egg batches.

Females lay their eggs in vegetation dominated by rushes and mosses. Eggs hatch and the second-generation larvae find their way into the soil where they develop through four larval stages or 'instars', taking about four weeks. The second generation of adults emerges in about mid-June and the mating/feeding cycle is repeated. The subsequent larvae, however, go into a dormant state when they reach the fourth instar in late August or early September. They remain as fourth instar larvae throughout the winter, pupating the following spring and forming the first generation of adults the next year.

The adult midge has a wingspan of less than two millimetres. The female's instruments of torture are two toothed mandibles and a maxillae which are used in a scissor motion to cut their way into the victim's skin, releasing a pool of blood from the capillary blood vessels. The female then inserts her mouth parts into the cut and continues to withdraw blood, unless detected, for several minutes. A typical meal is one ten millionth of a litre, so the victim will not succumb to anaemia unless attacked by ten million midges. Some victims would claim that this is a distinct possibility; a hectare of suitable land is estimated to contain 24,000,000 midge larvae. However, if it is any consolation, only pregnant females bite; the males are vegetarian.

The body's immune system releases a histamine at the source of the bite. White blood cells rush to the spot and start to repair the wound. It is the body's repair mechanism that produces most of the itching and swelling as a reaction to the proteins left by the visitor.

In the Tyne uplands the midge 'biting season' stretches from late June till the end of September but with the peak time in July and August. When the female is pregnant, the main trigger that cues her biting activity is the level of light; if the light level falls below a certain threshold (260 watts/m^2), then the midge is stimulated to seek out its victim. Hence the hour just before sunset and the hour just after sunrise are the worst times, but dull, calm weather is also prime biting time.

The attraction of a particular individual to a midge depends on body odour together with the different reactions of people to midge bites. Biting midges have about 500 olfactory receptors on their antennae, some of which respond to a small number of chemicals (specialists), and some to a broad range of chemicals (generalists). Recent research shows that the midge is highly selective in its victims depending on their sweat. One extract of sweat placed overnight in a midge trap attracted 26,000 insects.

The Kielder area has the reputation for being the worst midge area in the Tyne catchment, perhaps because the trees reduce the ambient light and wind velocity to a level suitable for biting. There is little problem with midges downstream from Wark. The moorlands of the South Tyne also create favourable conditions for midge breeding, but bad midge days are less frequent due to higher wind speeds on the open moorlands.

ALIEN INVADERS

An alien (or exotic) species may be defined as one which has reached its present habitat either by deliberate or accidental human intervention and now survives unaided in the wild. Its introduction may have been comparatively recent, as in the case of the mink, or much more ancient, as in the case of the rabbit (introduced by the Normans and for some years maintained in domestic warrens). Some are now widely accepted as part of the natural local flora or fauna whilst others are resented because of their vigorous colonisation, the displacement of true native species or other undesirable characteristics. Nevertheless, ecologists disagree about the extent to which aliens should be controlled. Some purists would argue for the control and even removal of all introductions but are particularly vehement about certain species such as the mink. Others make convincing arguments about the mink's right to live and the charm of the coypu (a large south American rodent which has been introduced to East Anglian rivers).

To put aliens into perspective, the definition above would include river species such as carp, rainbow trout and Canadian pondweed, and more generally, snowdrop, most daffodils, raspberry, sycamore, beech (native only in the southern counties of England), all pines except Scots pine and all deer except red deer. Clearly many of these species are now welcome; besides it would be impractical to consider exterminating them. Nevertheless some aliens of the river and riverbank are considered highly undesirable including the first two of the following examples.

Giant hogweed (Heraculeum mantegazzianum)
Giant hogweed is a native of the Caucasus and has been on the loose in the British countryside for over a century (Plate 13). It was originally introduced to gardens from which it escaped to make its home principally along riverbanks although it is now also found marching up hedgerows and covering areas of waste ground. It is a biennial member of the parsley and carrot family.

It is an impressive contender of the title of worst weed. It can grow to a height of four metres with vast prickly leaves shading out any potential competitors. Huge, flat flower heads develop from late May onward and it is ready to shed its cargo of seeds from August into the autumn. Each plant can produce 15,000 seeds in one year. The seeds can remain viable for over a decade and the plants seem to find riverside sandbanks an ideal seed bed. Finally, giant hogweed is dangerous to people; its caustic sap burns on contact with naked skin and if the contact occurs in sunlight, really serious burns can develop.

It is mainly found in the main Tyne downstream from Hexham to the upper estuary at Ryton, with particular problems in the Ovingham area. At one point the Environment Agency had a five-year plan to eradicate the plant by spraying with glycophosphate but this was unsuccessful and the programme has been discontinued. The EA has no statutory duty to control riverbank weeds.

Japanese knotweed (Fallopia japonica)
Japanese knotweed is another garden escape, introduced as an ornamental plant to Victorian gardens. It has rather attractive foliage with its mottled stems and fresh green spade-shaped leaves; it can reach three metres in height. It is now a common riverside plant along the Tyne especially at Wylam (Plate 14). However, its appearance belies its triffid-like tendencies. It is a perennial plant with spreading rhizomes from which shoots grow up in spring to form dense thickets shading out other plants. The rhizomes may extend as much as seven metres from the parent plant and reach a depth of two metres. It regenerates vegetatively and is highly efficient. Only fingernail-sized fragments of rhizome and stem are needed to produce new growth and in riparian areas it is readily spread downstream in flood flows.

Japanese knotweed is dioecious which means that male and female flowers are carried on separate plants. However all the British (and European) plants are female, thus precluding sexual reproduction. So, if it is any consolation, at least it doesn't spread by seed. It is also interesting to note that the entire British population is a clone from a single plant source.

The problem of controlling Japanese knotweed is twofold. It is not very susceptible to permitted herbicides and, even cutting and burning do no more than remove the top growth. The plant remains ready to rise again immediately control ceases.

Japanese knotweed is a 'controlled' weed and its disposal is regulated by law. All material even after treatment must be buried at a depth of not less than five metres and it must be disposed of either on site or at a designated 'special waste' tip. Anyone who has seen Japanese knotweed bursting up through concrete will know that this vegetable thug is a serious adversary. Typically, effective control costs over £1 per square metre (similar to the cost of de-mining!). Failure to control it now may lead to far greater expense in the future. Biological control based on natural pests in its native East Asia may prove effective, but introducing another alien carries its own risks.

Snowberry (Symphoricarpos albus)

More ambivalent feelings can be expressed about snowberry, a North American shrub of the honeysuckle family which has become such a common feature of gardens and countryside that it is now hardly recognised as an alien. In addition several generations of British children have taken pleasure in popping the small white fruit under their feet. But note, the fruit is not edible. It is also planted by gamekeepers to give cover to young game birds and provides a good cover for other wildlife..

Nevertheless, snowberry is a ruthless exploiter of riverbanks. It spreads both by seed and vegetatively, and once established creates a monoculture thicket that excludes all other plants. It can survive flooding and associated cover by river sand and helps to stabilise banks which grow steadily higher with successive floods.

Himalayan balsam (Impatiens glandulifera)

As its name suggests this plant originates in the Himalayas and came to Britain as a garden plant from which it has escaped mainly to colonise damp river banks. It is an annual and spreads by seed. In my view this alien can be forgiven; it has pretty pink flowers with a decorated helmet shape (hence its alternative name 'policeman's helmet') and a distinctive balsam smell that goes home with autumn riverbank users. When ripe, its seed heads explode on contact or on exposure to the sun. It is also a favourite with bees.

Himalayan balsam can become dominant and is a prominent component of the flora throughout the main Tyne catchment and parts of the North Tyne.

Monkey flower (Mimulus sp.)

The bright orange monkey musk (M. moschatus) and the larger yellow brown blotched flowers of M. guttatus are a familiar sight in the upland parts of the catchment. These introductions from North America were first naturalised in Wales, where they escaped from Victorian cottage gardens, but they have since spread throughout the British Isles. They have eased their way into the local flora without causing any particular problems. They are present but not dominant in riparian upland floras and do not seem to have displaced any native species. If only all introductions could be like this!

THE TYNE — A SPECIAL RIVER

Despite the long industrial history of the North East and the reputation of Tyneside until recently as a blighted industrial landscape, first-time visitors to the Tyne are surprised at the natural unmodified appearance of the river. The river looks pristine right down to its tidal limit.

How has the Tyne escaped the appearance of a post-industrial river and how has it retained its excellent water quality? The Tyne might be said to be a fortunate river by reason of the geology of its catchment. Had the Coal Measures straddled the Pennines, then the upper dales would now look something like the mining valleys of South Wales. Had the Pennine Orefield been in slates rather than in limestones, then the metals would have been far more toxic to river life in a calcium-poor environment than they actually are. In the North Tyne episodic acid flushes of upland tributaries amplified by Kielder Forest are balanced and buffered by storage and mixing in Kielder Water. The harsh climate, poor soils and steep slopes of the upper part of the catchment have discouraged the intensive agricultural development of the catchment and channel modification, seen for example in the rivers of the Midlands. The ecology of the river appears to have recovered from the ravages of gravel extraction. The kaleidoscope of gravel-bed microhabitats, shaken up and modified but not destroyed by each flood, provides the basis for a thriving biodiversity.

6. THE TYNE FISHERY

TONY CHAMPION

THE ARRIVAL OF FISH IN THE TYNE

On a geological timescale salmon (and other fish) are comparative newcomers to the River Tyne. Around 18,000 years ago at the height of the last Ice Age, the valley was filled with perhaps a thousand feet of ice. The English Channel did not exist and the southern limit of the North Sea was situated somewhere on a line from Norfolk to Holland. Where not covered by ice, Northern Europe as far south as the Alps, had permanently frozen ground (permafrost), so there were no perennial rivers running from this arctic desert into the North Sea.

The ice started to melt about 15,000 years ago. Authorities differ over how long it took, but it did clear before returning again to the Lake District and the Scottish mountains for about a thousand years 12,000 years ago, during the period known as the Younger Dryas. The ice then vanished very quickly as the climate changed yet again. It is difficult to form an opinion on the probability of salmon returning to the Tyne in this period. The climate would have been suitable, but the river may not have provided a suitable habitat for fish of any description. The melting ice would have generated huge floods heavily laden with boulders, gravel and silt surging down a river with a highly mobile bed in which there may have been no stable gravel suitable for spawning salmon. This process will have continued for long after the ice had gone, and it may not have been complete until about 8000 years ago when many European rivers assumed their present meandering characteristics.

Since the Dover Straits did not open until about 6500 years ago, any salmon recolonising the Tyne before that time would have been wanderers from the west coast or even further south from France or Spain. The Tyne may even have been a tributary of the Rhine which would have been recolonised from the same source. It is anybody's guess where the coarse fish came from, but they probably arrived at about the same time, possibly down the Rhine. Suggestions are that their eggs were transferred by birds or, no less fanciful an idea, in the thick fur of mammoths, a much more suitable medium for the transfer of fish eggs than the bare feet of ducks.

Significantly, at about this time Mesolithic man was re-establishing himself in Europe, and it is generally supposed that in his trek north, as the ice receded and the land became habitable again, he followed the deer and the salmon up the river valleys. Certainly he had the technology to take salmon, and salmon bones have been found at a Mesolithic site at Hauxley on the Northumberland coast. Mesolithic man made nets out of vines and barbed spears out of bone. Some authorities even claim that he fished for salmon with barbed fish hooks. This seems doubtful. Every salmon angler knows in his heart that a rod and line is a highly inefficient way of catching salmon, and few would be prepared to rely on their efforts for food. By all accounts Mesolithic man was no fool and, with a family unit or possibly a tribe to feed, he will have used the most efficient method available to him. His crude nets would not have gilled fish, so one can imagine they were used to herd the salmon into shallow water where they could be dispatched. They could also have been used to guide the salmon migrating upstream and to keep them close enough to the bank to be reached with a spear. Spawning grounds in the upper reaches were probably hunted in the same way. Spawning fish and kelts (the depleted salmon after spawning) are now despised as food, but hunger, no doubt, provided a different dietary perspective.

Coarse fish such as roach and dace can withstand very cold conditions but they do require warm weather in the early summer in order to breed successfully. Currently, dace which live in the Tyne are near their northern limit for the east coast. However, in the period from about 8000 to 4500 years ago the climate was warmer than at present; so it is probable that coarse fish thrived in that period. It is possible that they died out in the several later cold periods, notably in the 'Little Ice Age' of approximately 1300 to 1800 AD. In several winters at the end of the eighteenth century the Tyne froze over at Newcastle. Unfortunately, although there are many records of salmon in this period, coarse fish do not rate a mention other than in the ponds of the numerous monasteries of those days.

ROMAN AND MEDIEVAL FISHERMEN

The Romans fished for pleasure with rod and line, and although there are no records to suggest that they fished for salmon in the Tyne, they were familiar with the species in Gaul and Aquitaine. It seems unlikely that visiting dignitaries would not have taken advantage of the opportunity. Neither do we know for certain if the soldiers garrisoned on Hadrian's Wall ate salmon, but to this day soldiers in the field will eat pretty well anything that comes their way. It is inconceivable that conscripts from the Atlantic valleys of France and Spain or from the Rhine did not recognize the fish swarming in the Tyne and take the necessary steps to supplement their diet. It is equally unlikely that the native tribes would have ignored such a valuable source of protein. They would have taken fish by whatever method seemed most appropriate, possibly using stone or wooden groynes and traps, carefully repaired every spring, and would have fished on a daily basis when the salmon were migrating.

During the Middle Ages the record of conflict between different fishery owners (recognizing that the fisheries are valuable resources) provides the main source of information on Tyne fisheries. In 1344 Edward III granted a commission to the Barony of Prudhoe "to view and search the water of Tyne in order to destroy weirs and keddells which had been set up to the injury of the fisheries and contrary to ancient custom". This is probably the first record of conflict between a fishery owner and others competing for the same fish. The fishery at Ovingham, which was then in the barony, fed the inhabitants and so was of some importance. Thus this commission was frequently repeated.

However, there seems little doubt that this was not the first conflict of interest on the Tyne. In the time of King William Rufus, or possibly his son Henry I, about 60 salmon fishing stations between the Stanley Burn and Tynemouth were named in a list which apportioned the fisheries between the Bishopric of Durham, the County of Northumberland and 'free' fisheries. They were clearly of great value. It is not surprising that out of the 60 only eight were designated as 'free' and these were in the middle of the river.

Records clearly show that netting and trapping of salmon was a major industry on the Tyne until the end of the nineteenth century. Disputes over rent and ownership were frequent, and in 1598 there is a record of armed affray when a gang "armed with staves and swords broke open the locks of the dam (at Bywell) and entered into her majesty's possession of a fishery". It is not clear from the records how these stations were fished. Many of them were associated with mill dams, and in 1525 there is a record of payment for maintenance of a dam at Ovingham and associated boats and nets. It therefore seems likely that this was a seine net fishery for fish lying below the dam. Others, particularly in the tidal waters, seem to have been associated with groynes, which presumably were placed in such a way as to deflect migrating salmon into fixed nets or traps or possibly just into shallow water where they could be netted by hand or gaffed.

No mention is made of sea trout until the nineteenth century. Even then it is not clear whether they were usually included in the records as salmon, or whether they were simply beneath contempt and not worth recording. Certainly sea trout in the Tyne today are frequently as large as small salmon, and although it is easy to distinguish between the two species some experience is helpful. Moreover, although some people today prefer to eat sea trout because the flesh and the taste are finer, it seems unlikely that the peasants or ordinary townspeople of the first 900 years of the last millennium were too fussy.

Undoubtedly anglers fished for salmon, but few records exist of their efforts. Thomas Bewick in his Memoir[1] notes that his grandfather (around 1700) was an expert angler, and in 1760 it is recorded that an angler landed a small silver cup which had been washed down from Corbridge..

A TIME OF PLENTY
It is difficult to know how many salmon were taken from the Tyne. There is no doubt at all that salmon fishing by nets was a major industry on the Tyne, and it is puzzling that so few records still exist. There are occasional statements of the numbers of fish taken at a fishery, but it is never clear whether the number referred to is the total catch or just a part of it, or if the fishery was only worked for a short period. Two landings are certainly worth mentioning. The first was reported in the Newcastle Courant on June 12th, 1755, a day when over 2400 salmon were taken in the Tyne, and the second on August 6th, 1761 when 260 salmon were taken in one draught. Fishing records also show that many of the fish being caught were of large size, the longest being 5.5 feet, weighing 54 lbs. But where were the sea trout? It is inconceivable that there were not some sea trout in the catch.

Thomas Bewick in his Memoir[1] referring to his childhood in the 1760s relates by far the most famous story of Tyne salmon:

"Before or perhaps about this time there had always been an article inserted in every indenture in Newcastle that the apprentice was not obliged to eat salmon above twice a week, and the like bargain was made upon hiring ordinary servants — it need not be added that the Salmo tribe then teemed in abundance in the Tyne"

The folklore is that certain apprentices rebelled against their masters because they were fed salmon so frequently. Anyone who has eaten salmon every day for a week will sympathise with the apprentices and believe implicitly in the tale. Carefully boiled salmon with new potatoes and cucumber whether hot or cold is delicious fare if not repeated too often. Salmon boiled in bulk, overcooked and served every day is less attractive.

Tweed salmon also passed through Newcastle possibly in even greater quantities. Defoe[2] pointed out in 1723 that although great quantities of 'Newcastle salmon' were always available in London, they had in fact been caught in the Tweed and had been:

"... brought by land on horses to Shields, where it is cured, pickled, and sent to London ... so that it ought to be called Berwick salmon, not Newcastle."

FIGHTING THE WRONG BATTLE?
By the beginning of the nineteenth century the writing was on the wall for the river fisheries. Industrialisation increased rapidly and by mid-century the Tyne estuary was lined with coke ovens and iron, chemical and alkali works (Chapter 13). The rod fisheries upstream were beginning to decline, and it is now that more information becomes available and the voice of anglers and rod fishery owners is heard for the first time. But then, as possibly now, they barked up the wrong tree.

It is a strange and sorry fact that throughout the last century salmon anglers as a body concentrated on ridding themselves of competitors for a dwindling resource rather than on protecting that shared resource from damage. Thus they have concentrated their fire on netting, predators and illegal fishing rather than on the destruction of the fish's environment. It is of course true to say that there probably would not be salmon in many of our rivers today if it were not for the pressure from the angler's lobby. However, it is also true that there would be many more if instead of focussing their attention on the nets they had concentrated on the catastrophic effects of domestic and industrial pollution in the estuary and, in more recent times, on irreversible effects of gravel abstraction and damaging farming methods grant-aided by government.

The first recorded instance locally of this blinkered attitude seems to be a meeting of the South Tyne Association in 1834, at which it was agreed that the decline in catch was not due to the factories lining the banks in Newcastle but to fishing in the closed season. No mention was made of the increase in lead mining in the tributary streams of the South Tyne (Chapter 8).

The decline in catch cropped up again in 1891 when, in evidence given to a Royal Commission, the Clerk of the Fishery Board would not venture an opinion on the level of netting but detailed a horrific litany of pollution and dead salmon and smolts in the estuary. He also attributed the total absence of salmon in the South Tyne to pollution from lead workings and in support of this supposition cited a case where gravel abstracted from the river was spread on a carriageway resulting in the early demise of the abstractor's hens from lead poisoning. There was no doubt in his mind that the decline of the salmon fisheries was a direct result of pollution.

The Chairman of the Fishery Board, who was a riparian owner and angler, had a different opinion. He largely blamed the river nets for the decline in his catches from an average of 147 salmon in the 5-year period beginning in 1880 to 43 salmon in the period from 1895 to 1899, but he based his opinion on information that is unlikely to be correct. He believed that of a total of 121,600 salmon (and sea trout?) netted in 1871, at least 110,000 were taken in the river nets. However, in 1873, the first year in which records of the number of nets in use are available, there were only 27 drift net licences issued for the river compared with 163 for the sea. Like many other members of the anti-net lobby, he apparently did not stop to consider that the fishing pressure from the nets had been greater in the past (see discussion of sea net fishery below) and that he should be considering not how to get a larger slice of the cake but how to stop the whole cake shrinking. During this period the total rod catch for the river varied from 3201 in 1885 to 123 in 1898. His statements regarding estuarial pollution were ambivalent in that he seemed to regard it as a temporary problem in low flows despite the fact that on his own admission most of the estuary was grossly polluted.

The Commission reported that "the present polluted state of many rivers materially impedes the access of salmon to the upper waters and thus, by limiting the available spawning area, must have a most prejudicial influence on the salmon fisheries of the country". However, they missed the point that whilst adult salmon can often successfully negotiate polluted estuaries during heavy spate conditions, smolt migration (Fig. 6.1) can be triggered by small variations in flow, causing the migrants to pass downstream to their doom. This was still the case in the spring of 1974 when smolts could be seen on the intake screens of Stella power station near Blaydon. They were not sucked onto the screens by the high velocity of flow but rather drifted onto them, dead or in a moribund state. This vulnerability was appreciated by the Board of Conservators for the Fishery District of the River Tyne which reported in 1959 that, 'The floods.... necessary to enable the smolts to reach the sea did not materialise and, as always happens, large numbers of these fish were killed on entering the tidal stretch.... It is extremely improbable that they reached the sea in any numbers'. That year, coincidentally, was the first and only year in which no report was received of a salmon taken by rod and line.

Despite a peak catch of 3361 in 1927, the rod fishery had for all practical purposes ceased in the early 1930s, with an exceptional low of 15 in 1933. The combination of added pollution from new coke works, exceptionally low

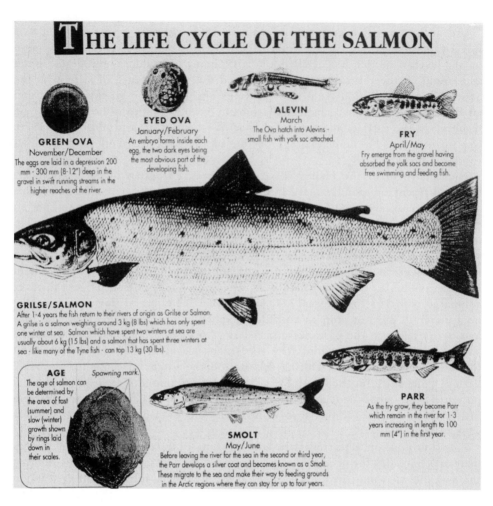

THE LIFE CYCLE OF THE SALMON

GREEN OVA
November/December
The eggs are laid in a depression 200 mm - 300 mm (8-12") deep in the gravel in swift running streams in the higher reaches of the river.

EYED OVA
January/February
An embryo forms inside each egg, the two dark eyes being the most obvious part of the developing fish.

ALEVIN
March
The Ova hatch into Alevins - small fish with yolk sac attached.

FRY
April/May
Fry emerge from the gravel having absorbed the yolk sacs and become free swimming and feeding fish.

GRILSE/SALMON
After 1-4 years the fish return to their rivers of origin as Grilse or Salmon. A grilse is a salmon weighing around 3 kg (8 lbs) which has only spent one winter at sea. Salmon which have spent two winters at sea are usually about 6 kg (15 lbs) and a salmon that has spent three winters at sea - like many of the Tyne fish - can top 13 kg (30 lbs).

AGE   Spawning mark.
The age of salmon can be determined by the area of fast (summer) and slow (winter) growth shown by rings laid down in their scales.

SMOLT
May/June
Before leaving the river for the sea in the second or third year, the Parr develops a silver coat and becomes known as a Smolt. These migrate to the sea and make their way to feeding grounds in the Arctic regions where they can stay for up to four years.

PARR
As the fry grow, they become Parr which remain in the river for 1-3 years increasing in length to 100 mm (4") in the first year.

Fig 6.1 The life cycle of the salmon (*Environment Agency, by permission*)

summer rainfall in 1932 and 1933, and increased gravel extraction upstream brought about this dramatic decline. The river net fishery, which was banned by byelaw in 1934 in an attempt to save the rod fishery, had long since lost favour with the markets because of the tainted tarry flavour of the fish. In hindsight it is easy to see that this taste was probably due to the phenols discharged from Derwenthaugh and Norwood coke works. Even after the recovery of the Tyne started in the late 1960s, it was popularly said that a flood that raised the water over Hexham weir by four feet was needed to clear the estuary to allow salmon through. Fish would then run clean and fresh for about a week, but later arrivals tasted of creosote. This phenomenon ceased when the coke works were closed. However, 1959 was undoubtedly the nadir for the Tyne (Fig. 6.2). Anglers and riparian owners had lost interest or despaired of maintaining their fisheries - their voices had been drowned by those who wanted to be rid of effluent, both chemical and sewage, in the cheapest manner possible.

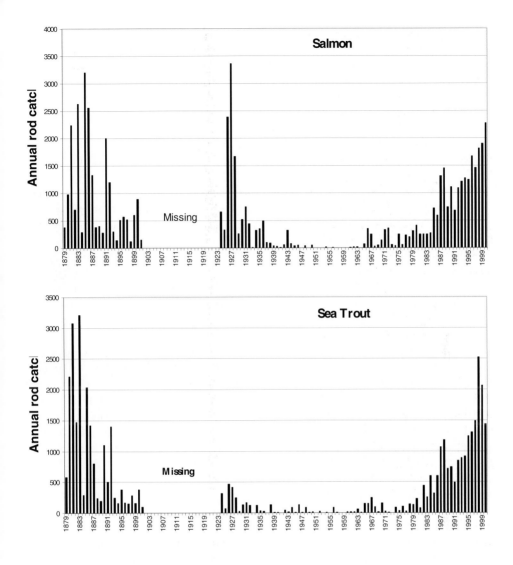

Fig 6.2 Salmon and sea trout rod catches from 1879 to 2000

Some landowners with no further interest in the fishery saw a quick killing in extracting gravel from the river (Chapter 4). They were unconcerned that it had taken an Ice Age and thousands of years of floods to sort it and put it in nice heaps in the river, and that it might take another ice age to replace it. Gravel extraction undermined the foundations of bridges, and civil engineers, in bolstering the foundations, built weirs that would prove impassable to salmon. Further erosion increased the weir height, thus necessitating the construction of fish passes, as at Hexham bridge. In the building of the first fish pass at Hexham about 30 years ago, the work exposed a complete oak tree which had been used as part of the foundations. The engineer had nightmares about what would happen if he cut into the oak, for he suspected that the bridge would be weakened and might collapse with the next flood to the possible detriment of his career prospects. The plans were quickly modified; the top resting box of the fish pass was installed but with insufficient depth. As a result the flow of water in the box circulated in the wrong direction and obliged resting fish to sit on the bottom and face downstream. Fish have short memories; so when they were rested they promptly jumped back downstream again. The problem was ultimately solved by filling the box with boulders so that the migrating salmon had to keep going without a rest.

Thus were the problems of the salmon exacerbated by decades of neglect. The sole glimmer of hope for later years was that salmon are a persistent species and some were always present in the river. It now seems unlikely that the Tyne race of salmon was extinguished.

THE SEA NET FISHERY

The salmon sea net fishery has always been a bone of contention with anglers. Conflict may have started in a small way when Tynemouth Priory first sent boats out to sea to catch fish for sale in Newcastle. However, salmon are not specifically mentioned as part of the catch, and it is more likely that the monks preferred to take salmon from their netting stations in the estuary, a safer and more efficient option. Even in relatively modern times the history of netting for salmon off the North East coast has not been easy to decipher, although there is good reason to believe that drift netting started round about 1840. The confusion arises because Bucknall, the Inspector of Salmon Fisheries, in his report dated 1879 says that a large proportion of the Tyne salmon were caught at sea in hang nets (nets in which the salmon were enmeshed and 'hung' by the gills), which were invented about 35 years previously. In his report the following year Bucknell made the contradictory claim that hang nets were introduced in 1867, and he described as many as 107 boats fishing at sea with 600 yards of hang net.

In 1882 his successor reviewed the history of salmon conservation in the Tyne more thoroughly. He traced to 1838 or 1839 the introduction of stake nets, which may either have been nets supported by poles in such a manner that they formed traps or simply hang nets fixed on poles. He described the spread of this instrument along the coastline subsequent to the Tyne Fisheries Act 1842, which abolished their use in the immediate vicinity of the river mouth. He further discussed the invention of the hang net to evade this law and described how these nets were anchored or tied to the shore and frequently laid right across the river mouth to an anchored boat. This practice was prohibited by the Salmon Fishery Act 1861, but the prohibition may not have been rigorously enforced until 1867 when a licensing system was first introduced in the Tyne. The hang nets then licensed could only have been drift nets. Thus Bucknall's later claim that drift netting started in 1867 must have referred to licensed netting, and his earlier comment to the effect that the method had been introduced some 30 years earlier is more likely to be correct.

Throughout the history of drift netting in the North East, fishermen from the Tyne ports of North and South Shields seem to have taken the lead, but even there the published statistics are unreliable and in some cases contradictory. In 1867 Buckland describes drift net fishing three to fifteen miles out to sea; yet in that year large numbers of sea trout were caught with an average weight of only 4 lbs. Folk history has it that the mesh size used in these drift nets was approximately 3" knot to knot. Sea trout averaging 4 lbs in weight could not have been enmeshed in nets of that mesh size. Today significant catches of sea trout are only made close to shore. Clearly drift or fixed hang nets of smaller mesh size must still have been used on the beaches. A drift net method that survives to this day is to set a net out from the beach and allow the free end to drift around whilst judicially anchoring the inner end so that the net does not quite become illegal.

Drift netting at sea was conducted entirely at night and, with increasing motor traffic up and down the coast, must have become increasingly dangerous from small unmotorised cobles. It is not surprising that there was a decline in catches and in the number of licences issued from 1870 to 1920. The subsequent slight rise in the number of licences issued in the 20s and 30s may have been due to the introduction of the motor coble, which is quoted as being the catalyst for the start of drift netting in the Coquet area around that time. However, drift netting virtually ceased during the second World War because no lights were allowed on board the boats.

The net fishery began to recover in the early 1950s, with a steady increase in the number of licences issued by the Northumberland and Tyneside River Board until 1964. Then the Board took action to limit cropping rates by introducing legislation to control the number of licences issued. The average annual catch of salmon per licence, having declined since the 1870s, started to recover through the 1950s and early 1960s, but did not regain its former level until the late 1960s when nylon twine nets were first used to a significant extent. It is not known whether this material was more efficient than the traditional hemp or cotton nets when in the water. However, the mesh size was smaller (approximately 2.5" knot to knot); it was clearly an easier material to use and meant that the fishermen could spend more time with their nets in the water.

The slightly later introduction of monofilament netting has been the most significant change in recent years as it no longer restricted effective fishing to the hours of darkness and bad weather. (Salmon could see and avoid the traditional nets in calm bright weather). By 1970 the new nets were used by all licensed netsmen with the result that there was a rapid increase in catch per licence; the effective fishing effort had probably doubled. Demand for licences also grew. It was not until 1976 that further steps were taken specifically to protect the residual stock of Tyne salmon, which was showing signs of recovery. Agreement was reached with local netsmen for the imposition of a prohibited area one mile wide for a distance of 2 miles to the north and 4.3 miles to the south of the Tyne estuary. An exception was made for two beach netting stations immediately to the south of the river, in which netsmen were allowed to use 'T' nets, a type of fixed net forming a trap similar to the bag net in common use in Scotland. Despite claims from anti-netting lobbies that drift netting would destroy salmon stocks, the rod catch in the Tyne continued to rise.

The drift net fishery was based chiefly on salmon heading for other rivers, mainly the Tweed. It was from there that the majority of local opposition to drift netting for salmon had been orchestrated, on the grounds that the income from the valuable rod fisheries on the Tweed was limited by the drift net fishery and that the local tourist income from fishing was also diminished. The conservation argument was also invoked. Stocks were apparently endangered by drift netting and could be in danger of extinction. The fact that, like rod fishing on the Tweed, drift netting is a commercial enterprise and therefore will cease when it becomes uneconomic, thus allowing stocks to recover, was ignored. The objective was to conserve salmon from exploitation at sea so that they could be exploited in the river. This objective has been achieved, and the drift net fishery is now to be phased out. Undoubtedly as a result more salmon will enter the Tyne as well as the Tweed, but English taxpayers will subsidise the Tweed fisheries because they will be lumbered with the cost of policing the Northumbrian coastline to prevent illegal fishing.

THE RECOVERY OF THE TYNE FISHERY
The seeds of recovery of the Tyne salmon were already apparent in the Tyne during the 1960s when catches by rod and line exceeded 200 in several years. However, the major breakthrough did not occur until the late 1970s when three major changes occurred.

1. Coke works production went into decline and finally stopped in the early 1980s, and the associated effluent discharges rapidly diminished. This was certainly the cause of the rapid reduction in ecologically-damaging ammonia concentrations in the estuary (Fig. 6.3).
2. The Tyneside Sewage Treatment scheme was commissioned in 1980 and grew by steps in the following decade to serve a population of nearly one million (Chapter 9). All the effluents which were previously discharged raw along the estuarial Tyne were intercepted and carried to the treatment works at Howdon, where the sewage was subjected to primary treatment and then returned to the estuary.
3. River regulation by Kielder commenced in 1981. Although the effect of releases is probably not entirely positive, the associated commencement of salmon stocking from the Kielder Hatchery provided a boost. In 1981 a maximum yearly number of 400,000 parr/smolts were introduced into various parts of the Tyne.

The rod catch of salmon rose steadily from less than 200 in 1976 to over 1000 in 1987 and reached the 2000 mark for the first time in 2000 (Fig 6.2). The news was still not all good A reduction in estuarine pollution encouraged greater numbers of fish to return to the river to spawn, but conditions in the estuary, particularly dissolved oxygen levels during the summer, were not always satisfactory and led to sizeable fish kills. Dead salmon often had serious fungal

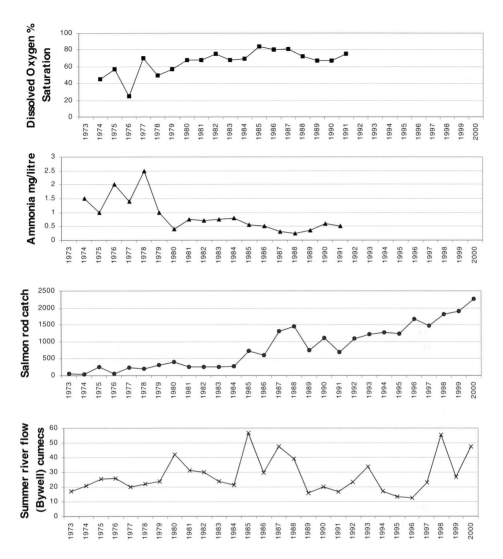

Fig 6.3 Comparison of fish catches during the period of recovery with pollution levels

infections but these were found to be secondary infections. After a period of intensive investigation the main problem was found to be low oxygen levels in the Newburn area (Chapter 8). Oxygen injection into the river was used, but this led to only marginal improvement. Special releases from Kielder were also made to increase flow and oxygen. The problem of fish kills has persisted throughout the 1990s especially during hot dry summers, but it is anticipated that the introduction of secondary treatment at Howdon in 2000 will provide further alleviation.

Recovery has occurred, but by the standards of the eighteenth or even the nineteenth century the patient still has a long way to go. Regrettably much further improvement seems unlikely for two reasons. We appear to be in a period of global warming, and the feeding grounds of the salmon in the Northern Atlantic have been reduced by an incursion of warm water which have resulted in lower survival rates of salmon in the sea. Returning salmon numbers have declined not only in Europe but also in North America. In addition, the long-term build up of oxygen-devouring mud in the Tyne estuary may take many decades to clear.

THE IMPACT OF RESERVOIRS

The River Derwent is neither a salmon river nor a highly successful coarse fish river. It has several strikes against it. In the past it has suffered from serious pollution, from the lead mines in the headwaters to the Derwenthaugh coke works near its confluence with the Tyne, from effluent from Consett steel works and from coal minewater drainage at Blackhall Mill in between. Most of this pollution has now gone, but the Derwent is still largely inaccessible to salmon entering from the estuary because of barriers at Derwenthaugh and Winlaton Mill. Besides these factors the flow regime in the Derwent has been seriously affected by the construction of Derwent Reservoir (Chapter 1). Without the regular large floods of the past the river still contains a heavy silt load from the construction works so that gravel beds are blocked, and even brown trout are not always able to spawn successfully.

The construction of Kielder dam also caused siltation of the river, but this seems now to have cleared. The effect of changes in the temperature regime of releases[3] is likely to be more persistent despite the fact that since 1992 water is preferentially drawn from the surface layers of the reservoir. Generally, release water temperature is lower than in the natural river in spring and summer but higher in winter. Thus, in the immediate vicinity of the dam, egg development is accelerated during the winter, but the water may be too cold in spring to initiate feeding with consequent risks to fry mortality. The greater the release discharge, the further the influence of temperature extends downstream; an adjustment to the release policy has been made since 1995 to hold back releases during the most critical spring period. It is not yet clear how significant temperature is for fry or for the growth rates and smoltification of parr.

Kielder Water inundated 11 kilometres of salmon spawning area and prevented access to significant tributary reaches such as Kielder Burn and Scaup Burn. In evidence given to the first Kielder Inquiry, the Northumbrian River Authority proposed to construct a fish pass at the dam to provide access for spawning to such reaches. However, subsequent study suggested that some potential tributary spawning gravel had been extracted for forestry road construction and that if salmon managed to negotiate the 52 metre lift of the fish pass, they would find difficulty in spawning. Returning smolts might find even greater difficulty in descending. In addition, it did not seem likely that migratory fish would provide a basis for a fishery in the reservoir.

Following consultation with anglers and riparian owners in 1975 it was agreed to scrap the fish pass and instead to build a hatchery and restock the Tyne system with 160,000 salmon parr per year. In the interests of rehabilitation this number was exceeded, and for the first ten years an average of 250,000 parr were introduced, chiefly into areas not normally spawned by salmon. Survival was high in some batches. Microtag return data demonstrated a recapture rate of up to 2% from net and rod fisheries. Although it is popularly supposed that the intensive restocking over and above that required to compensate for the destruction of spawning beds under Kielder reservoir has been a major factor in the recovery of the salmon stocks of the river, in fact sea trout stocks recovered as quickly as the salmon without restocking. Restocking has its own long-term dangers. The immediate vicinity downstream of Kielder dam is stocked with hatchery parr because the natural spawning is unsuccessful due to the unfavourable temperature regime. Indications are that most of the returning adults in this immediate area are chiefly of hatchery origin. Brood stock are captured from the river, chiefly in the area below Kielder dam; therefore the fish are mainly of hatchery origin and inadvertently are being selected as those most successful in a hatchery environment. In the long term it may well turn out that such fish are not the best adapted for life in the wild.

The River Rede also has a reservoir at its head, which destroyed some of the spawning ground. Additionally, compensation water for the river is released from the bottom of the reservoir and causes some of the same problems as Kielder.

OTHER LAND USE ISSUES

Afforestation on a wide scale has affected watercourses both below and above Kielder dam. It causes acidification of minor watercourses, affecting both the average pH and the severity of acid flushes. However, with respect to the main North Tyne downstream from Kielder, the reservoir effectively buffers the effects of incoming acid flushes and maintains a fairly steady pH level which is nearly neutral.

Runoff from mature coniferous forest is also much lower than from grass moorland; much of the rainfall is intercepted by the forest canopy. The amount depends on the species and age of the trees, but studies in Kielder[4] have shown that 25-year old stands of Sitka spruce and lodgepole pine intercept 30%, and a 63 year old stand of Sitka spruce around 50% of the 1000 mm annual rainfall. The resulting reduction in summer flows can particularly affect tributary suitability as a fish habitat.

Moorland drainage, either to improve pasture (South Tyne) or as a prelude to afforestation, (North Tyne) can release a heavy silt load into the river and reduce spawning suitability. Experimental studies in the Kielder forest[5] show that, in contrast to the effect of afforestation itself, drainage increases runoff and does not significantly diminish low flows. The influence of drainage and afforestation on the river regime and ecology thus depends on the length of time after drainage and planting has occurred.

Fortunately the Tyne has not suffered the ravages of intensive cattle rearing or maize cultivation, which has done so much damage to some rivers in the West country. Heavy use of fertiliser occurs on some land bordering the main river, but generally the catchment of the Tyne has not lent itself to intensive farming. Although the main river can carry heavy infestations of algae in the summer, the all-important upper reaches are generally free.

Pollution problems remain in the South Tyne and its tributaries from flow from old mine adits and from drainage of spoil heaps (Chapter 8). Gravel extraction in the middle reaches of the South Tyne in the mid-twentieth century has also affected spawning suitability (Chapter 4).

It is inevitable that activities on the catchment will have an impact on the river flow regime, water quality and sediment and that these will affect the ecology and fishery of the river. However, in the past the consequences of industrial, mining, agricultural and forestry policy and practice on the river were rarely considered. It is to be hoped that the recent emphasis on catchment management planning within the Environment Agency will ensure better coordination between land activities and the river environment.

PREDATORS

Avian predators and mink have also been targeted by the angling lobby, but in the wild there is enormous selection pressure on juvenile salmon from predators. Any parr or smolts that are less than 100% fit for survival are quickly eaten and it is this that keeps salmon stocks healthy. The brown trout was probably the main predator on salmon parr in years gone by although pike were present in the river. Now brown trout populations have declined to the point where angling clubs have to sustain them with hatchery-reared introductions which are themselves products of careful selection for hatchery rather than wild survival. It is doubtful if these fish are capable of weeding out the less suitable salmon parr. Only the cormorants and goosanders will be capable of that. Goosanders have re-established themselves in the Tyne in the past 30 years and cormorants have become regular visitors; doubtless they take many thousands of parr, but whether or not they actually affect the survival rate from parr to adult is open to question. It can be argued that a salmon parr that is unable to evade a goosander is unlikely to evade the predators it will meet in the sea. However, the angling lobby is targetting piscivorous birds because, and only because, they take fish which it is believed will one day provide sport for angling. Many thousands of brown trout are stocked into the Tyne catchment every year. It is not surprising, if all this food is spread out on the table for them, that the birds respond.

OBSTRUCTIONS TO FISH PASSAGE

Historically there have been numerous weirs on the Tyne and its tributaries to provide a head of water for the operation of mills or specifically for trapping fish. These weirs have acted as obstructions to fish passage. Two high weirs at Bywell (Fig. 6.4) and at Winlaton Mill on the Derwent were cited as reasons for the decline in salmon catches before 1800. In 1862 after difficulties in constructing a fish pass, the weir at Bywell was removed, and in 1870 a dam at Woodburn on the River Rede was also demolished. The weir at Winlaton Mill remains.

A proposal was made by Northumbrian River Authority at the Kielder Inquiry

Fig 6.4 The weir at Bywell. Note the fisherman in the river and another dragging a large salmon up the bank (from a print by Thomas Allom 1834)

to carry out works on downstream tributaries to make them accessible to salmon. Work was done shortly thereafter on the Tarset Burn and Houxty Burn, but the River East Allen remains inaccessible above Catton. The recent construction of a fish pass on the Devil's Water has successfully reintroduced salmon; kelts have already been recorded above the fish pass.

There remain six obstructions to the passage of migratory fish in the main river and in the North and South Tyne. It is very difficult to quantify the extent to which salmon fishing is affected by these obstructions, but they are always a source of dispute amongst anglers and fishery owners upstream who believe that an obstruction keeps the fish in the water of downstream anglers, who then exploit them without mercy. The firm belief always seems to be that the agency responsible, now the Environment Agency, should utilise public money to provide fish passes in the obstructions so that upstream anglers can do the same.

Unfortunately for the Environment Agency and the various bodies that have been responsible for protecting fisheries in the past, civil engineering in rivers is very expensive. The design of fish passes is not yet an exact science, and short of removing an obstruction it is probably impossible to ensure that all fish immediately find the right way through at all states of flow. Moreover, salmon tend to migrate upstream on above average flows and stop when they tire or when they feel exposed in shallow water. The cheapest fish pass in a large river like the Tyne is likely to cost at least four or five times the revenue received from Tyne anglers. Therefore it is difficult for any protection agency to justify major works merely to resolve competition for a limited resource. Thus the size of fish passes has always been likely to limit their efficiency to relatively low flows; some fish fail to find the pass in high water and some stop below these obstructions.

It is interesting to note that the obstructions at Haltwhistle, Haydon Bridge, Hexham and Wylam have all been caused by the lowering of the river bed as the gravel substrate has been displaced from downstream of the level bridge footings. Modifications to the channel upstream and downstream from Wylam have considerably improved salmon passage, but Hexham remains a problem in low flows. Chollerford weir was a mill dam which for many years was a serious obstruction to migratory fish on the North Tyne, but the construction of a fish pass enables fish to ascend at virtually all flows – as shown by a fish counter.

The only modern obstruction is Riding Mill dam. This structure consists of two weirs at different levels and a fish pass adjacent to the channel of the lower weir. Unfortunately under high flow conditions migrating salmon can miss this channel and then jump fruitlessly at the higher weir. Also, despite the careful design and construction of a scale model, the velocity of water below the entrance to the fish pass is high and may be a problem to smaller fish, particularly migrating dace.

However, all these obstructions can be passed, with or without delay, and it is very unlikely that they affect in any way the distribution of spawning fish and thus the production of future generations. Other obstructions exist on the tributaries, but few of them are likely to provide much of an increase in fish production if they are equipped with passes.

THE IMPACT OF POACHING

Anglers also become choleric about illegal fishing - or poaching to use the more emotive term. On the Tyne all salmon anglers must be in possession of a valid licence to fish with rod and line; this is the only allowable way of removal of salmon from the river by fishermen. The responsibility for law enforcement lies with the Environment Agency. Enforcement costs far more than the income that body derives from the licencing system, but there is an expectation amongst fishery interests on the river that poaching should be minimal. This is not an unreasonable aim, but there often appears to be a lack of perspective in what is considered to be a reasonable level of enforcement. This limited perspective stems from the fact that the fishery interests who are the beneficiaries do not have to pay directly for the service. It might be argued that the maintenance by the taxpayer of very valuable fisheries and providing enforcement for the benefit of well-to-do riparian owners is inequitable. However, a recent government review makes very persuasive arguments in favour of existing practice and recommends that fishery owners should not be charged.

FUTURE DIRECTION FOR FISHERIES MANAGEMENT

It is upon the resolution of this argument that the future of the Tyne fisheries depends. The Environment Agency is charged with the management of the fisheries of the Tyne although they neither own the fisheries nor have the necessary powers to manage them in the business sense of the word. Despite the fact that successive governments (albeit inadvertently) have invested heavily in fish habitat destruction in order to help farmers produce more food, they have starved the Agency and its predecessor bodies of the necessary funding not only to protect fish habitat but, more importantly, to monitor the environment and conduct research into the ecology of native fish.

The Agency now has a programme of research. However, under the present level of funding it will be many years - if ever - before the information produced will be adequate to drive a protection and improvement programme based on demonstrable and quantifiable knowledge of the actual problems as well as reliable prediction of what will happen if certain steps are taken. Recently the Agency has banned the killing of salmon in the spring throughout England and Wales on the grounds that spring salmon have been diminishing in number because of over-exploitation by anglers. This ban has also been applied to the Tyne despite the fact that the Tyne has a substantial spring run and there are no signs of it diminishing, although the proportion of spring fish in the rod catch has gone down since the commissioning of Howdon sewage works. It is interesting to speculate that the continuing existence of this run may be due to years of selection pressure from the polluted estuary which allowed passage of salmon only during floods with the result that few salmon could get through in the summer and therefore encouraged the development of a race of spring-running salmon. The removal of this constraint on summer migration coupled with the phase out of the drift net fishery means that the numbers of summer migrants will increase further and the breeding population of spring migrants may be swamped and lost.

Fishery management has always been a political skill. As long as the government controls the purse strings and is pushed by vested interest, it will remain so. However all is not lost; there are still salmon in the Tyne. They returned after the Ice Age and have survived the ravages of intensive netting, pollution and mismanagement through ignorance. The angling lobby is still strong, and although they have sometimes collared the wrong culprit for falling catches, they remain as persistent in their advocacy on behalf of the fish as in pursuing their sport. Short of global disaster the biggest threat to the Tyne salmon and the coarse fish will be a ban on angling. However, it will be interesting to see whom anglers blame if their catches fall after the nets have gone!

REFERENCES
1. Bewick, T. (1975) *A Memoir of Thomas Bewick* (Edited with an introduction by I Bain), Oxford University Press, London (first published 1862).
2. Defoe, Daniel (1723-5) *A Tour through the Whole Island of Great Britain.*
3. Cave, J.D. (1985) The effects of the Kielder scheme on fisheries, *Jour Fish Biology*, **27**, 109–121.
4. Anderson, A.R. and Pyatt, D.G. (1986) Interception of precipitation by pole-stage Sitka Spruce and lodgepole pine and mature Sitka spruce at Kielder Forest, Northumberland, *Forestry*, **59**, 29–38.
5. Robinson, M. (1998) 30 years of forest hydrology changes at Coalburn: water balance and extreme flows, *Hydrology and Earth Systems Science*, **2**.

7. FISHING THE TYNE

AIDAN POLLARD

INTRODUCTION

In its natural state the River Tyne was brimming with salmon (Chapter 6) and from the medieval period was heavily exploited by net fishermen who used a succession of fishing weirs along the river. From the nineteenth century offshore netsmen took an even larger number of fish – though not all of their catch was destined for the Tyne. Yet through this period, the river continued to yield a good harvest both for the commercial fisherman and for the angler. It was only in the last half of the nineteenth century that the growth of pollution from the urban population and industry began to take its toll on the salmon. This decline continued into the twentieth century, with the discharge of increasingly toxic chemical pollutants and the despoliation of spawning gravels, to the point that not a single salmon was caught in the Tyne in 1959. Through this period and during the recovery of salmon and sea trout in the past forty years, the angler has proved to be a most hardy species. Even in the depths of decline and salmon famine there were still anglers fishing the Tyne, perhaps more with hope than good judgement.

Optimism and patience are the hallmarks of the angler. To those who are not fishermen it remains a considerable puzzle that children and adults from every walk of life can exercise such virtues when the rewards are infrequent or altogether absent. Fishing is said to be the sport (or recreation as the case may be) with the greatest number of active participants in Britain; they cannot all be deluded. What is it then that attracts the fisherman? It cannot be simply the prospect of the evening meal — though fishermen do enjoy such benefits — since many fish, including salmon are now returned to the river. A visit to the fishmonger will yield a greater and more certain return than will the money spent on licences and permits, along with the time invested in securing a catch.

In explanation I give a personal account of the joys and attraction of fishing and, in particular, the pleasure of catching a salmon for the first time. Perhaps the uninitiated will be encouraged to join our ranks.

THE FIRST SALMON

The thrill and excitement of your first salmon is unsurpassable. No matter how many you catch in later years you will never forget the first salmon - every detail of the take (the first contact from the fish) and the playing of the salmon on the rod. Eventually landing the fish, you are able to appreciate the subtle shades of colour and the quivering beauty of form and fin. The details of the river, riffle, pool and banks are imprinted on your memory; you will remember the quality of light, the colour of the water and you will experience the great sense of achievement. To return unharmed such a fish only enhances the experience and then, as Chaytor[1] observes, "to fish on with hugely increased expectations" is a truly wonderful experience.

The puzzle of the uninitiated has been solved but the mystery remains. Why did you catch the fish in that particular pool rather than at many a similar location? What did you do better than or differently from your previous unsuccessful hours or days? Was it simply the happy coincidence of the salmon's presence, its inclination to take, and the casting of your line with a particular fly or lure at precisely the right moment and place? How much did the catch depend on good luck and how much on good practice? The angler's mind is constantly filled with such questions and theories. It is only with time and experience that one acquires an understanding of fish behaviour, habitat and the condition of the river and so begins to distinguish between luck and good practice. Time spent by the river offers ample opportunity for such reflection.

As the angler's experience and awareness increases, the challenge is then to catch a fish when the conditions are difficult — when the water level is extremely low or heavy with sediment. To succeed in catching a fish in such adverse conditions, when no one else is succeeding, arouses similar sensations to those of the first ever salmon. The search for knowledge and an understanding of these wonderful fishes never ceases; there are always new experiences, always something different, always another puzzle to unravel.

Salmon in the Tyne offer a great challenge. Being truly wild, migratory fish, their presence and abundance in a particular reach (or beat) vary from day to day and are influenced by the current local conditions, but also by spawning success in the river three or more years ago, by mortality on the high seas, and by success in negotiating the remaining hazards of the Tyne estuary. At a particular spot, the fish may be resting or running, ignoring any fly or lure, or occasionally in a 'taking' mood, offering the angler the chance of a catch. Knowledge provides a guide to the expert fisherman, but the mysteries remain and are worth keeping.

AN ANGLER'S VIEW OF NATURE

Whether fishing for salmon or coarse fish, anglers have a unique opportunity to observe in solitude the ever-changing river, and its flora and wildlife. Chaytor[1], who gained most of his experience of salmon fishing on the Tyne at Dilston remarks:

> "Since the time of Walton the first thought of the true fisher is of the fresh air, the rushing water in his ears, the cool evenings, the glowing sunsets, the flowers and the trees, the birds and all the river-loving things in furs and feathers. ....the kingfisher skimming the water with his gleam of blue and orange over some luckless minnow. ....A great grey heron slowly and clumsily arises and flaps off."

Sometimes a day on a river is pleasantly satisfying even without catching a single fish; indeed it is the quality of the day that matters; a salmon is a bonus.

Many more anglers now seek that quality day; more fish than ever are returned unharmed to the river. These fish add to the spawning potential.

A particular delight is the fact that otters have been increasing steadily through the 1990s and are now seen regularly. Some fishing beats have 'no fishing areas' where otters are known to breed. Otters are totally unfazed by anglers; both spend time watching each other. The occasional otter has been known to inspect the competition, especially at dusk.

Seals are rather more surprising visitors to the freshwater river. Twice over the past fourteen years, seals have travelled upriver as far as the dam and fish pass at Riding Mill. Whilst seals often spend considerable time in the tideway, it is quite a shock to have a large seal suddenly appear close-by whilst you are wading in the river. Roe deer have often been seen swimming the Tyne.

The rich and varied bird life is also of great interest to most anglers and a good pair of binoculars should always be at hand. Occasionally the harsher realities are seen. I have seen noctule bats feeding in daylight make an easy meal for a sparrow hawk

THE FISH

Despite the restriction on access due to foot and mouth disease in 2001, a new record of 2,500 salmon caught by the rod angler was achieved. Many anglers feel that this continuing success is not only due to improving water quality, important as this is, but is also attributable to the Kielder salmon hatchery and the efforts of Peter Gray, the Hatcheries Superintendent, in restocking the river annually.

Anglers often talk about the 'Tyne salmon' as a distinct race. Typically it is a short, very deep fish of high average weight. Salmon of 20 to 25 lbs are quite common with most years producing one or two over 30 lbs. In the first two years of restocking from the Kielder Hatchery brood stock were obtained from other rivers. Although these contributed to the gene pool of Tyne salmon, anglers generally believe that distinctive character of Tyne fish is more influenced by the river environment than by genetic variation. Brood stock from the Kielder salmon hatchery are now, of course, obtained from the Tyne, and tagged fish represent over 10% of returns for brood stock in subsequent years. This percentage is all the more remarkable, given that only one in thirty fish are tagged on release. The high survival rate of Kielder hatchery salmon can be attributed to the fact that the hatchery is continually fed by water from Kielder Burn, and the juvenile salmon are subjected to the natural vicissitudes of chemical water quality and temperature, making them well suited to survival in the wild.

But the Tyne is not only about salmon. Good runs of sea trout occur, and occasionally fish up to 15 lbs (or more) are caught. The main Tyne does not seem to produce as many sea trout as do the North and South Tyne, probably because few anglers fish specifically for sea trout on the main Tyne. As I write (2002), an earlier and larger run of sea trout than usual is evident, reflected in bigger catches and many more greater than 10 lbs.

Brown trout have declined in numbers recently. A major factor may be a decrease in the annual restocking of these beautiful fish. In the 1970s the River

Authority sold the trout hatchery at Reivers Well. As a result the annual stocking of some 72,000 brown trout in Northumbrian rivers and streams ceased. Another reason may be that as salmon fishing rents have increased, some clubs have stopped purchasing trout for restocking in order to keep subscriptions as low as possible. A third reason could be the increase in fish-eating birds particularly goosanders. This sawbill duck has enjoyed a very great increase in population since the 1970s. Some good trout fishing still exists, particularly in the Rivers Rede and Derwent. The Derwent is still regarded as a trout and grayling river and is stocked regularly. Good feeding in the Derwent produces some very nice plump trout.

Grayling, 'the lady of the stream', is increasing in the River Derwent. Some good fishing is available throughout this Tyne tributary and is at its best from October to the beginning of March. Fishing is with weighted fly. Grayling to 1½ lbs are frequently caught and most anglers return all fish.

I can remember vast shoals of dace in the Tyne in the 1950s, most readily seen from Hexham bridge. Dace are still present but no longer as plentiful. The reason for the decline is still subject to speculation in spite of investigations by the Environment Agency. Some blame the cold water from Kielder, but a major factor could be the cleaning of the river. Far less raw sewage enters the Tyne now, and the nutrient available is correspondingly lower. This problem may not be unique to the Tyne; there are recent press reports of anglers complaining that the River Trent is now too clean for coarse fish. The Environment Agency has carried out some restocking of the Tyne with coarse fish. I don't yet know how successful this has been. The cormorants look happy.

Some sizeable chub can be caught. In recent years fish to 4½ lbs have been caught every summer by salmon anglers fishing in low river. Small chub are often seen attacking minnow shoals in the warm shallows. Very occasionally perch are caught. The lower main river Tyne is where most coarse fishing takes place although I am advised that some decent catches of dace are possible on the River Rede.

STARTING TO FISH

Most fishermen catch the bug when they are young. They go fishing with father and in turn their friend tags along. Until the 1970s most aspiring game anglers would be introduced to fishing on a river. Nowadays the introduction is more likely to be on a commercial stillwater fishery where the emphasis is quite different from river fishing. Commercial fisheries focus minds on bag limits and catching large soft-bodied hand-reared trout. The novice angler may then come to river fishing with unrealisable expectations. Wild fish can not be found to meet the high catch rate generated by the 'put-and-take' fisheries. Angling on the river requires more thought and understanding of fish behaviour and habitat. However, the rewards in terms of enjoyment are far greater.

Anglers do benefit from the apprenticeship of stillwater fishing since basic casting tuition is readily available, and novices are exposed to a wide range of equipment. When they have mastered the basics of casting, those seeking a more challenging pursuit can turn to the River Tyne. In practice, one cannot simply choose a reach of the river and go fishing. A license and permits are required. Fishing rights for particular reaches (or beats) are owned and some are leased to fishing clubs. There are often limits to membership of clubs and limits to the number of rods per river beat. Many clubs have waiting lists. These practical arrangements ensure that the river is not over-exploited.

Salmon licences, currently £60 per year, are valid for the whole of England and Wales and are available from the Environment Agency (Rod licence Sales 0870 166 2662) and from local agencies including all Post Offices. The same licence is also valid for trout, but a licence for trout only costs £17 per year. Youth licences (12 to 16 years) cost £5, whilst children under 12 do not require a licence.

ACCESS TO FISHING

Access to Tyne fishing clubs and costs of membership are highly variable. The Tyne offers access to the river via free water (very limited), council waters (limited), clubs in association, syndicates and private day or season lets. A good approach is to seek out angling friends or neighbours who can introduce a guest to a local club water. Most angling clubs are eager to help with free advice: when to start, where to fish and how to read the river. Local tackle shops are also well informed and keen to help. As an angler gains in experience, the Tyne can offer better water or more privacy to suit the individual's skill, enthusiasm and pocket. More than thirty clubs, organisations and individuals offer access to fishing on the Tyne. Permit prices range from £5 per day to several hundred pounds per day for the best beats in peak season. There follows a selection of more accessible organisations for visiting fishermen or for those at the early stages of their fishing careers. Contact details are shown in the Appendix.

Corbridge offers a 200-metre reach of free fishing for salmon, trout and coarse fishing whilst Tynedale District Council[a] has a stretch at Tyne Green for visitors as well as residents, at low daily and seasonal rates.

The Northumbrian Anglers Federation (NAF)[b] offers an affordable introduction to fishing the Tyne for salmon and sea trout. Seasonal or two-week visitor permits give access to the Tyne at Ovingham and Merryshield (below Bywell Bridge) as well as reaches of the River Coquet. Membership of NAF is open and there is no waiting list for people who live in the North East. Tyneside Anglers Syndicate[c] also provides ready access to several reaches of the Tyne and Rede both for salmon and mixed fishing.

Anglers who are so devoted to their sport as to choose to live where there is ready access to salmon fishing could satisfy their needs by living in Corbridge, Wylam or Haydon Bridge where local clubs are open to village residents.

Limited-membership clubs and syndicates also provide access to game fishing. Membership of some is by introduction to a waiting-list; others are more accessible and advertise in the press or local tackle shops. West End Anglers[d] are a well organised club with interests on the North, South and main Tyne.

Some very fine salmon fishing can be had on estate water on the Tyne with a regulated number of rods per beat, private access and waters suitable for fly fishing. Visitor access can be had by means of daily and weekly lets, for example at Chesters estate[c] on the North Tyne below Chollerford Dam and at Chipchase Castle[f] also on the North Tyne. The Bywell Salmon Syndicate[g] has extensive double-bank fishing on the main Tyne only eight miles above the tidal limit and offers good fishing conditions from February to October.

Coarse angling is readily available and those coarse angling clubs situated on the Tyne can also offer the chance of a salmon. These clubs are easy to join and charge comparatively low fees. They are friendly, well-organised and with opportunities for competitive fishing. Coarse anglers generally have a good understanding of their quarry and the environment, including temperature, oxygen and feeding patterns. Their knowledge of where and when to fish often amazes the 'stockie basher' of the trout angling world. Local tackle shops are again a good source of information and can usually sell the necessary day ticket.

The Axwell Park and Derwent Valley A.A.[h] offers good trout and grayling fishing both for members and visitors on the River Derwent whilst Tyneside Anglers Alliance[i] provides coarse fishing opportunities on the Tyne.

WHEN AND WHERE TO FISH
The fishing season
The salmon season opens on the Tyne on 1 February and lasts until 31 October. Currently anglers are not allowed to keep any salmon caught until 16 June. The season for sea trout is from 3 April until 31 October. Sea trout can be retained throughout the season. The brown trout season is from 22 March until 30 September. The coarse fishing season depends upon the venue, and coarse fish anglers can fish throughout the year by switching between rivers, ponds and lakes

Salmon and sea trout season
A decline of early season salmon is evident on some English rivers. These 'springers' are much sought after. Although the total number of salmon and the percentage of the annual total is much smaller during the spring than during the autumn (as shown in Fig. 7.1), neither numbers nor proportion have declined in recent years on the Tyne. It would seem that springers suffer greater fishing pressure than later-arriving fish and it is thought that as many as 30 to 50% of the arrivals are caught. In some years the number of spring salmon caught has equalled the number registered on counters. The records in Fig. 7.1 are from fish counters on the weirs at Riding Mill on the main Tyne and at Chollerford on the North Tyne. The records are suspect for Chollerford where fish frequently bypass the fish pass and counter; a much smaller proportion bypass at Riding Mill.

The main Tyne has the best of the early season sport; Wylam, Ovington and Bywell all produce fish in February if river flow is suitable. March continues to give good sport in these areas and also at Corbridge and Hexham. It is usually in late March that the North Tyne and lower South Tyne produce their first fish of the season. At this time sea trout appear in a 'good wet' year and salmon and sea trout run on each tide. Excellent fishing has been had in May and early June on the whole river. Chesters on the North Tyne has produced wonderful

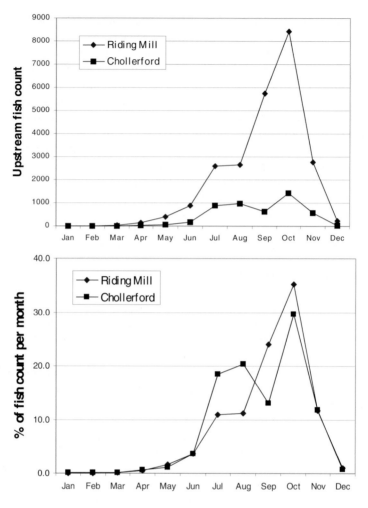

Fig 7.1 a. Monthly number of salmon registered travelling upstream on the counters at Riding Mill and Chollerford, b. Proportion of annual total by month.

results after spates, with very clean - often sea-liced - fish of a good size, many in the range 12 to 15 lbs. Sea trout are mainly caught above Hexham.

As a reflection of conditions off the estuary, net caught salmon and sea trout are often at their lowest price of the season around the third week of July. Large offshore catches are often made particularly during low water conditions in the river. If a flood occurs, these fish will run very quickly through the river system. Given a good flow, a marked increase in the numbers of salmon and sea trout is evident from July onward. All the beats now fish — at Chesters, Chipchase Water, Nunwick, Parkend, Countesspark, and Bellingham on the North Tyne, and on the Rede. Anglers will also enjoy fishing on the South Tyne where runs of salmon and sea trout increase steadily through the summer, through the beats of Haydon Bridge, Lipwood, Ridley Hall, Willimontswick, Melkridge and up to Eals.

August rain brings some exciting fish, salmon of 8 to 10 lbs, wonderfully fresh and full of fight. Some of these fish will be larger grilse, their speed and dash being much appreciated.

It is in September and October that the heaviest runs of both sea trout and salmon occur. The whole river provides good fishing from Wylam virtually to the source. The largest salmon and sea trout of the year are generally caught in this 'autumn run'. Whilst many fish are coloured and must be returned to the river to spawn, some fish are very fresh and well worth keeping. Sea trout appear to 'ripen' with egg more quickly than salmon, and even bright fish may be soft with roe and should be carefully returned. Some salmon have numbered tags in their adipose fin. These are springers that have been caught by anglers, tagged and released. Any fish that is caught with such a tag should be released again and the Environment Agency informed of the tag number.

Changing angling conditions
The salmon angler must apply his experience to adapt to changing seasonal conditions of the weather, the river and the fish. The river is never constant; level, flow, temperature, water colour, tidal effect, barometric pressure and oxygen levels all change through the day, with the season, and with the changing weather. With the changes in light and air temperature the angler has endless opportunity to experiment. The same angler has also many excuses to hand for the lack of success. Anglers rarely mention 'lack of skill and understanding' as a reason for failure!

Fish respond to changes in their environment which anglers are often slow to understand. Why, for example, is it that a quiet dusk after a bright day can greatly increase fish activity – and possibly success?

Weather conditions on the lower Tyne are not necessarily a good indicator of what is happening over Cross Fell or on the North Tyne moors. Upland storms can create unexpected spates and freshets in the lower reaches, leading to disappointing fishing and occasionally to danger for fishermen. The Environment Agency provides a 'rivercall' telephone service for river level updated daily on 0930 107701. Upstream levels, and whether these are rising, falling or steady on South Tyne, North Tyne and Rede, can be used by anglers along with the weather forecast to assess and predict downstream conditions, up to a day later.

In addition, Kielder reservoir releases may greatly affect fish and fishing. Generally Kielder releases up to 15 cumecs benefit angling, particularly on the North Tyne. On the main Tyne releases in spring and autumn, if at times of increased natural flow, are believed to be disadvantageous to fishing. Releases in low water, particularly in warm weather and linked to spring tides, are of great benefit to salmon and encourage them to migrate from the relatively risky estuary. Information on planned releases for the current week are available on 01434 240463.
FAMOUS TYNE POOLS

Pools below natural or man-made obstructions often provide the most exciting fishing, as salmon and sea trout wait for favourable conditions before ascending. However, such pools frequently attract criticism if their advantage is exploited too ruthlessly to the detriment of upstream river users. Downstream river erosion may result in an obstruction becoming a progressively more severe barrier to fish passage and may justify works to raise downstream river levels.

Wylam Bridge pool (Wylam Angling Club)
This pool, situated at the very top of the tidal Tyne, is wholly owned by Wylam Angling Club whose members are drawn from local residents, but non-residents can fish as a guest of a member. In the 1980s and early 1990s this pool accounted for a remarkable number of salmon and possibly up to one third of the spring run. Requiring low water, tide-liced fish rest in the pool prior to ascending the bridge footings. The salmon are caught on spinning tackle or by 'spinning' a fly. Graham Heaney, a Wylam rod who regularly fishes this pool has accounted for many salmon; it is not unusual for him to land more than thirty sea-fresh salmon in one season. Graham is also one of the first people to notice any changes in the behaviour of the fish and his prompt response has given early warnings of problems, particularly during the estuary fish kills of the 1990s. It is worth noting that salmon now swim the bridge footings much more easily than in earlier days, following installation of a boulder box downstream by the Environment Agency.

Fish pass and Beeches (Bywell Syndicate water)
The pool below Riding Mill weir and fish pass (Broomhaugh Pool) is possibly the first to fish after a flood (Plate 15). Catches in this pool greatly increased after the weir was completed, as fish initially found difficulty in ascending in certain flow ranges. The Riding Mill weir is a complex structure having a main high level weir and a lower gated section with an adjacent fish pass. The main weir is impassable at most flows, whilst swift and turbulent flow downstream from the fish pass also used to delay the passage of fish. The problem was alleviated by installing a boulder box (as at Wylam) and fish now ascend much more readily. In high water, angling effort on this pool (particularly in the 1980s and early 1990s) was high. Now more fish are caught in pools downstream, particularly at Beeches (known in the 1920s at Bywell High Water). This reach between the A68 bridge and the gauging station, which consists of a glide in the middle of a long pool, was not fished seriously for many years but now fishes to both fly and spinner, with a good number of summer sea trout taken.

Hexham Bridge Pool (Hexham Fly Fishers)
This pool downstream from the Hexham Bridge appears to hold more fish now than ever before, as the bridge footings have become more difficult for fish to run. The height of the obstruction has increased with progressive downstream erosion — an inheritance from gravel extraction more than two decades ago (Chapter 4). It is fortunate that both groups of anglers who fish this pool are very considerate and do not abuse their privilege. The south bank is reserved

for fly fishing only. Many salmon are landed here in middle to low water conditions. This pool is well watched and offers good views of running fish. A well-known and liked rod is Billy Glendenning of Hexham who has fished this beat for decades.

The Waters Meet, Hexham (Waters Meet Fishery; Warden A; Kingshaw Green)
The confluence of the North and South Tyne is probably better known for the meeting of the waters than for its fishing. Nevertheless the Waters Meet pool generally yields a good catch each year and benefits from freshets from either or both tributaries.

Above Waters Meet, the Chesters Estate has some of the finest fishing on the North Tyne. One can debate the merits of each pool. With the right river conditions, Upper and Lower Island offer some fine fly fishing. Late May and early June floods seem to draw salmon through the main river, and it is here that the salmon are found. Conditions for wading are satisfactory in these pools, unlike many other pools on the North Tyne. The owner of the beat is George Benson who is a keen angler and, like his father, has worked hard to preserve this beat.

Redburn Pool, South Tyne
Ownership of this pool is shared between Network Rail on the left bank and Willimontswick Farm on the right bank. This pool is at its best with a freshet, and in falling water is rarely without salmon from May onwards (Plate 16). The fresh water brings a new run of fish and it is these rather than resident salmon that are more often taken.

EQUIPMENT AND TACKLE FOR THE TYNE
The next section is mainly intended as advice for visiting anglers, but local anglers may wish to compare notes on lures with the recommendations I have made.

Safety is of paramount importance and precaution is necessary on a wide river with deep pools and dark waters. When fishing the larger pools and far-off lies, chest waders, preferably with studded or felt soles, are essential. Flotation jackets or life preservers are also advised. A wading staff is a great aid; the water and river bed are often dark, making it difficult to see obstacles. Good polarising sunglasses are helpful for wading and for reading the water.

Salmon fishing is either by fly or spinning. Natural salt water prawn and shrimp have been used but are becoming less favoured. Anglers new to the river would do well not to use these baits if only to be seen to be fair sportsmen.

The prospective angler has a huge range of rods, reels, and associated equipment from which to choose. Whether fly-fishing or spinning good strong tackle is essential as salmon on the Tyne can be 30 lbs or more. The pools are often wide and long casts are helpful. With these criteria in mind many anglers prefer a 15-foot or longer fly rod. The neutral density line or sink tip is generally preferred in cooler water, whilst floating lines (and small flies) are often used with shorter rods with the arrival of warmer weather.

Spinning rods 9 to 10 feet long are often used, with a fixed spool reel or multiplier being the norm. A recent innovation is the braided spinning line of high test strain but fine diameter. This line increases casting distance and gives direct contact without stretch using the lure *salmon on rocks*. Early and late season lures are usually larger than those used in summer.

My own choice of essential equipment would include a good quality knotless landing net, which is important if you wish to land fish quickly and return them unharmed.

Anglers have their own favourite flies and lures and no doubt would want to add to or subtract from the following short list which is based on my own experience of fishing the Tyne for 30 years. Since the water is often peat-stained, highly visible flies often work best.

Ally shrimp is a good standby (sizes 4 to 14, in standard dressing or a red or yellow version with some 'lure flash' in the long tail)

Black dart is a good option in peaty water (various sizes from a 1½ tube to a No. 12 double)

Garry dog, willy gunn and munro killer are also recommended in fresh, coloured water

The silver s*toat tail* is recommended in clearer water.

Blue charm has proven effective on the rare occasion when the river is very clear. One April in the 90s a visiting rod landed six springers to a *blue charm*; this was very much contrary to local practice at the time.

Recommended sea trout flies include *peter ross* and *black pennell*, but some stillwater type lures will also work. The *cascade* will take both salmon and sea trout as will *stoat's tail* and *ally shrimp*.

Recommended flies for brown trout include *dark olive hatches*, which give sport with some good, albeit short, rises. *Greenwell, partridge and orange* and *hare's ear* will also give sport with the addition of *sedges* on the arrival of warmer weather.

Spinning is more often used in high or coloured water although some experts fishing with fly tackle do well in difficult conditions. From a huge range of spinners, the *rubber tail* and *flying 'c'* in various colours are popular fish catchers. *Tobies* have their adherents as do *yellow belly* and other *devon minnows*. Some anglers take fish on a Finnish lure, the *rapala*. These can be very good but are difficult to cast. *Mepps, blair spoon* and *quill minnows*, also have their adherents.

Use whatever you have confidence in. Remember that fishing with rod and line for salmon and sea trout is a rather inefficient way to catch fish. The emphasis must always be on having fun.

THE CHANGING RIVER TYNE

The decline and regeneration of the river, chronicled in other chapters, has been reflected in the changing spirits of the angler; only the salmon itself is more sensitive to changes in the river environment. Diaries regularly kept by anglers provide a record not only of catches, but of despair, hope and a measure of satisfaction at the changes over the last four decades.

In 1952 Col. Bobby Barnett, a regular rod at Chesters and Countesspark, recorded no salmon. A succession of frustrating seasons followed, although occasional wet years, or those with the rain at the right time, provided some encouragement. Signs of improvement were evident from increasing catches in the early 1960s, but with the outbreak of UDN (ulcerative dermal necrosis) the Tyne suffered, though not quite as badly as neighbouring Coquet and Tweed. Fish succumbed to a virulent fungal infection and were covered by white patches. Not only did many salmon die - adults, smolts and parr - but anglers were put off their sport by the scabby appearance of the fish they caught. The cause of the disease was never discovered but it seems to have petered out naturally.

Concerns at the construction of Kielder Dam and the loss of spawning grounds were tempered by improvements brought about by Kielder hatchery and by changes in the estuary. The decline of industry and the construction of the Tyneside Interceptor Sewer certainly improved water quality in the estuary but the improvement was fragile. Although catches began a steady improvement in the 1980s, appalling fish mortalities occurred in the early 1990s in the upper estuary, demonstrating continuing water quality problems in drought years. It is the angler's hope that the completion of secondary treatment of Tyneside sewage in 2000 will see an end to such losses in drought years.

The steady increase in salmon catches in the Tyne in recent years contrasts with many other English rivers. The Tyne Anglers' Code of Practice, introduced by anglers themselves, is certainly helping to protect stocks. The Code requires that no more than two salmon per day or six per week may be kept, whilst all coloured (ripe) fish are to be returned. This voluntary Code reinforces legislation requiring the return of all spring fish until 16 June. Further improvements are expected to follow when and if the buy-out of net fishing is completed. Anglers contributing to this buy-out would like to see improved enforcement against illegal netting of salmon which apparently takes place year round. Perhaps a ban on the sale of wild salmon would help most of all. The Tyne is a river returning to its former greatness. Long may it continue!

The return of the salmon is of increasing benefit to the local economy. The Tyne is a very affordable river to fish, thereby attracting more visitors each year. A sensible balance of visitors and local fishers can and should be maintained.

FISHING TALES

Fishermen have a reputation for telling stories often with some element of embellishment or economy with the truth. The 'one that got away' is a by-word for an unverifiable exaggeration. Some fishermen may live up to their reputation, but my experience is that fishermen are no more deceitful than the average and may even compensate for their reputation by ensuring that their fishing prowess is verified by photographs, etc.

Chaytor describes records as 'that curse of true sport'. Nevertheless, he cannot refrain from indulging in the general angling interest in 'biggest' and 'most'. His biggest Tyne salmon was 40½ lbs; in his best season he landed 78 salmon and on his best day 9 (Fig. 7.1). Such catches in the early twentieth century could not be matched for many decades given the deteriorating quality of the river. However, with increasing salmon runs in recent years fish catches and

Fig 7.2 The early glory of fishing on the Tyne – a Chaytor catch of 7 September 1908. We would hope for this productivity to return, but not the urge to kill.

size have begun to approach the old standards and in most years someone will catch one over 30 lb. Mike Walton of Yorkshire caught a huge cock fish in the 1990s at Bywell, conservatively estimated at 35 lbs. This would be Bywell's second 35+ lb fish in recent years.

Graham Heaney of Wylam has landed a 35½ lb salmon, along with hundreds of other salmon over many years of fishing. As this is written (spring 2002) a 35 lb salmon has been caught and released on the North Tyne. Fish in excess of 42 inches and with great girth are now present every year and spawn successfully, as evidenced by the massive kelts found in spring.

Increasingly, large sea trout are being caught with fish to18 lbs recorded whilst 10 lb fish are quite common. Many of these sea trout are caught by rods fishing for salmon.

Fishing obsession

Occasionally anglers become a little too intense in their pursuit of fish. Some years ago a fishing gentleman whom we shall call Mike was fishing a well-known pool. A retired fellow named George often sat on a log by the pool for many an hour and observed all. He was friendly and talkative, offering advice whether requested or not.

Mike had seen a large salmon move in the pool and was becoming obsessed with this fish to such an extent that he began to fish without thought. Old George could see this and suggested that a different approach was required. In a brief, blunt response Mike told George not to speak to him as he wished to fish quietly and privately. George was quite miffed. Mike 'thrashed' away without success, making himself late for home but vowing to return early the following morning.

Next day, first light found Mike again fishing hard in the same place. After an hour had passed, George appeared and quietly sat down. Mike had little time before going to work, but such was his obsession that he persisted in fishing on, still without success. Eventually frustrated, fishless and very late, he reluctantly packed his gear and turned to leave. As he passed the old fellow, George smiled and said, "If I could have told you, that fish was caught last night. Young Pearson got it; 18 lbs it was — but then I mustn't talk to you. Good day."

A fishing 'competition'

In October 2001 Gerard Maynard of Corbridge was an angling guest on the Tyne. The river was moderately high and Gerard was happily 'spinning' for salmon. Having lost a fish in play earlier in the day and seeing plenty of salmon, his hopes were high. Gerard's concentration was soon rewarded; a good pull on the line – a fish was on. At first the salmon ran down and across the pool. Gerard maintained a steady pressure on the salmon, and after showing on the surface the fish settled. Gerard began to work the fish towards the bank when suddenly it 'went heavy' and began to move away towards the bushes on the far bank. Surprised, the angler applied more pressure and again began to draw the salmon in. Amazingly the tail of the salmon appeared vertically out of the water and, without apparent means of motion, began to move away. Further pressure on the salmon and some line was recovered. Then again the salmon appeared as before and moved away. At this stage Bernard Lynch of Stagshaw, having sharp eyesight, asked Gerard to look at the brown head on the back of the salmon. An otter had grasped his catch. The struggle continued with the otter slowly gaining. Then moving into faster water, the otter held on till the hook became free.

Far from being annoyed, Gerard had to laugh and concede defeat – a rare and wonderful experience. The otter won but no one (but the salmon) lost.

REFERENCES

1. Chaytor, A.H. (1910) *Letters to a Salmon fisher's Son* (Reprinted 1983, in Modern Fishing Classics, Andre Deutsch).

APPENDIX – ANGLING CONTACTS

a. Tynedale District Council, c/o Tourist Information Centre, Wentworth Car Park, Hexham, NE46 1QE.

b. Northumbrian Anglers Federation, Mr Alan Bagnall, West Thirston Mill, Felton, Northumberland, NE65 9EH.

c. Tyneside Anglers Syndicate, Mr Bill Carrick, Rothgar, Woodside Lane, Ryton, Tyne and Wear, NE40 3NE.

d. West End Anglers, Mr George Turnbull, 15 Grasmere Crescent, Whitley Bay, Tyne and Wear, NE26 3TB.

e. Chesters Estate, Ms Heather Mather, Cluttons, Matfen Hall, Newcastle upon Tyne.

f. Chipchase Castle, Smiths Gore, Chrtd. Surveyors, Eastfield house, Main Street, Corbridge, Northumberland.

g. Bywell Salmon Syndicate, Mr Aidan Pollard, 2 North Lodge, Stagshaw House, Corbridge, Northumberland, NE45 5PG.

h. Axwell Park and Derwent Valley A. A., Mr Alan Dodd, 63 Sherburn Park Drive, Rowlands Gill, Tyne and Wear.

i. Tyne Anglers Alliance, Mr G Atkin, 82 The Glebe, Dunston, Tyne and Wear, NE11 9NQ.

8. THE DEATH OF THE TYNE: RIVER POLLUTION

DAVID ARCHER, ROGER INVERARITY and SAM JAMES

INTRODUCTION

The generation of waste products is an attribute of all living creatures, and human beings are no exception. Most of the products decompose naturally in the environment and do not cause detriment to other organisms sharing their living space. Over most of his life history man has also lived in harmony with his environment, or his population numbers have been insufficient to generate serious polluting loads. Little by little the population has grown and become concentrated in towns and cities. A favoured location for towns and villages has been on river banks, for available water supply, mill power and river trade. Rivers have been seen not only as a source of drinking water but also as a convenient means for the disposal and carrying away of effluent, domestic refuse and industrial waste. Whilst concentrations of population were small and unsophisticated, the results were inconsequential but with urbanisation and escalating growth of polluting industry during the industrial era, the habit of careless disposal of waste devastated rivers throughout Britain. The River Tyne was a prime example especially in its tidal reach; the freshwater River Tyne fared better but did not escape entirely. Too late did we realise the environmental dictum: "We all live downstream".

The narrative first traces the early growth of pollution by inference from the known by-products of industries and mineral extraction and by the effect on fisheries, then by reference to public health, and finally to measurements of the chemistry and biology of the river. By the mid-twentieth century the tidal reach of the river was virtually lifeless. But there was no waving a magic wand. In spite of the assertions of less practical environmentalists, the bung-and-knot solution is no more feasible at the municipal and community level than it would be at a personal level. It took far-sighted decisions, costly and extensive engineering works, legislation, and watchful monitoring to restore life and beauty to the river, as we shall see in Chapter 9. And we may not be entirely into clear water yet......

WHAT IS POLLUTION?

River pollution may be defined as occurring when water "is altered in composition or condition directly or indirectly as a result of the activities of man so that it is less suitable for any or all of the uses for which it would be suitable in its natural state"[1].

There are three significant aspects of this definition. Firstly *"as a result of the activities of man"* rules out natural variations which may be detrimental to river life. For example, high water temperature associated with power station outfalls would be regarded as thermal pollution whilst similar temperatures occurring as a result of low flows during a hot summer would not.

"Composition and condition" refers to three features of water quality — physical, chemical and biological. Physical properties include turbidity and temperature as well as those aesthetic properties of colour, taste and odour, noticed most in drinking.

Chemical properties clearly include those substances which are directly toxic to river life such as cyanide, ammonia, heavy metals and pesticides. In addition and perhaps more important or more pervasive, the presence of organic matter by means of oxidation reduces the dissolved oxygen content of river water. Micro-organisms (bacteria) act to break down the organic matter to gases, minerals and stable organic compounds but in doing so remove oxygen from the water. Dissolved oxygen (DO) is critical for the sustenance of fish and other river life and is generally referred to in percentage of saturation (0 to 100%). An alternative measure of the oxygen status of the river is *biochemical oxygen demand* (BOD) which defines the consumption of oxygen by micro-organisms and is measured in milligrams per litre (mg/l). Water from an unpolluted river generally has a BOD of less than 1.5 mg/l, treated sewage of less than 20 mg/l, raw sewage typically of 300 mg/l, but many industrial effluents of over 1000 mg/l. High biochemical oxygen demand from pollution causes low levels of dissolved oxygen and may arise not only from domestic sewage in breaking down organic matter, but also from food (milk, beer, etc.) and other industrial wastes.

Biological properties refers primarily to the presence of micro-organisms at a level and of a type which are harmful to other river life or to humans. Most river-borne organisms — even those derived from sewage — are harmless, but a small number of pathological organisms associated with these bacteria, such as those which cause typhoid, cholera and dysentery can wreak havoc.

"Suitable for use" indicates a need for assessment of water quality in relation to use. Potential uses form the basis of river water quality classification and objectives. These first became a statutory requirement under the Water Act 1989 and are now enshrined in EC legislation. Of course, after several millennia of occupation of the Tyne catchment it is not practical to return the river in its entirety to a completely natural state, so objectives are set for specific realizable uses for particular river reaches. Each use class such as potable water quality or migratory fishery has associated physical, chemical and biological standard values.

THE NATURAL RIVER

Natural rivers show some variability in water quality, due in part to the chemical quality of rainfall on the catchment. Rain, even when uncontaminated by atmospheric pollution, is naturally somewhat acidic (pH 5.6) largely because it contains carbonic acid derived from dissolved carbon dioxide. To a greater extent river water quality, including acidity, depends on the soils and underlying rocks with which the rain comes in contact before reaching the river. Upland catchments with high rainfall and a peat cover tend to produce acidic river flows whereas calcareous bedrock tends to have alkaline waters. The Tyne fortunately has both, resulting in a natural flow in the Tyne and its main tributaries which is nearly neutral. The Tyne catchment is underlain almost in its entirety by rocks of Carboniferous age, including the main Coal Measures in the east and Carboniferous limestone in the west. The interbedding of limestone between bands of shale and sandstone in many upland tributaries ensures that even these are not on average unduly acidic.

Nonetheless there are variations with time in a given reach of river, depending on how long that water has been in contact with the underlying rocks, i.e. longer in droughts (when the river is sustained by groundwater) than in floods. It is possible that even in the natural river occasional episodes of acidic runoff would have occurred in association with high flows. The first flush of autumn rain after a dry summer would (as now) have produced peat-discoloured water, rich in humic acids and therefore more acidic than normal.

Natural variations of physical and chemical water quality place some limitations on the plant and animal species which can colonise the river and its channel. Water quality, along with the hydrological regime described in Chapter 1, contributes to the 'personality' of the River Tyne. There is one area in the Tyne basin where it is possible that, even in the natural state, the quality of the river water may have severely limited the species which could colonise. Parts of the South Tyne catchment, notably its tributaries the Nent and West Allen, are underlain at depth by an intrusion of granitic igneous rocks with associated lead and zinc mineralisation extending to the surface. Although exploitation of these minerals has derogated some tributary reaches (as we shall see below), it is not clear to what extent the natural river also suffered from zinc contamination which would have inhibited plant and animal colonisation and growth.

THE IMPACT OF MINING

The first serious impact on the water quality of the River Tyne was almost certainly from mining, not in the first instance from coal, but from the mining of lead and zinc in the tributaries of the upper South Tyne. The Romans may have mined lead but there is more definite evidence of medieval workings - the beginnings of an industry that continued until the mid-twentieth century.

However, the early technology would only have allowed the exploitation of ore deposits near the surface. Large-scale mining in the Tyne catchment began early in the seventeenth century[2]. By the late eighteenth century, with advances in mining, preparation and smelting technology, the northern Pennines (South Tyne, Wear and Tees catchments) became Britain's leading lead and zinc producer. Lead production reached a peak in the mid-nineteenth century and zinc production peaked around 1900 with the growth of the food-canning industry. The last metal mine in the Tyne basin closed in the early 1930s although reworking of spoil heaps for zinc recommenced during World War II and continued until the early 1950s. Mining sites are shown in Fig. 8.1.

Mining and processing left ample opportunity for lead and zinc, and associated cadmium and copper, to enter the river system in solution or as sediment.

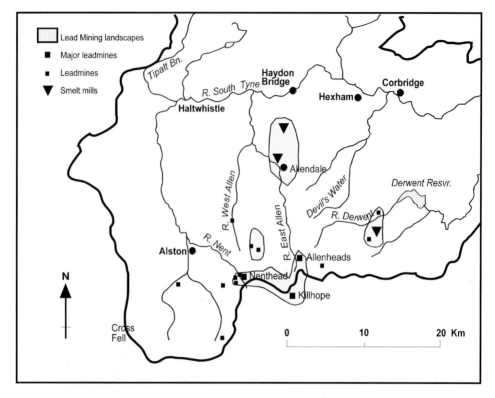

Fig 8.1 The distribution of metal mines and sources of mineral pollution in the South Tyne and Derwent catchments

Exploration by 'hushing' (Chapter 13) had a significant effect; the resulting rush of water washed away soil into the river system and exposed the underlying rock which could then be inspected for ore. Repeated hushing on the same site left deeply-gouged valleys on the hillside, an example being Dowgang Hush southwest of Nenthead.

Mining was followed by crushing and dressing and then gravity separation of ore in water which was then discharged to the river. Waste water was led through tailings dams where sediment settled, leaving clear water to enter the river. The tailings dams, now left dry and filled with fine sediment, still have a high residual lead content on which few plants survive. The river has also transported metal-rich sediments downstream and deposited them on shingle banks and in fine sediments on the floodplains[3]. The heavier lead appears not to have been transported as far as the zinc, which is present in significant concentrations on the floodplain as far as the estuary, but particularly on the South Tyne, Allens and Derwent. The metal rich shingles, being inimical to the growth of most plants, are very bare but have a characteristic flora of metallophytic plants (Chapter 5).

Adit drainage of minewaters (Fig. 8.2) with high levels of metals, along with the weathering and erosion of spoil tips, still remain sources of fluvial pollution.

Zinc concentrations are much higher than those of lead or associated cadmium due to zinc's greater solubility, and no doubt minewater concentrations were much higher during the period of mining. Zinc is toxic to many species of aquatic invertebrates and thus has a knock-on effect on zinc-tolerant algal growth. The filamentous green alga, *Mougeotia sp*[4], flourishes in the Nent due to the absence of grazing invertebrates.

As described in Chapters 12 and 13, the mining of coal and the coal trade through the port dominated the life of Newcastle and indeed of the whole Tyne estuary from the medieval period to the early twentieth century. In the mid-nineteenth century there were nearly 20,000 sailings per year from Newcastle, the majority of them bearing coal to London. Much of the coal was mined within

Fig 8.2 A mine drainage level from ancient workings high on Cross Fell, discharging clear but mineral-rich water *(Photo: David Archer)*

a few miles of the river or even within sight of it. It was inevitable that coal and coal dust found its way into the river whilst in transit or in loading from the coal drops. Yet there is no strong evidence that coal mining or the coal trade had a seriously detrimental effect on the estuary. Salmon continued to pass through the estuary to reach their spawning grounds and their smolts returned to the sea. It was not until the early twentieth century that the coal trade took a nosedive.

Coal is normally biochemically inert and perhaps the main influence was waste water from coal washeries. The polluting effect was primarily due to suspended solids which were deposited in watercourses, blanketing the bottom and destroying plant and animal life. Coal waste also did not improve the aesthetic quality of the river. However, except when it contains exceptionally high levels of sulphur, coal is neither toxic nor does it exert a biochemical oxygen demand.

One issue which has raised its head in recent years since the demise of underground workings in the Northumbrian coalfield is the drainage of minewaters. Mine drainage of working pits using Newcomen's engines commenced in the early eighteenth century and drainage water was discharged to the Tyne and its lowland tributaries. Under the Rivers Pollution Prevention Act of 1876, it was no offence to discharge minewater into the river if it were discharged in the same condition that it was raised from the mine. Although the 1963 Water Resources Act placed a requirement for a consent to discharge minewater, there remained no effective statutory control on the quality until 2000. The Durham coalfield required extensive pumping to keep coastal mines from flooding, and the largest of these is at Kibblesworth into the River Team, providing a significant proportion of the total flow to that tributary in dry weather.

The closure of pits created new problems. Whilst the mines were in operation the water level was kept below the working area of the mine. When the mines closed and pumping ceased, the water level rose up through the workings and eventually discharged as springs to the river again. The combination of water, air in the shafts, and impurities in the coal could potentially create a highly polluting ochreous discharge containing manganese, iron and sulphides. An example is the Red Burn which flows through Acomb – red both by name and nature from drainage of ancient coal workings. The polluting discharge received special treatment in 2000 using reed beds, a technique championed by the author of the final chapter, Paul Younger, nearly fifty years after the discharge first emerged.

THE SPECTRE OF DEATH

Citizens of Tyneside at the beginning of the twenty-first century give little thought to the fact that water arrives through a tap and is carried away down a plughole or round the bend. But take these conveniences away for a few days or even for a few hours, and we realise how fundamental they are to our civilisation.

We all produce waste and it has got to be disposed of somewhere. In pre-industrial rural communities the injunction of the Mosaic law which returned the organic matter to the soil seemed adequate.[5]

"And thou shalt have a place also without the camp. And thou shalt have something to dig with: and it shall be when thou ease thyself abroad, thou shalt dig therewith and shalt turn back and cover that which cometh from thee."

The availability of flowing water to riverside communities provided an alternative sink for waste of all kinds and Linsley in Chapter 12 outlines how medieval Newcastle quayside and adjacent streets were founded on the waste of a previous generation. The problem of disposal of domestic sewage and other wastes grew with urban development. It became critical in the nineteenth century when the population of Newcastle quadrupled in 60 years (27,500 in 1811 to 128,500 in 1871) with migration from surrounding rural areas and an influx of 'poor' Irish in the wake of the Irish famine. The overcrowding and lack of sanitation created a squalor unrivalled even in the worst urban slums of the present developing world. There were cholera epidemics in 1832, 1848 and the worst in 1853. The Report of the Cholera Commission[6] the following year makes grim reading.

In 1851 the population of Newcastle was 88,000 with 9450 houses and an average of more than two families to a house. In the crowded slums of Sandgate and elsewhere there were often more than 15 living in a single room. Of these houses only 1451 had water closets, some of which discharged into cesspits which overflowed through overuse or rainfall to be carried at the behest of gravity. In Gateshead some were discharged into old coal workings. Perhaps another 1500 households had access to private privies or ashpits often built against the porous walls of houses so as "to allow the liquid filth to ooze directly through the walls into the living and sleeping rooms". Some privies were simply converted cellars. They were infrequently emptied and often depended upon irregular visits from neighbouring farmers who carried off the nightsoil to fertilise their fields.

The remaining two-thirds of the households had no drains of any kind even for storm water. Occupants had the options of public privies of which there were only 21 in Newcastle, most unlit at night, or more commonly the use of chamber utensils (locally called kits). Overcrowding obliged occupants to use these in the one and only room in which more than one family cooked, ate and slept and to store them in the room or at stair heads. The contents were often emptied into open gutters or out of windows onto the surface of entries courts and alleys. The houses themselves were said to be "almost devoid of a proper means of ventilation".

The Commission Report enumerates the conditions of squalor:

○ Extensive diffusion of faecal matter on paved surfaces
○ Perpetual soakage and stampage of excrement into the soil
○ The generally unemptied and uncleansed condition of ashpits and privies
○ General accumulation of offensive matters in places not designed for their reception
○ Aggravation of these accumulations from slaughterhouses, tripe boileries,

bone dealeries, tanneries and fish cureries

"The whole town may, almost without exaggeration, be said to have been breathing continually an atmosphere of its own excrement".

Upon this scene in the summer of 1853 stole the spectre of death in the form of *Vibrio cholerae* — cholera. In a period of nine weeks in Newcastle 1530 perished, or 1 in 60 of the population. A similar ratio succumbed in Gateshead where 433 died. In one case 8 out of 31 occupants perished in a single house and at its height more than 100 died of the disease in a single day. Unlike previous outbreaks, the disease was not confined to the overcrowded slums but extended to the new streets built by Grainger with their private water supply, water closets and drains connected to main sewers.

It was not realised that the main cause of the disease was not the miasma and foul odours of the town but the water supply. Although the Commission concluded that there was grave suspicion about the water supply, it did not amount to certainty. The news of John Snow's unequivocal discovery in 1853[7], of the connection between an outbreak of cholera in Soho and a particular water pump in Broad Street, appears not to have reached the Commission.

At the beginning of the nineteenth century water was being supplied to the city by Newcastle Fire Office from springs at Coxlodge and elsewhere, and was supplemented from 1832 by pumping from the Tyne[8]. Abstraction from the Tyne was augmented in 1834 by a pumping station at Elswick but the quality of the water steadily declined with pollution of the river. In 1845 the Whittle Dean Water Company (to become after 1863 the Newcastle and Gateshead Water Company) was formed and received Royal Assent, with the laudable intention of providing a cheap and constant supply of pure and wholesome water for both poor and rich of Newcastle and Gateshead. The works comprising five impounding reservoirs at Whittle Dean and a pipeline to Newcastle were completed in 1848. The water was supplied to individual houses (less than 10% in 1844) and the remainder took their water from 52 public fountains and pants, but all received supplies from the same sources.

Demand for the clean water grew rapidly from 1.5 million gallons per day (mgd) in 1848 to 2.5 mgd in 1852 and included industry as well as domestic users. The original reservoirs proved insufficient to meet the increased demand in the drought years of 1850 and 1853, and the Water Company took the fateful decision of topping up the supply by reinstating pumping from the river at Elswick. The water supplied after 5 July 1853 was a mixture of one-third Tyne water and two-thirds Whittle Dean water and was undoubtedly the source of the epidemic. The Water Company recognised the dangers of taking polluted water from the river and attempted to minimise the danger by abstracting only on the ebb tide. What they did not seem to realise was that polluted water carried upstream on the incoming tide polluted the river over the full tidal cycle. Rainfall at Whittle Dean enabled the Company to stop pumping from the river on 15 September and the rate of deaths from cholera began to drop sharply from 19 September.

The separation of the functions of water supply and sewage disposal was clearly a problem. The water company took the responsibility to bring water only so far as the house but householder and Corporation retained the responsibility for getting rid of it. There was an inadequate infrastructure in place to carry the water off to places where it could do no harm. Newcastle had main sewers which followed the track of the ancient rivers, the Lort Burn, Erick Burn and Pandon Burn, but few and improperly constructed branch sewers and house drains to connect to them. Whilst there was a clamour for piped water there was no equivalent clamour for sewage disposal — and no effective body to respond to any such clamour. Divided responsibility and the lag between supply and disposal provided opportunities for foul water to reach new locations and was clearly an aggravating factor in the spread of the epidemic. The functions remained separate over much of the country until the Water Act of 1973 which focused on integrated river basin management. It was not until the amalgamation of North East Water and Northumbrian Water in 1995 that the functions came within the same organisation on Tyneside..

The epidemic of 1853 was to prove pivotal in the attitude to public sanitation and sewage disposal in Newcastle. With respect to water supply, the Water Company immediately abandoned the Elswick abstraction and implemented further step by step development of sources. The Newcastle Corporation's response with respect to sanitation and drainage lagged behind that of the water supply company. However, it now became more active in enforcing its powers concerning the connection of foul drains to sewers, which had become mandatory under the Public Health Act of 1846. However, it failed to appoint a Medical Officer of Health until 1872 and sanitary conditions in many overcrowded districts remained poor.

What has all this to do with the River Tyne? Whilst sewage and other waste lay festering and putrefying in cesspools and roadsides, it reached the river only in quantities sufficient to promote human disease but not in sufficient amounts to deprive the river entirely of oxygen. In this respect it was probably helped by the larger ratio of freshwater to saltwater flow in the estuary before navigational dredging and 'improvement'. The progressive increase in piped water supply and drainage of foul sewage to the river in the second half of the nineteenth century gradually transferred the trouble from town to river. In spite of this, the salmon population as illustrated by rod catches (Fig 6.2) seems to have held up remarkably well and salmon numbers did not decrease dramatically until well into the twentieth century.

PASSING THE BUCK
The need to avoid the dangers of disease and filth in towns conditioned attitudes to sewage disposal throughout the second half of the nineteenth century and the beginning of the twentieth. The 'sanitary idea' of the time was to get rid of the sewage and where more obvious than the nearest river. Thus the sanitation problem of the town was substituted by an environmental problem in the river. The tidal river deteriorated as population and urban sewerage systems grew.

Fortunately the freshwater Tyne had an advantage over many other large English rivers such as the Trent and the rivers of south Yorkshire in that there was little industrial development (apart from the lead and zinc mines) in the headwaters. The waste of small rural towns could be adequately diluted by the substantial river flow of the Tyne (average of 44 cumecs and an absolute minimum of around 3 cumecs).

The law was also different for inland rivers and tidal estuaries. The Rivers Pollution Act of 1876 made it an offence to discharge solid or liquid sewage into an *inland* watercourse without first rendering it inoffensive. However, it was all very well to pass such an act but implementing it was another matter. The science and engineering of sewage treatment was still in its infancy and in the late nineteenth century consisted mainly of what would now be referred to as preliminary treatment — screening to remove debris and grit.

Many rural towns continued to depend on ashpit and bucket netties even as late as the 1950s. The responsibility for sewage disposal lay with urban and district councils. A common sight was the donkeyman and his cart removing nightsoil and ash from the backs of terraced houses and taking it either to spread as fertiliser on fields or to the local midden. Ron Edgar (who died aged 89 in 1995), a village historian from Ovingham, recalled a large midden heap on the south bank of the Tyne just downstream from Ovingham bridge, which received the waste from the coal-mining town of Prudhoe over several decades. Its situation next to the River Tyne allowed the midden to drain and carry its oxygen-demanding organic matter into the river. It was probably in violation of the 1876 Act but enforcement was lax or non-existent. Ultimately, when the use of the midden ceased, the remaining organic matter decomposed and was leached, leaving a hill of ash and cinders. These found a use as foundation material for the 'new' road from Ovingham bridge past Prudhoe Castle to the town in the 1930s. Sufficient cinder remains in the river bank to provide a source of archaeological interest for children visiting the Riverside Park in search of broken clay pipes and Victorian pottery — not realising the original source of the material.

Gradually the science of sewage treatment developed. A Royal Commission on Sewage Disposal was set up in 1868 and between then and 1915 produced ten reports based on continuing research and practice. In 1882 they proposed settlement tanks for separating solid and liquid (primary treatment — as described in Chapter 9). By the tenth report in 1915 they were recommending the use of biological (percolating) filters which accelerate the aerobic processes of natural purification (secondary treatment). Circular filter beds with their rotating and sprinkling arms came to be a familiar sight near many towns and villages after about 1930. They had the advantage that they could operate virtually without power and with limited unskilled manpower, and could be scaled to the size of the settlement. A second phase of sewage works construction and reconstruction occurred in the 1950s and 1960s with the implementation of the Rivers (Prevention of Pollution) Acts of 1951 and 1961. This followed the assumption of powers by the newly-created River Boards to issue consents which required works to meet standards with respect to suspended solids and BOD in treated effluent, so that it would do no harm to the receiving river.

The freshwater Tyne throughout its history retained a water quality sufficient to support a thriving brown trout and coarse fishery. Indeed, it is said that the nutrient provided by inadequately-treated sewage enhanced the coarse fishery. Apart from the despoliation by gravel extraction, the state of the freshwater river remained suitable for migratory salmon and sea trout if only they could pass safely through the estuary.

The situation was quite different for the tidal river. There were no controls on discharge to tidal estuaries until the Rivers (Prevention of Pollution) Act of 1961, after which new or changed discharges had to be consented by the River Authority. Not until the Control of Pollution Act of 1974 was there a legal basis to control long-term existing discharges to the estuary. By that time, apart from industrial discharges described below, the river received untreated sewage from a Tyneside population of over 700,000, plus the waste from industry. The only sewage works in the whole of Tyneside was at Felling and that discharged its effluent into the non-tidal river Don.

WASTE FROM INDUSTRY

Although domestic sewage had a serious impact on the estuary, it was probably industrial or trade wastes which did the most damage to the estuary and all but destroyed the river for salmon by the mid-twentieth century. The absence of statutory control over discharges to estuaries no doubt encouraged industries to be lax in their attitude to discharges of trade effluent. Indeed the Royal Commission of 1972[9] was of the view that some industries gravitated to estuaries simply in order to avoid the cost of treatment.

Until the end of the eighteenth century industries were mainly based around agricultural products from which the organic waste was polluting predominantly in its requirement for oxygen for decomposition. The Cholera Commission of 1854 had already noted the offensive waste from animal slaughter and processing, including the production of tripe, cow gum from bones, and tanned hides. Slaughterhouse wastes have a BOD of around 1000 mg/litre, appreciably more than raw sewage; blood, one of the components of waste, has a BOD of more than 100,000 mg/litre. It is possible that in the nineteenth century the waste was incorporated in middens and other disposal sites for domestic refuse, but likely that by the twentieth century much of the liquid waste was discharged to the estuary (Fig. 8.3).

In contrast, tanneries have often been located adjacent to rivers, abstracting water for their processing and discharging waste back to the river (Fig. 8.4). A typical site was along the Cockshaw Burn in Hexham. In Newcastle several sites were away from the river to the west of Newgate Street from whence the waste would certainly have found its way to the Tyne. The processes of soaking, liming and tanning involve the passing of hides through a series of pits with liquors of increasing strength. The spent liquors, containing ammonia and sulphides, were highly polluting with a BOD of 1000 mg/litre or more. As late as 1953, Isaac[10] noted that "there is no method of treatment in general use in Great Britain by which tannery wastes alone can be rendered fit for discharge to surface waters". Untreated it would certainly have wiped out the biota of small tributaries such as the Cockshaw Burn and would have made a significant

Fig 8.3 A foul discharge from an abattoir to the river Tyne. Unfortunately the black and white photo does not convey all the gory details of the discharge *(Photo by courtesy of Kinghorn Davies)*

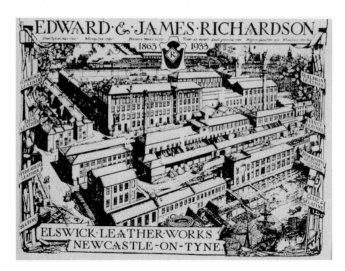

Fig 8.4 Richardson's Elswick Leather Works: The Quaker Richardson family were tanners in North Yorkshire from the seventeenth century and later on Tyneside. In 1863, the company moved to a riverside site at Elswick to create the largest such works in the region, complete with workers' housing in 'Shumac Village', shown towards the top left in the illustration. Dependent upon the river for import and export, the works quay can be seen at bottom right. The works closed in the 1970s.

116

contribution to deoxygenation of the estuary.

Perhaps surprisingly, brewery waste and beer itself is very highly polluting. The waste is primarily the liquor which is used to steep the barley (to allow it to germinate under controlled conditions in malting) and washings from vats and casks. Occasionally spoilt beer was also discharged. Perhaps it goes against the grain for a Geordie to see beer poured into an opening other than the one for which it was intended but such disposal was actually a statutory requirement as a means of avoiding the payment of excise duty on spoiled beer. Sam James recalls one such incident at Scottish and Newcastle Breweries in the early 1960s when beer was poured into the sewer under the eye of the Excise Inspector. Beer has a BOD of more than 75,000 mg/litre and would again have exerted a significant deoxygenating impact on the estuary.

Perhaps the most devastating of all the industries in the Tyne estuary were those concerned with the processing of coal for coal gas and coke (Chapter 13). The processes are similar. Inflammable gas, consisting mainly of hydrogen and methane, is given off when coal is heated out of contact with air, and coke is the residue left in the retort. However, there are also various volatile products, including coal tar, ammonia and ammonia salts, phenol, cyanides and sulphides, which pollute both because of their direct toxicity and their oxygen demand. The volatile by-products are condensed to produce ammoniacal liquor, typically at a rate of 200 litres per tonne of coal. Initially the entire liquor would have been discharged to the river but a use was found for the coal tar extracted from the liquor. Later methods for extracting ammonia were also developed, but the final effluent to the river was still highly toxic and deoxygenating. Champion in Chapter 6 notes the tarry flavour of salmon caught in the estuary in the earlier part of the twentieth century — almost certainly due to coke works effluent.

Production of gas for public consumption started in Newcastle in 1817 with gas works (Chapter 13), first at the Manors and Forth Street and later at Elswick and Redheugh, together providing street lighting for most of Tyneside by the late nineteenth century[11]. The industry grew in the twentieth century to provide most of Tyneside with domestic coal gas for cooking. Coke works were initially on a small scale and grew up alongside collieries in the nineteenth century. The demand grew with the requirement for coke for iron and steel-making, particularly for the works at Consett alongside the River Derwent. The largest coke works were those at Norwood, discharging to the lower Team, and Derwenthaugh on the lower tidal Derwent, with plant for the latter having been taken from Germany as part of World War I reparations. Both continued to operate until the early 1980s though with rapidly declining output during the previous decade. Together, at their peak, they discharged a polluting load equivalent to that of over one million people

Besides these there were numerous other industries along the estuary. Alkali manufacture at Walker-on-Tyne from 1796 produced over 30,000 tons of bleaching powder a year, with highly toxic chemical waste, including calcium sulphide, which was dumped at sea. Also contained in the toxic wastes were arsenic, cyanide and hydrogen sulphide gas. Copper was produced from pyrites with an output of more than 150,000 tonnes per year. The glass, arms and munitions, and shipbuilding industries each added their contribution of waste.

An interesting reflection on the change in government and public attitudes to the environment, is the fact that water leached from the contaminated land at Derwenthaugh coke works and at the Walker alkali works now receives sophisticated treatment at the site, whereas formerly a much greater discharge of highly toxic waste from the working plant went straight into the river.

A contributory cause of low dissolved oxygen in the upper part of the estuary was the construction of power stations, first at Dunston in 1910 and later at Stella and Stella North. These discharged large quantities of warm water and raised the temperature of the river by up to 8°C. This increase not only reduced the solubility of dissolved oxygen, but in turn raised the temperature of the fish, increasing their metabolism and requirement for oxygen.

In 1941 another important development — this time in the freshwater river — was the building of the ICI factory at Low Prudhoe which manufactured both ammonium sulphate for fertiliser, and ammonia which could be used for explosives. A significant amount of water was abstracted from the river and returned as effluent laced with ammonia, and the Spechells continued to leak ammonia to the river for some years after the closure of the plant in 1967. The powdered chalk by-product was dumped on floodplain land, known from late-medieval times as the Spechells. This name is now given to the line of flat-topped hills along the river. Annually up to 300,000 tonnes of chalk a year were also shipped as fertiliser as far afield as Yorkshire and Scotland. The remaining white chalk was hand-turfed to avoid its use as a navigational guide by German bombers. The chalk now appears to be inert and the hills are appreciated for their unusual biota of lime-loving plants and associated butterflies.

CHARACTERISTICS OF THE POLLUTED ESTUARY

In 1960 around 275 major discharges of untreated water (domestic and industrial) entered the estuary. Contrary to popular assumption, the scour of tides does not immediately dispose of such wastes to the sea. Some are carried upstream, linger in suspension and are finally deposited in bottom muds where they continue to deprive the river of oxygen. The physical characteristics of the estuary (as modified by dredging) have an important bearing on the behaviour of pollutants. This interaction between estuary and pollutants was first elucidated in a King's College report in 1960[12] and has been an ongoing subject of survey and analysis by regulatory bodies, most recently the Environment Agency.

These studies have shown that there is a very rapid response in the estuary to what is happening in the open North Sea. The time of high and low water does not vary in the estuary by more than 15 minutes. Up to Ryton the longitudinal water profile at high and low waters is horizontal. In each tidal cycle from low water to high water there is a tidal inflow to the estuary of 33.7 million cubic metres (Mm^3) for a spring tide and 17.0 Mm^3 for a neap tide. This implies an average inflow through the piers over the flood tide of 1500 cumecs on a spring and 750 cumecs on a neap tide. At mid-tide the rate of flow would probably be twice these rates. Even passing Newburn, the net upriver flow is still considerable — 75 cumecs in springs and 40 cumecs in neaps. These flows are large in comparison to the freshwater flow at times of low flow when fish are most likely to be stressed (say, 5 cumecs). In addition they are large in comparison to the freshwater flows that can be generated by releases from Kielder. The average inflow into Kielder is about 7.5 cumecs and the maximum possible release rate is around 50 cumecs. Releases from Kielder cannot be expected to have an impact in improving the water quality beyond the upper part of the estuary though they may be effective in encouraging upstream migration.

Although the water swills up and down the estuary with each rise and fall of the tide, the net downstream movement of water and any suspended material and pollutants is only about 400 metres per tidal cycle. Moreover, this movement is complicated by stratification of the water due to density variations between saline water and freshwater. Less dense freshwater stays near the surface and has a net movement downstream more rapid than the average (of 400 m), whilst saline water of higher density near the bed has a net movement upstream. As a consequence the fate of polluting materials entering the estuary depends on their specific gravity. Materials which dissolve or remain in fine suspension move with the upper layers and may leave the estuary after a few tidal cycles. Denser materials like sludge tend to stay longer in the estuary and are carried upstream. They may stay in the estuary indefinitely until decomposed. Materials like recalcitrant organics and heavy metals are likely to accumulate unless removed by dredging.

These mechanisms are responsible the build-up on the bed of banks of mud rich in organic matter. Although some consider these unsightly at low water, they are host to huge numbers of worms and crustacea, which provide rich feeding for an increasing number and variety of ducks and wading birds. However, the mud also exerts an oxygen demand: surveys in 1995 and 1996 have shown that it contained up to 20% organic matter. Calculations suggested that these bed deposits accounted for nearly half the oxygen uptake in the estuary. Tracer studies undertaken at that time also showed that fine particulate material was transported from Howdon upstream as far as Newburn, carried by the inland movement of the saline water which enters the estuary on every tide. It is ironic that, while the Tyneside Interceptor Sewer carries effluent from Prudhoe to Howdon for treatment, some of the residuum is carried more than half this distance back upstream!

This upstream transport of organic-rich sediment, which adds to the oxygen demand on the estuary, is one of the mechanisms that have contributed to salmon deaths in the upper estuary. In recent years, as the estuary's water quality has improved to allow the passage of salmon virtually all the time, some have died in most summers. More have died in relatively warm, dry summers, when they are less inclined to leave the apparent sanctuary of the relatively cool but lethal estuary for the safe but uncomfortably warmer river.

The commissioning in 2000 of secondary treatment at Howdon has reduced almost tenfold the amount of oxygen-depleting organic material in the discharge and has already resulted in a significant increase in oxygen concentration in the lower estuary. However, there are substantial amounts of mud in the estuary, from South Shields to Newburn and the organic content of the mud is expected to decline more slowly. It may be some years before the full benefit is apparent in the upper estuary. Meanwhile, the risk, albeit lower than before, of substantial numbers of salmon dying in the upper estuary is still with us.

KEEPING THE TYNE CLEAN

For most of its length the Tyne and its main tributaries is a first-class river suitable for migratory fish and for the abstraction of drinking water. It has to be so, because we depend on the Tyne for the water supply to Tyneside. In dry summers the Tyne also ensures the continuity of supply for Wearside and Teesside (Chapter 10).

However, so far as both fish and our drinking water are concerned, it is essential that there are no momentary lapses from the high standard of water quality, or, if lapses occur, that measures are in place to cope with them. Unfortunately accidents do occur and people can be careless. It is the role of the EA to ensure that accidents are minimised and that effective action is taken to respond with respect to the river. In turn, Northumbrian Water must ensure the continuing quality of water abstracted for domestic supply. Protective procedures have been considerably strengthened in both organisations in the last decade. The following are examples of incidents which have heightened awareness.

During the hot dry summer of 1989 the natural flow in the Tyne diminished to the point where Kielder releases were being made to maintain the minimum flow. Water was being abstracted both for water supply to Tyneside and via the Kielder Tunnel to augment the supply to Wearside. At this point somebody (identity unknown) released about one litre of phenol into the river, perhaps as a component of some other substance. There was little water for dilution in the Tyne. The pollutant abstracted from the river, was chlorinated and released, much diluted, to supply. Now phenol in its original state is nearly colourless and tasteless but when chlorinated it becomes TCP (trichlorophenol), the familiar antiseptic which the sensitive palate can taste at one part per billion. The amounts in supply were harmless (much less than a TCP mouth gargle) but extremely worrying to householders. The incident also rang warning bells for the water companies who have strengthened the barrage of monitors to ensure that processes are halted before tainted water can enter the supply system. These include:

- Automatic continuous chemical monitors
- Fish monitors which detect abnormal activity of fish in a tank which is constantly fed with water entering the treatment works
- Water tasters – the final human line of defence

Three other incidents on the River Derwent, with quite different sources, highlight potential pollution of the river. The first in 1982 involved the deliberate release of a tank of waste cyanide down the drain from a paint works which had gone into liquidation at Leadgate. On reaching the river it wiped out the fish and most other life in the river for a considerable reach downstream. The incident was the subject of a successful prosecution.

In November 1984, after a period of heavy rain and a rise in groundwater levels, lagoons associated with the Consett steel works overflowed, releasing a large volume of polluted waste. This again caused a massive fish kill and the death of animal and plant life.

Finally, in the early 1990s in a road accident at the A68 bridge over the River Derwent, a tanker loaded with acrynol (a rubberised liquid used amongst other things in the manufacture of condoms) crashed and overturned in the River Derwent. It released nearly its entire contents into the river, which became white as milk over a stretch of more than one kilometre, and the polluted reach gradually progressed to the Tyne estuary. However, in this case, in spite of its worrying appearance, there was no detectable impact on river biota.

The Environment Agency has four main strands to minimise such incidents:

○ Education
○ Inspection of sites (factories and farms, etc.) to ensure that where there are hazardous chemicals or substances, they will be contained by bunding in the event of spillage
○ Rapid response teams to isolate hazardous material
○ Legal enforcement through fines for causing or permitting pollution to occur

This final paragraph is intended to contribute to education by addressing the reader. Look at the shelves of your medicine cabinet, garage and greenhouse. They are all full of toxic chemicals used for a variety of purposes — pesticides, herbicides, solvents, paints, oils. If pesticides can kill insects in your garden, they can kill them in the river. Do not be tempted to put unwanted residues in the drain, neither the foul drain nor the surface water drain. Put them in a sealed container in your solid refuse or, if in doubt, call the Environment Agency. Only by our own vigilance can we ensure that the River Tyne remains as a sparkling river full of life.

REFERENCES

1. Raistrick, A. and Jennings, B. (1965) *A History of lead mining in the Pennines*. Longmans, London, 347pp.
2. Key, A. (1956) *A general survey of water pollution in Europe*. WHO, Geneva
3. Macklin, M.G. and Dowsett, R.B. (1989) The chemical and physical speciation of trace metals in fine grained overbank flood sediments in the Tyne basin, north-east England. *Catena,* **16**, 135–151.
4. Patterson, G. and Whitton, B.A. (1981) Chemistry of water, sediments and algal filaments

in groundwater draining an old lead-zinc mine. In: *Heavy Metals in Northern England: Environmental and Biological Aspects,* P.J. Say and B.A. Whitton (eds.). University of Durham, 65–72.

5. Holy Bible, Deuteronomy Chap. 23, Verses 12–13.

6. *Report of the Commissioners appointed to inquire into the causes which have led to or have aggravated the Late Outbreak of Cholera in the Towns of Newcastle upon Tyne, Gateshead and Tynemouth* (1854), HMSO, London.

7. Snow, J. (1853) *On the prevention of Cholera*

8. Rennison, R.W. (1979) *Water to Tyneside. A History of the Newcastle and Gateshead Water Company.* Newcastle and Gateshead Water Company 359pp

9. Royal Commission on Environmental Pollution (1972) *Third Report: Pollution of some British estuaries and Coastal Waters,* HMSO, London.

10. Isaac, P.G.C. (1953) *Public Health Engineering* E. & F.N. Spon, London.

11. Bevan, J.R. (1992) Public utilities in the 19th century: Gas and Electricity. In, Burke, M. and Buswell, R.J. (eds.) *Newcastle's Changing Map*, Newcastle upon Tyne City Libraries and Arts.

12. Allen, J.H. and Hall, D.G. (1960) *Hydraulic and Sediment Survey of the Estuary of the River Tyne.* Report 20, Dept. of Civil Engineering, Kings College.

9. THE REGENERATION OF THE TYNE ESTUARY

TONY FOSTER

INTRODUCTION

The story of the regeneration of the River Tyne estuary spans almost the entire twentieth century, and continues into the twenty first. In many ways it reflects the changing priorities and perceptions of the public, especially over the last three decades, the growth of environmental consciousness, and willingness to commit very high levels of investment to the resolution of environmental problems.

Although the main historic driver for the clean-up scheme was water quality – the absence of nuisance and the passage of migratory fish – its biggest impact has been economic and social. The regeneration and redevelopment of the banks of the Tyne, most particularly in central Newcastle and Gateshead, simply would not have been possible without the improvement in water quality which resulted from the elimination of sewage outfalls to the river.

It was said of Barcelona that it was a city which had "...turned its face away from the sea" until the redevelopment associated with the 1992 Olympic Games gave new life to the waterfront and changed the city's focus. Similarly, Newcastle had turned its face away from the river, with the city's focus steadily moving northwards, but now it has turned back to the river again. The quayside area has become the social heart of the city and the location of choice for many businesses, while Gateshead's creation of the Millennium Bridge, followed by the Baltic Centre for Contemporary Art and soon the Sage Music Centre, will further enhance the appeal of a formerly-neglected area.

Thus the regeneration of the River Tyne estuary has been central to the physical and economic regeneration of the area round the estuary, as well as improving the passage of migratory fish up the river. Although unglamorous and usually unseen, effective sewerage and sewage treatment systems are about as fundamental to modern civilization in terms of health and amenity as it is possible to get; the Tyneside Scheme is a source of pride and satisfaction to the many people who have been associated with it over the last thirty or more years and might reasonably be regarded as £150 million well spent.

HISTORY — SURVEYS, REPORTS PLANS AND COMMITTEES

Urbanisation and the growth of industry on Tyneside led to a progressive deterioration of water quality in the estuary (Chapter 8), as waterborne sewage systems were constructed, with sewers discharging directly into the estuary. Through the nineteenth century there was little environmental awareness or concern; pollution was largely regarded as an inevitable and acceptable

Fig 9.1 Postcard entitled 'Canny Newcastle – the Pride o' the North' with smoking chimneys and shipping on the River Tyne in the background, produced in 1905 by A. Denholm Brasg, bookseller and artistic stationer.

(By permission: Beamish, the North of England Open Air Museum)

consequence of development (Fig. 9.1). As Johnson[1] wrote of Tyneside in 1895, "smoke-ridden, grimy, noisy as it all is, what is it but the free expression of nineteenth century energy". The first glimmerings of environmental concern came early in the twentieth century, but it has taken nearly 100 years of committees, surveys, reports, plans and finally engineering action to restore life to the estuary.

The first surveys of dissolved oxygen, the key indicator of river health, were carried out from 1912 to 1931, and total depletion of dissolved oxygen, rendering the river 'septic', was recorded at Newcastle Quay on 16 October 1912. Chemical and biological examinations of sewage and trade effluents were carried out in this period, together with tests on fish immersed in sewage, trade effluents and river water.

The then Ministry of Agriculture and Fisheries set up a Standing Committee on River Pollution in 1921 and they in turn appointed a River Tyne Pollution Sub-Committee, which accumulated evidence from 1922 to 1931. Dr H.O. Bull, Reader in Marine Biology at the Dove Marine Laboratory, was appointed biologist to the Sub-Committee and summarised all available evidence for the period 1912 to 1931. The involvement of King's College, then the University of Durham and subsequently the University of Newcastle upon Tyne, has been a feature of the regeneration of the estuary, through both the Dove Marine Laboratory and the Department of Civil and Environmental Engineering.

A Joint Committee of the local authorities on Tyneside together with the Tyne Fishery Board pursued further research work on pollution. The Joint Committee first met in December 1931 and, with the benefit of earlier work, issued a report in January 1933. The report described conditions in the estuary as "nauseating and thoroughly objectionable" near some sewer outfalls, with the pervasive 'rotten eggs' smell of hydrogen sulphide. It gave details of gross deficiency of oxygen (0 to 10% of saturation values) in the summer months from Ryton to Wallsend. The Joint Committee concluded that '...the saturation point when untreated sewage can be discharged into the estuary with safety has been reached and passed', and recommended Local Authorities and government departments to consider this situation.

The Commissioner for the Special Areas (England & Wales) appointed a Tyne Sewerage Committee in 1935, and obtained advice from consulting engineers Sir George W. Humphreys, and Messrs J. D. & D. M. Watson[2]. Their joint report of November 1936 proposed the first practical scheme for dealing with pollution in the estuary and recommended that the natural drainage area should be considered as a whole rather than each administrative district separately.

The report proposed that, in the first instance, sewage from the greater part of the Tyneside conurbation was to be conveyed to a site near Jarrow where it would receive partial treatment. Partially treated sewage was to be discharged into the sea from an outfall situated between Lizard Point and Souter Point, and sludge was to be shipped for dumping at sea. Sewage from areas between the river and the intercepting sewers was to continue being discharged untreated into the river in the early life of the scheme. Sewers were designed to serve 685,000 people at 120 gallons per head per day and the treatment plant was to serve 600,000 people. The estimated cost of the scheme in November 1936 was £2.25 million.

Unsurprisingly, there was no further progress during World War II and for some years afterwards The scheme was discussed again between the local authorities and the then Ministry of Housing and Local Government in 1953 but it was not until 1958 that a conference of Tyneside local authorities considered the information available at that time. The constituent authorities decided to set up a Working Sub-Committee on Tyneside Sewage Disposal, consisting of one elected member from each of the then 18 authorities, '...to examine the present and projected schemes for sewage disposal and to explore the possible ways of creating for the area a modern system of sewage disposal'.

The Working Sub-Committee immediately appointed a Technical Sub-Committee consisting of Engineers and Surveyors to the constituent local authorities, together with co-opted technical representatives from other interested bodies. This group met for the first time in January 1959 under the chairmanship of the City Engineer of Newcastle upon Tyne.

A series of reports from both the Technical Sub-Committee and other experts were produced, culminating in a final report in July 1964, of their proposals for reducing pollution in the estuary[3], and designed to be read alongside a consultant's report on sea outfalls[4], seen as a part alternative to a land-based solution. The Committee also recommended that the Minister of Housing and Local Government make a Statutory Order that the area of the constituent local authorities be constituted a 'combined district' for the purposes of sewerage and sewage disposal, and so, with the *Tyneside Joint Sewerage Order* of 1966, the Tyneside Joint Sewerage Board (TJSB) was born.

This history is interesting from a political perspective as it involved collaboration between many local authorities from the first Joint Committee meeting in late 1931, and their ultimately ceding power in this particular sphere to a new sub-regional joint board, one of very few such boards in the UK. This made possible a solution which was both technically elegant and economically sensible, and which was a forerunner of the increasing regionalisation of the water industry. The TJSB was absorbed inot the newly-formed Northumbrian Water Authority on its creation in 1974.

AN OUTLINE OF SEWAGE TREATMENT PROCESSES

Before continuing with the story of the regeneration of the River Tyne estuary, it may be worth briefly setting out what sewage treatment is, and what it does, so that some of the issues faced, and decisions made, can be better understood.

Sewage is the liquid waste from a community. It flows along *sewers*, pipes or tunnels in the ground, which together make up what is called the *sewerage* system.

That liquid waste is made up of discharges from domestic property, from lavatories, baths and showers, clothes washing, washing up and from anything else, like garbage grinding, which results in a waterborne discharge. It also includes liquid waste discharges from businesses and from factories. The latter, of course, have the potential to include a much wider variety of materials, including chemical and potentially toxic wastes. In the past there was little control of such trade discharges to the estuary and some individual industries such as coke works had a major additional influence on estuary water quality. The overall volume and strength of trade discharges has decreased with the decline in industry, and in any case they are now subject to control at source, which determines what can and cannot be discharged to the public sewerage system. The discharger may be required to pre-treat the waste before its discharge to a sewer.

Tyneside sewage is therefore essentially domestic in character. This means it principally consists of organic material, compounds of carbon, oxygen, hydrogen, nitrogen and sulphur, and its biggest polluting impact on a watercourse is the absorption of dissolved oxygen from that water, endangering marine life and potentially rendering the watercourse septic and smelly. Sewage also contains lots of debris, including sanitary and contraceptive products, which make discharges aesthetically offensive. Finally, sewage contains very high levels of bacteria, many derived from the human gut, which are potentially harmful.

The preceding section on the history of the scheme constantly refers to sewage *disposal*, reflecting the view at the time, rather than sewage *treatment*, which is where current emphasis would lie.

Sewage treatment normally consists of three stages, with the possibility of a fourth being added where circumstances so demand. The first stage, preliminary treatment, consists of removal of debris by screening, and also the removal of grit. Because many (especially older) sewers take surface water from premises and roads as well as sewage itself, in a 'combined' rather than 'separate' sewerage system, there is often a lot of grit conveyed by the sewer which has to be removed to protect machinery used in treatment, especially pumps.

The next stage, primary treatment, consists of the removal of settleable solid material in very large tanks, where about two-thirds of the suspended solids in the sewage will settle onto the floor of the tank, from where they can be scraped out and removed as sewage sludge. This process also reduces the propensity of the remaining liquid to pollute, as measured by its Biochemical Oxygen Demand, or BOD, by about one-third.

Following this, secondary treatment further reduces the polluting impact by removing in excess of 90% of the BOD. It does this by providing an environment where bacteria and other microscopic organisms, in the presence of oxygen, can convert the organic compounds in the sewage to harmless end products. This environment may be (usually circular) beds made of clinker or a similar material with a rotating arm sprinkling the sewage onto them, or tanks where sewage is aerated by surface agitators or by bubbles passed from below, called the "activated sludge" process. In both cases, agglomerations of organic material 'feed' on the sewage, converting it to oxidised end products such as carbon dioxide, water and oxides of nitrogen and sulphur. The process also produces new cells, more than are needed to keep the process going, and these are removed in the final settlement stage (part of the secondary process).

Although the final effluent produced by such a process has had its polluting impact massively reduced, it still contains very large numbers of bacteria. Until recently, this has not been regarded as an issue in the UK, but modern bacterial standards for bathing waters have led to the increasing use of disinfection, commonplace in sewage treatment particularly in the United States for many years. This can be achieved by the use of chemicals, especially chlorine (although this itself may give rise to unwanted compounds), or by physical processes, such as ultra-violet radiation.

Final *disposal* of the treated effluent would normally be to the nearest appropriate watercourse, but the screenings, grit and sewage sludge left by the treatment process still have to be dealt with. Screenings are washed and may be buried or, in some cases, incinerated. Grit can be washed and used on roads or taken to landfill sites as volumes are not usually particularly large. Sewage sludge is much more problematic. Disposal to sea in approved dumping grounds was allowed until the late 1990s, but no longer. Further heat treatment by digestion can pasteurise the sludge, or it can be stabilised by the addition of lime. In this state, it can be used as a fertiliser and soil conditioner, but it is deficient in potassium and there are increasing concerns about its use on the land. It can also be heat-treated to produce a low grade fuel, or incinerated. What needs to be remembered is that ultimate *disposal* of sewage and the by-products of its treatment has to be to somewhere — either to rivers or the sea, to the land or to the air (via incineration). It won't just disappear — and it will keep coming!

THE PROPOSED SCHEME

The scheme recommended in the 1964 report was for a land-based sewage treatment works at Howdon, on the north bank of the Tyne adjacent to the old Northumberland Dock. Interceptor sewers would be constructed along either bank of the river to intercept more than 200 existing outfalls and convey the sewage to Howdon. Flows from the south bank of the river would be conveyed to Jarrow, where they would receive preliminary treatment before crossing under the river, via an inverted siphon, to the Howdon site. Sewage would initially receive only primary treatment at Howdon and the final effluent would be discharged into the estuary.

One exception would be the south-west part of the catchment, south of the river and west of the high ground at Gateshead. Because of the topography, the report recommended that this catchment area, with a future estimated population of approximately 300,000, should be separately drained to a new sewage treatment works at Dunston, where it would receive both primary and secondary (biological) treatment.

The sludge resulting from the treatment processes at both Howdon and Dunston would be taken out to sea by vessel for disposal in an approved dumping ground.

Because most of the existing sewerage system was combined, carrying both sewage and surface water drainage from roofs and roads, storm overflows would be provided at the points where the new sewers intercepted the existing outfalls, to make sure the new sewers were not overwhelmed by severe storm flows.

Finally, that part of the catchment which was too low to drain into the new interceptor sewers, essentially a narrow strip adjacent to each river bank, would continue to discharge directly into the river initially, and would be re-sewered and the flows pumped back to the interceptors over time, as redevelopment took place.

This land-based scheme was favoured over the alternative, a long sea outfall extending roughly east-northeast from under The Links at Whitley Bay, primarily for economic reasons.

THE PLANNING PROCESS AND PUBLIC INQUIRY

After establishment of the Tyneside Joint Sewerage Board, the scheme was worked up in more detail, and the board's proposals were submitted for approval to the Minister of Housing and Local Government in November 1968. In May 1969, the board applied to Tynemouth Corporation for planning approval for the Howdon Treatment Works. This application was subsequently 'called in' by the Minister because of the change of land use and an objection by Associated Lead Manufacturers (ALM), whose Hayhole Works was immediately adjacent to the proposed sewage treatment plant. Subsequently, ministerial inspectors held a public inquiry at Tynemouth during March, 1970, which was immediately followed by a technical investigation into the proposed works.

In March, 1971, the report of the public inquiry was released, accompanied by the refusal of planning permission for the works at Howdon. The key reasons were, firstly, that it was considered impossible to be certain that gases generated in the sewers or at the treatment works would not affect products manufactured at the Hayhole Lead Works (the concern was over the loss of reflectance in white lead pigments used in paint because of their potential reaction with hydrogen sulphide). Secondly, there was some doubt over the validity of the grounds for the board's decision to adopt a land-based treatment solution rather than a sea outfall

Between March and July 1971, discussions took place between technical officers of the ministry and the board which involved *inter alia* a re-examination of the relative economics of sea disposal and land-based treatment. These discussions culminated in the preparation and signing of a joint agreement and the issuing by the Secretary of State of a statement affirming that land-based treatment was the best technical solution.

Steps were then taken to address the other major outstanding problem, the potential effect of hydrogen sulphide on lead products. After meetings with ALM, it was agreed that the works at Howdon would be covered and any gases generated within would be processed (scrubbed) to ensure that the concentration of hydrogen sulphide was below ambient level or the concentration which would damage ALM's products. In return, ALM agreed not to object to a further planning application, which was approved. So Howdon became perhaps the first sewage treatment works with an air emission standard (2 parts per billion of hydrogen sulphide) as well as a standard for its liquid effluent.

At this point, the total estimated cost of the proposed Stage I works, including the proposed treatment works at Dunston, was some £46 million.

CONSTRUCTION OF THE INTERCEPTOR SEWER

Construction of the scheme proper began in 1973 (Fig. 9.2). The total length of sewers involved in the scheme as originally conceived was around 62km, with internal diameters ranging from 0.6m up to 3.0m. A substantial part of that length was both large diameter and deep, and constructed in tunnel, with the shallower and smaller diameter lengths consisting of concrete pipes laid in open trench. Tunnels were constructed of steel or concrete segments and lined with concrete or brick.

Tunnellers cut in places through layers of Tyneside's history. Along the Tyne river banks they faced difficulties not only from polluted urban and industrial wastes but also from naturally wet and weak alluvial deposits. They also risked breaking into long abandoned coal workings or strata weakened by subsidence. Sometimes they required special methods of ground stabilisation to allow construction to proceed.

At Neville Street in Newcastle, construction of an interceptor sewer shaft in water-bearing fine sand necessitated ground freezing using liquid nitrogen at a depth of ten to twelve metres. The excavation was carried out using explosives, and very slowly, as progress was handicapped by the presence of twin water mains close to the upper part of the shaft. There was also a severe lack of oxygen, and miners controlling the inlet valves during the sinking of the shaft had to wear breathing apparatus. After passing through this sand lens, further construction was delayed for three months to allow the strata to thaw sufficiently for normal working.

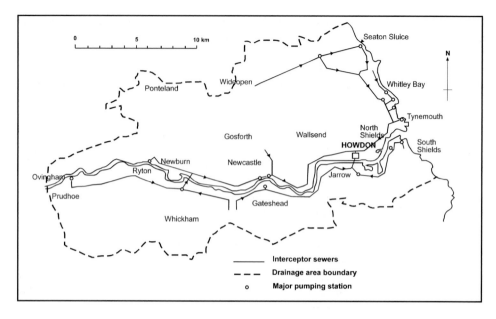

Fig 9.2 The area served by the Tyneside Sewerage Scheme

Elsewhere, notably in the sewer tunnel leading to the Don Valley Pumping Station, problems were caused by water-bearing silty sands, requiring construction in compressed air. Part of this tunnel drive passed through small buried valleys in the Jarrow area which had been filled in the past with chemical waste. This produced hydrogen sulphide within the compressed air tunnel drive, requiring additional ventilation and suitable protective equipment for the miners.

A short section of the North Bank Interceptor Sewer through Newcastle crosses a partially-filled valley above ground. The valley fill was largely loose granular material which was stabilised by vibrating probes to produce a series of columns of vibrated crushed stone at approximately 2 m spacing. The sewer was constructed as a reinforced concrete culvert sitting on top of these 'stone piles', and the valley was then filled to the level of the adjoining ground.

A new River Tyne crossing was constructed to carry sewage from the south bank, which received preliminary treatment at a works at Jarrow, across to the main treatment works at Howdon. The Tyne Siphon, not far from the Tyne Pedestrian and Vehicular Tunnels, consisted of vertical access shafts on each bank connected by a 3.2 m diameter dry tunnel in which were installed three one-metre diameter steel pipes to carry the sewage flow. Again, because of the difficult ground, much of the construction, including the tunnel drive, was carried out in compressed air, largely as a safety precaution against the breakthrough of water from fissures and gullies beneath the river bed, some of which were probably the result of long-completed mining subsidence.

It is interesting to note that, while construction of the sewers was under way during the 1970s, both the Tyne and Wear Metro and the Kielder Water Transfer

Works (Chapter 10) were also being built, making the North East something of a tunneling Mecca and putting considerable demand on specialist resources.

CONSTRUCTION OF THE HOWDON TREATMENT WORKS

The Howdon site itself (Plate 17) was also interesting from a geotechnical perspective. Construction of the North Bank preliminary treatment works and the large sedimentation tanks for both north and south bank flows necessitated the preparation of two major plateaus at different levels, which in turn required the excavation (up to 16 m deep) and removal of about 1 million m^3 of clay soils, mineral deposits and fill. The Howdon works was built on the site of a network of coal wagonways which formerly served Northumberland Dock and, during the initial excavation, an accumulation of some 16,000 tonnes of coal was salvaged and sold to the National Coal Board.

The major tank structures were all constructed from reinforced concrete, and backfilled with Pulverised Fuel Ash, a lightweight material then readily available as a by-product of coal-fired power stations.

Alongside the works itself, a jetty was constructed to allow berthing of the new vessel, *Northumbrian Water*, which would be used to take sewage sludge out to an approved sea dumping ground.

Construction of both sewers and treatment works continued through the 1970s. The preliminary treatment works at Jarrow, giving screening and grit removal to the south bank sewage, was commissioned in 1978, though sedimentation of the south bank flows did not begin at Howdon until 1980. In 1981, the north bank interceptor sewers from upstream of the Ouseburn branch to Whitley Bay were connected, and the scheme was officially declared open by the Duke of Edinburgh at an opening ceremony at Howdon on 6 November 1981. Towards the end of 1983, the north bank interceptor sewer from Denton to the Ouseburn was commissioned.

THE SOUTH WEST AREA

As indicated earlier, the topography of the south bank of the River Tyne to the west of Gateshead created a separate catchment area, to be dealt with independently of the main catchment draining to the North and South Bank interceptor sewers. This area contained major residential and industrial developments between West Gateshead, Whickham, Blaydon and Ryton, including the Team Valley Trading Estate and, since 1986, the MetroCentre.

The original intention, set out in the 1964 report, was to build a full sewage treatment works at Dunston. A feasibility study carried out in 1982/3, however, indicated that substantial savings could be realized by utilising spare capacity available in the North Bank Interceptor Sewer.

At the time of the feasibility study, the North Bank sewer had been constructed and commissioned as far as Denton Dene in the west end of Newcastle and was operating at about half its design capacity, having been designed to accept ultimate flows forecast for the year 2054. It was therefore likely that this capacity would suffice for at least 40 years before any alternatives might need to be examined.

In 1983 the decision was made to build a pumping station at Derwenthaugh, just south and east of Scotswood Bridge and not far from the originally-proposed sewage treatment works site. From here, sewage from the South West Area would be pumped through a little over one kilometre, and lifted some 25 m, to the North Bank Interceptor at Parmontley Street in West Denton. The route of the rising main went across Scotswood Bridge and fitted within the box girder construction beneath the bridge deck. The pumping station itself was built between autumn 1985 and spring 1987.

The interceptor sewers running east and west from this pumping station are of necessity close to the banks of the River Tyne, and the routes were carefully chosen in consultation with Gateshead MBC so as not to restrict future development and to provide sewerage facilities for what were then developing enterprise zones and Garden Festival sites. As the new sewers were so near the river, existing sewers were intercepted very close to their discharge points, so minimizing continuing discharges to the river.

The westward extension of the drainage area to Ryton was completed in 1991, but a further, previously unforeseen extension followed not long afterwards. The sewage treatment works at Prudhoe, rebuilt in the 1970s, was the cause of periodic complaint primarily because of odour problems from the sludge press house, and development of the Riverside Park had also opened up the river bank adjacent to the works as an amenity area. A study was undertaken to examine the possibility of pumping the sewage from Prudhoe to the head of the new interceptor sewer at Ryton, thence draining to Derwenthaugh Pumping Station and, ultimately, to the Howdon Sewage Treatment Works. The proposal was accepted, so now the Prudhoe catchment represents the most westerly fringe of the Tyneside Sewerage and Sewage Treatment Scheme (Fig. 9.2).

ENSURING WATER QUALITY AT NORTH TYNESIDE BATHING BEACHES

As part of the original Tyneside scheme, new sewers had been constructed up the coast to intercept sewage from the North Tyneside area and take it to Howdon. In line with the standards of the time, however, overflows for storm sewage were installed, which discharged via existing outfall pipes into the sea. These outfalls were very short; only two of the nine discharged below mean low water level.

Seawater quality standards were laid down in a European Community Directive (the 'bathing water directive') in 1976. This Directive laid down mandatory bacteriological and viral standards for designated bathing waters which must not be exceeded for 95% of the samples taken fortnightly during the bathing season. There was an exception allowed for samples taken following "...floods, other natural disasters or abnormal weather conditions", but the precise meaning of this phrase became the subject of widespread debate throughout the Community. In the UK, the requirement was interpreted to mean that there should be no storm discharges as a result of storms with a frequency of up to once in five years; for such events, all flows should be taken for treatment.

The discharges from existing storm sewage outfalls were thought to be the cause of occasional failure to comply with the directive's standards, while the very coarse screens fitted to the overflows meant that any discharge was particularly aesthetically distasteful.

Since the bathing water directive required full compliance by 1995, Northumbrian Water commissioned consultants to carry out a coastal strategy study for the entire Northumbrian coastline. Following this, a specific scheme was prepared for North Tyneside, encompassing the coastline between the mouth of the River Tyne and St Mary's Island, Whitley Bay.

The solution chosen was to construct a second interceptor sewer, providing storage for storm sewage flows, and a new long sea outfall. The new interceptor extends for 3.6km between North Point, Tynemouth and Brierdene. A pumping station at Brierdene lifts the sewage into the existing interceptor flowing to Howdon.

The new long sea outfall, fitted with fine screens, is over a kilometre in length and takes what limited storm overflow discharges still occur from the pumping station into deeper water further from the shore. The outfall is constructed from steel pipes with an external concrete coat, protected from external corrosion by coal-tar enamel reinforced with glass tissue wrap. The pipes were joined on land and pulled out to sea by a very large floating rig.

IMPACT ON THE RIVER

The most significant effect of the Tyneside Sewerage Scheme was an immediate reduction in gross visual pollution and smell. Over 200 sewers along the river immediately ceased discharging. Some small discharges from riverside properties continued discharging into the 1990s but now virtually all are picked up. For the observer on the river bank, the transformation was dramatic; the river had become an amenity rather than an eyesore. The way was opened for new development along the river corridor.

The state of the river was helped by the decline in industry and associated industrial discharges but there was one small but significant additional factor in the improvement. The freshwater river was still bringing down much floating debris in flood (the wrack of Chapter 5). This material tended to coalesce and move up and down the estuary with the rising and falling tide, accompanied by unsightly urban debris. A water surface 'hoover' craft, the Eager Beaver, was devised to skim this debris and it has removed several thousand tonnes of floating debris since it came into operation in 1989.

In spite of these improvements it had to be recognised that the typical throughput of a quarter of a million cubic metres per day through Howdon works was receiving only primary treatment. The only standards being enforced by Northumbrian Water on itself, and subsequently by the National Rivers Authority and the Environment Agency, were for suspended solids, where the limit was 150 mg/litre, and for some heavy metals. There were no standards for biochemical oxygen demand (BOD – Chapter 8) nor for ammonia such as were statutorily applied to sewage works discharging to freshwater rivers. The removal of huge quantities of solids from the raw sewage inevitably also reduced the BOD of the treated outflow discharge, but it still had a typical BOD of 170 mg/litre, more than half that of the untreated inflow.

Moreover this treated effluent was not, as had been anticipated, carried downstream and out to sea. Instead, because of the stratification of the estuary, between lower level salt water and surface fresh water, and differences in the way in which these layers moved in the estuary, part of the effluent gradually moved upstream with the salt water flow. The influence of Howdon effluent could be detected as far upstream as Newburn. Although there had been a rudimentary appreciation of estuary stratification and tidal movement from the 1960s, the extent of the problem only became appreciated after the hot dry summers of 1989 to 1991.

Whilst the riverside observer might be satisfied, the salmon and other river creatures were less impressed. Although salmon could pass safely through the estuary for longer periods of the year than previously, there were still occasions in hot summers with low freshwater flows when the fish succumbed to stress from low oxygen levels and from associated fungal infections.

It is likely that neither a public body funded by Government, nor a privatised Northumbrian Water, would have found the money for further treatment without the goad of the EC *Directive Concerning Urban Waste Water Treatment* of May 1991, which became a United Kingdom Regulation in November 1994. The directive specifies emission standards for sewage treatment serving populations greater than 2000, and seeks to protect the environment from the adverse effects of sewage discharges. These standards are based on the classification of the receiving waters, laid down by Government after advice from the Environment Agency.

The work at Howdon to meet the requirements of this directive are described below. The effluent standards for the new outfall imposed by the EA on Northumbrian Water require that the treatment process removes at least 70% of the incoming BOD. In practice, to ensure that the standards are met, the works actually removes an average of more than 90%. Such standards could hardly have been anticipated when the original works were proposed in 1964. Whilst the treated effluent from Tyneside is now as good as is ever likely to be needed, the organic muds of the river bed — short of dredging, which could create its own problems — will continue to exercise an influence for some decades more.

MEETING NEW STANDARDS
The implications for Howdon Sewage Treatment Works of the Urban Waste Water Directive were profound since the disposal of sewage sludge to sea had to cease by 31 December 1998 and secondary, or biological, sewage treatment had to be provided by 31 December 2000.

As part of an overall regional sludge strategy, a new plant was built at Bran Sands on the Tees Estuary which heat treats sewage sludge to produce pellets which can be used as a fuel. The sludge vessel, formerly used to take sludge out to the licensed dumping ground off the mouth of the Tyne, has been modified and can now carry sludge from Howdon to the Bran Sands Plant. In addition, equipment to allow sludge dewatering has been installed at Howdon, which allows a second disposal route to sanitary landfill. A lime dosing plant also permits chemical sterilisation of the sludge cake, offering a further disposal route to agricultural land.

A new secondary treatment works has also been built at Howdon on the eastern site (Plate 17). This uses activated sludge treatment of the effluent pumped from the primary sedimentation tanks on the western site, with fine-bubble diffused air aeration in large covered concrete tanks. Following final settlement in new circular sedimentation tanks, the final effluent returns to the existing outfall into the estuary. Construction of the new works was very rapid; site work began in August 1998 and the works was functioning as required by the end of 2000.

A by-product of the scheme was the enhancement of part of the eastern site designated as a Site of Nature Conservation Interest (SNCI) in the local structure plan with the creation of a new wetland. This also helped reduce costs, as spoil from the new construction site was used in creation of the wetland, rather than having to be removed from site.

It was expected that one of the benefits of secondary treatment would be an improvement in the bacteriological quality of nearby bathing beaches. The outcome easily matched this expectation. In 2001 all the officially designated bathing beaches in the area complied for the first time with the standards of the EC Bathing Water Directive and two thirds met it more stringent 'guideline values'. In 2002 disinfection of the effluent using ultraviolet light has been commissioned, and the beaches at Whitley Bay, Tynemouth and Whitburn have for the first time received the coveted Blue Flag award. Early results suggest that the effluent itself could be safe to swim in!

IMPACT ON THE RIVER CORRIDOR

In the early 1960s the stimulus of cooperation between local authorities for improvement of the river led to similar arrangements with respect to the riverside. An inter-authority committee was set up and carried out studies on the potential for environmental and recreational improvements. Some schemes like riverside parks at Felling and Hebburn were outcomes of such studies.

With the incorporation of the entire estuary into the Tyne and Wear Metropolitan County in 1974, there were prospects for better coordinated planning on the riverside. Though set up in 1975, the County Committee for Improvement of the Banks of the Tyne was disbanded in 1979, leaving the main planning framework in the County Structure Plan.

Although numerous local improvements were carried out, it was not until the Tyneside Interceptor Scheme was in place and visible improvements had occurred on the river, that public attitudes to the riverside changed and regeneration began to gain pace. Perhaps the pivotal event was the Tall Ships Race in 1986 when 70 sailing vessels lay at Newcastle Quay (Plate 18). Amid a carnival atmosphere, over one million people visited the quay. There was a sudden realisation that the riverside was a desirable place to work, live and play. The biggest transformation has been in the central bridges section. An early and visible indication of the change was the arrival in 1986 of the Tuxedo Royale which berthed on the Tyne as a night club. Its replacement, the Tuxedo Princess, is now one of many night clubs by the river. Planning for the Law

Courts and the Copthorne Hotel (both opened 1991) followed soon afterwards.

With the demise of the Tyne and Wear County and the return of district authorities, the Tyne and Wear Urban Development Corporation was established in 1988 by the Government for a ten year period with wide powers to regenerate derelict and contaminated land. TWDC was responsible of 1600 hectares along 30 km of the Tyne riverbank. It cleared and reclaimed over 500 hectares, spent £400 million and attracted private investment of over £1 billion. The effects on the riverside at the Eastern Quayside and the Royal Quays are particularly visible.

The momentum has continued with the Centre for Life, the Millennium Bridge, the Baltic Centre for Contemporary Art, and soon The Sage Music Centre and a Hilton Hotel in Gateshead. Tyneside has a renewed vibrancy and optimism as seen in its bid for European Capital of Culture in 2008. It is not too much to suppose that the cleaning up of the river played a germinal part in the new civic pride.

SOME REFLECTIONS ON THE TYNESIDE SEWERAGE AND SEWAGE DISPOSAL SCHEME

Looking back over more than thirty years of active development of the scheme, a few points stand out:

1. Although the main historic driver for the scheme was water quality — the absence of nuisance and the passage of migratory fish — its biggest impact has been economic and social as a consequence of the regeneration and redevelopment of the banks of the Tyne.

2. The initial scheme was an exercise of considerable political will, which involved many local authorities ceding power in this particular sphere to a new sub-regional joint board, one of very few such boards in the UK. This made possible a solution which was both technically elegant and economically sensible, and which was a forerunner of the increasing regionalisation of the water industry.

3. The impact of rising environmental standards, and in particular the role of the European Community in setting those standards, has been profound. The initial sewerage and sewage treatment scheme was directed towards achieving UK environmental standards which were regarded as entirely acceptable at the time, and with the acknowledgement that some improvements, particularly the interception of discharges from the 'riverside strip', were likely to take a very long time to achieve. The advent of European Directives, especially the Bathing Water and Urban Waste Water Treatment Directives, and their adoption into UK regulations, generated the need for massive additional investment over relatively short timescales with a significant impact on charges to customers. When the original part of the scheme was being constructed during the 1970s, no-one involved imagined they would see the provision

of secondary treatment, let alone disinfection, in their lifetime. Nor was sea disposal of sewage sludge, subject to proper quality checks, seen as anything other than an acceptable environmental option. Equally, they would probably not argue now about most of what has happened, such has been the change in environmental perceptions, although the enormous additional cost incurred, for example, to avoid the occasional sewage overflow to sea in very bad weather, might still raise the odd eyebrow.

4. It is interesting to consider what might have happened had the water industry in England and Wales not been privatised in 1989. Prior to this, there had been a very large squeeze on public investment through the late 1970s and 1980s, as such investment was treated as current expenditure within the Public Sector Borrowing Requirement (PSBR). Privatisation removed water company borrowing from the Treasury's grip but also enabled government to distance itself from the expenditure implications of new European standards and claim that these were a matter for the utility companies, their customers and the appropriate regulators, while the cost burden of rising standards fell fairly directly on those customers. Instead, a new battle developed between environmental standards setters, especially the European Commission, and economic regulators, in the form of the Office of Water Service (OFWAT), whose principal concern was to keep customer prices as low as possible. By and large, the environmentalists won, as the most recent episode of the Tyne estuary story shows.

ACKNOWLEDGEMENTS

The author wishes to thank the Chairman of Ondeo Services, Sir Frederick Holliday, and staff of Northumbrian Water Ltd for their assistance, especially Bill Williamson, Project Manager for the Howdon Secondary Treatment Works.

REFERENCES

1. Johnson R.W. (1895) *The making of the Tyne: a record of fifty years of progress.* Newcastle upon Tyne
2. Sir George W. Humphreys, and Messrs J. D. & D. M. Watson (1936) Report on sewerage and sewage disposal of Newcastle upon Tyne and the Tyneside
3. Bradshaw, D.T. (1964) Technical sub-committee on Tyneside Sewage Disposal, Final report on proposals for reducing pollution of the River Tyne estuary and adjacent sea beaches.
4. Messrs J. D. & D. M. Watson (1964) Final report on investigations of sea outfalls
Bradshaw, D.T. (1972) Go-ahead given for £46 million Tyneside Scheme. *The Surveyor.*
Norgrove, W.B. & Staples, K.D. (1975) The Tyneside Sewerage Scheme. *Proc. Inst. Civil Engineers.*
Frith, S.J. & Staples, K.D. (1995) North Tyneside Bathing Waters Scheme. *Journal Inst. Water & Environment Manage.,* 9(1), 55–63.

10. KIELDER WATER: WHITE ELEPHANT OR WHITE KNIGHT?

INTRODUCTION

The Kielder Scheme has undoubtedly had the greatest impact of any scheme on the landscape of the North Tyne, on the flow regime of the river downstream to the estuary, and on aspects of ecology and fisheries. It is possibly the most ambitious water resources project and certainly one of the most costly ever undertaken in the United Kingdom. It has two main components:

○ Kielder Water on the River North Tyne is Britain's largest man-made lake, with a capacity of nearly 200 million cubic metres, and covers an area of more than 10 square kilometres (Plate 19). The dam is 52 metres high and 1140 metres long (Plate 20).
○ A pumping station on the River Tyne at Riding Mill lifts water by a rising main to a small head pond at Airy Holme, from which the water is conveyed via a 34-kilometre tunnel, 2.9 metres in diameter, to outlets on the Rivers Derwent, Wear and Tees.

And yet, when the Queen drove to Kielder Water for the official opening of Kielder Dam on 26 April 1982, she was greeted by a large hoarding alongside the approach road which proclaimed "Kielder Water, White Elephant of the North". By the time the dam and the associated transfer works had been completed, it was widely believed that its construction had been midguided[1] and that it was unlikely that the water would be used in the foreseeable future. Criticism has persisted through the following two decades and the perceived failure of the elaborate planning process at Kielder has been used by environmental campaigners as a rod to strike at other proposed major water resources projects in the country. Some of the criticism has been fully justified, but Pearce's snide description in 1991[2] of Kielder as "Europe's biggest boating lake" has not been helpful; his assertion that "neither the reservoir nor the expensive tunnel and pipes built to take its water to the cities of the lower Tyne and Tees have ever supplied customers" was mistaken. It has been used, but not on the scale envisaged by its planners.

The Kielder Scheme was conceived during a period of unprecedented economic and industrial growth in the 1960s and it was assumed that the rate of growth would continue more or less unabated to the forecast horizon of 2001[3], by which time the added water resource provided by Kielder would be fully utilised[4]. If the forecasts had been fulfilled, the Northeast would already have had to endure further public debate on where the next supply source would be, Kielder Water would have nearly emptied in the dry summer of 1995, and the River Tyne flow would be dominated each summer by releases to match abstractions on the Tyne, Wear and Tees. The reality is that the demand for water has changed little since the Public Inquiries of 1972 and 1973; Kielder Water stays within a few metres of its top water level and the flow regime in the upper North Tyne is largely controlled by releases for hydropower.

Thirty years on from the Government's approval of the Scheme in 1973, seems an appropriate time to reconsider the role and impact of Kielder. To what extent have the promoter's claims and forecasts been fulfilled or fallen short? What major issues concerning the impact of the reservoir have come to light, which were not considered at the time?

KIELDER: THE HISTORICAL SETTING

The Kielder Scheme may be considered the last in a long line of water resources developments that have taken water from the Tyne and its tributaries. It differs from its predecessors not only in scale but, more significantly, in its ability to supply water not just to Tyneside but to the whole of northeast England. Such a regional scheme could not have been contemplated without the legal framework set up by the Water Resources Act of 1963 and the establishment of Northumbrian River Authority (effectively in 1965), which had a statutory duty to survey its regional water resources, estimate future demands, and formulate proposals to meet those demands. Previous reservoirs and water resources schemes had been built by individual companies and local authorities to meet the needs of householders and industry within their own supply area, or for sale in bulk to neighbouring agencies. A study of the River Tyne would be incomplete without reference to historical water supply to settlements in the Tyne catchment. Rennison[5] has made a thorough analysis of water supply to Newcastle and Gateshead, but within the Tyne catchment, in the late nineteenth and early twentieth centuries, there was a mosaic of private and public organisations which deserve further study.

Although riverside settlements have access to the river as a source of water, there has traditionally been a preference for the perceived purity of water from springs and wells, which also have the advantage that water can more readily be distributed by gravity. River water needs to be lifted to a holding tank or reservoir before distribution. Early supply to Newcastle appears to have been a mixture of river and spring sources.

The first record of pumped water from the Tyne is in 1680, when Cuthbert Dykes erected an 'engine' to pump water from the Tyne at Sandgate to Newcastle. Gateshead, on the other hand, was blessed with natural springs, and soon parts of Newcastle were to be supplied from the same sources via pipes laid over the Tyne Bridge. But even as late as 1755, only 161 individual properties in Gateshead and Newcastle had piped water; everyone else relied on irregularly-supplied public pants, albeit free of charge.

In 1797 the Newcastle Fire Office, an insurance company, took over the existing supplies to Newcastle and were able to offer a better supply by adding water pumped from coal workings at Coxlodge, but only on two days a week. A dry summer in 1831, combined with damage to the well at Coxlodge, forced

the Fire Office to distribute Tyne water in carts; if the arrival of a cholera
epidemic later in the year was coincidental, many believed that a connection
existed between the use of river water and the spread of the disease. A new and
rival supplier, the Newcastle Subscription Water Company, promised the
citizens of Newcastle 'an abundant supply of good wholesome water', for
although this company would still rely on river water, it would be filtered before
being pumped from Elswick to a reservoir at Arthur's Hill. By 1836, the new
company was supplying double the output of the Fire Office, and the two
concerns were amalgamated in that year.

Growth in demand for good quality water continued and in 1845 another
new concern, the Whittle Dean Water Company was formed, with the intention
of ridding the citizens of Gateshead and Newcastle of dependence on Tyne water.
However, they overestimated the amount of water available from their new
reservoirs at Whittle Dean (Fig. 10.1) and underestimated the demand, with the
result that in the dry summer of 1853 they reverted to river abstraction at

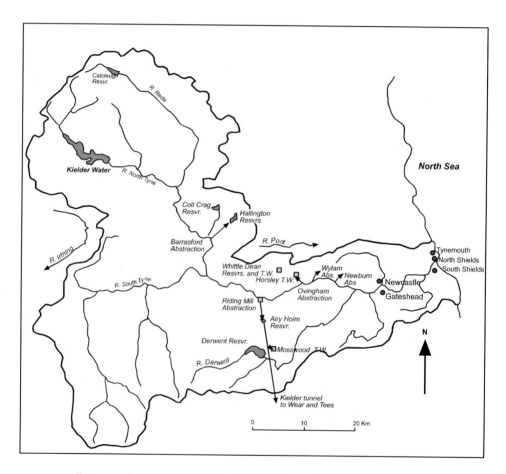

Fig 10.1 Water resources and water supply in the Tyne catchment

Elswick. The consequent epidemic is described in Chapter 8. The following year the water intake on the Tyne was moved upstream to Newburn, and the yield of the Whittle Dean system was extended through an aqueduct from the upper Pont and streams in the Ryal area. In 1863 the company was renamed the Newcastle and Gateshead Water Company (N&G) and over the next half century further source reservoirs, all in the Tyne catchment, were constructed at East Hallington (1871), Little Swinburn (1880), Colt Crag (1884) and West Hallington (1889). In 1905 the major scheme until that date at Catcleugh on the upper Rede nearly doubled the water available. Water was (and is) brought from all of these sources by pipeline and aqueduct to Whittle Dean for treatment before onward transmission to Tyneside.

Abstraction of water directly from the River Tyne continued to form part of the Company's strategy, but at points further upriver to avoid the progressively declining quality of the river. A new intake was established at Wylam in 1874 and the intake at Newburn abandoned in 1885. Later still, in 1940, a pumping station was built at Barrasford on the North Tyne and in 1977 at Ovingham (to replace the Wylam offtake). Since pumping involved greater costs than gravity supplies, these sources had their greatest use in dry summers.

The coastal towns of Tynemouth and North Shields depended initially on underground sources including minewater from within their own boundaries, but after 1870, with the growth in demand, the North Shields Water Company (founded 1786) and Tynemouth Corporation were obliged to purchase bulk supplies from N&G Water Company. The rivalry between coastal towns and Newcastle, which had characterised the navigational use of the river (Chapter 12) for several centuries, was again reflected in their competing demands for water supply and seems to have aroused strong feelings[6]. The coastal towns were denied their own supplies from the River Tyne but could not depend on delivery of the bulk supply from the N&G Water Company during drought, when the Company considered itself duty-bound to supply its own customers first. In 1898 Tynemouth Corporation absorbed the North Shields Company and sought an independent supply, which they secured in the Wansbeck catchment with the construction of Font Reservoir, completed in 1907. It is interesting to note that major enhancements of resources for both Newcastle and Tynemouth, which were to prove adequate for several decades, were secured within a period of two years when a regional approach might have suggested a more staged development.

South Shields, as well as neighbouring Hebburn and Jarrow on the other side of the Tyne, received water from boreholes in the Magnesian Limestone through the Sunderland and South Shields (S&SS) Water Company. These groundwater sources have medieval and Roman ancestry, and a third century stone inscription records the installation of a new water supply to the Roman camp at The Lawe, South Shields[7] (Fig. 10.2). Magnesian Limestone sources were much more reliable than those to the north of the river and there are even records of requests and deputations from Tynemouth and Gateshead around 1870 for water to be supplied to these boroughs. The company declined their requests.

The contrasting chemical quality of the water supplies either side of the river mouth was discovered to be reflected in the comparative dental health of school

Fig 10.2 Inscribed Roman stone from The Laws, South Shields inaugurating the Roman water supply. The inscription reads "The Emperor Caesar Marcus Aurelius Severus (Alexander) pious, august high priest, with tribunal power, father of his country, consul, grandson of the deified Antoninus the Great, led water into the camp for the use of the fifth cohort of Gauls under the direction of Marius Valerianus his legate, propraetor". *(Photo: by permission Tyne and Wear Museums)*

children; the fact that those on the south side enjoyed better teeth was found to be related to the occurrence of a small concentration of natural fluorine salts in the groundwater[8]. On the basis of this experience and at the request of the health authorities, most major treated supplies in the Tyne catchment now receive added fluoride, where it does not occur naturally.

Groundwater remained adequate for Sunderland and South Shields until the mid-1930s when the intrusion of seawater began to affect some boreholes. In seeking to augment their supplies the S&SS Water Company joined with Durham County Water Board to construct Burnhope Reservoir (completed in 1937) in the upper Wear catchment. These two organisations joined forces again in the 1960s to promote the construction of Derwent Reservoir and Mosswood Treatment Works which were completed in 1967. Until Kielder Water, Derwent Reservoir was by far the largest reservoir constructed in the Tyne catchment. Like all its predecessors it was a direct supply reservoir; water was taken directly from the reservoir to the Mosswood Treatment Works, and from there by pipeline to the companys' customers on the coast and in mid-Durham. The reservoir thus deprived the river of the abstracted water for the full reach downstream from the dam to the estuary, as described in more detail in Chapter 1.

Regional management of water resources from the Tweed to the Tees was initiated with the passing of the Water Act (1973), which set up Northumbrian Water Authority (NWA) from April 1974. In replacing Northumbrian River Authority (NRA) and its responsibilities for water resources, the new Authority received the baton (and the future embarrassment) of Kielder development. Whilst NWA also took responsibility for water supply from all local authorities within the area, the two large statutory water supply companies (N&G and S&SS) remained in place.

To bring the story up to date, the service sectors of water supply and sewage disposal were privatised in 1989 under Northumbrian Water (NW), whilst environmental regulation became the role of the National Rivers Authority, whose name changed to the Environment Agency in 1996 when it was given a broader role in waste regulation to land and air as well as to rivers. The statutory water companies merged as North East Water in 1992 when they were taken over by the international giant Lyonnaise des Eaux. The French company further acquired Northumbrian Water in 1995 and under its local name now has responsibility for water supply for the whole of the Northeast, with the exception of the Hartlepool enclave. Anglian Water took over the Hartlepool Water Company in 1997.

To make the privatisation of NW more palatable, the Conservative government wrote off the remaining debt for the Kielder Scheme. The dam and associated works as well as the tunnel from Tyne to Tees are thus owned by NW, who are operators of the Scheme and make releases from Kielder Water to the North Tyne. However, the Environment Agency effectively has control over the water in the reservoir and is responsible for policing the operating policy for releases, taking into account the requirements for abstractions, statutory minimum flows, flood control, ecology, fisheries, recreation and hydropower. The difficulties in striking a balance between these conflicting requirements are discussed below.

THE BEGINNING OF THE KIELDER IDEA

Water resources planning in the 1960s was imaginative and large scale. Planners saw the growth of industry and the associated demand for water, both for manufacturing and for more prosperous households, as continuing in the foreseeable future. Planning for growth was not just a Northumbrian phenomenon. It was fostered by the government and by the national Water Resources Board (WRB), which had been set up alongside the river authorities in 1963. By 1965 the WRB was already looking at the feasibility of massive barrages across the Solway Firth and Morecambe Bay to supply the growing needs of the north. It was the era of the 'white heat of technology'. As Brady[4] states in 1984, "The mood of the time needs to be fully understood. The conviction in the late 1960s that further major industrial expansion was in hand was just as strong as the present day conviction, that consumption will not rise appreciably in the North East during the next 20 years". The succession of reservoirs in the Tees valley had barely kept pace with the demands of the chemical and steel industry; Selset reservoir was completed in 1960, Balderhead in 1965, and Cow Green then under construction was completed in 1971. Without a major new source, there would be a shortfall on Teesside by 1976 (in spite of Cow Green), on Tyneside by 1973, and in Durham and Wearside by 1979. Based on extrapolation of the 1960s demand for water, there would be a regional deficit of over a million cubic metres a day by 2001[9]. The expected growth more than doubled the total usage of 1971.

Hence, when the Northumbrian River Authority set up shop in 1965, it applied itself urgently to assessing the magnitude and timing of deficiencies and what sources of supply could be used to meet the deficiency. It considered but discounted underground sources and desalination as insufficient or too costly. The NRA came to the conclusion by 1968 that there was no real alternative to surface storage in conjunction with a north-south aqueduct. The new storage would have to be a river regulating reservoir rather than a direct supply type to achieve the necessary yield and flexibility of supply.

The NRA investigated 28 potential dam sites from the River Coquet to the River Tees in terms of how much water each would yield, their total cost, and the cost per volume stored[10]. A site at Otterstone on the North Tyne came out on top in terms of water yield and the only one sufficient to meet the forecast need until the end of the century. A site on the River Irthing was the only one to offer lower storage costs but with only a third of the Otterstone yield. All the other sites gave smaller yield or double the cost of volume stored. The Irthing site, if selected, would need to be followed sharply by four other reservoirs; to meet the forecast demand and match the yield of Otterstone, the overall capital cost of a scheme based on Irthing would be over 50% greater than at Otterstone. Although a reservoir at Irthing would flood land of little agricultural value and no houses, the follow-on reservoirs would together cause much more environmental disruption and displacement of homes.

Until 1970 the proposed reservoir on the North Tyne was referred to as Otterstone Reservoir. By mid-1971 the name appearing in documents had changed to Kielder Water, although the village of Kielder is some ten kilometres from the dam site and is not even on the shores of the completed reservoir. However, it had already given its name to the Kielder Forest. It would appear that the new name was selected and enthusiastically promoted by the Chief Engineer for the River Authority, Urban Burston, in preference to Otterstone or the more flamboyant suggestion 'Dragon Lake' by the landscape architect for the Scheme, Sir Frederick Gibberd, with reference to the shape of the lake on the map.

THE PUBLIC INQUIRIES

Northumbrian River Authority made a formal application to the Secretary of State for the Environment for an Order (the Kielder Water Order) to authorise the Kielder Scheme in June 1971. In all, there were 188 objections to the Scheme and licences associated with the dam and the aqueduct. As a focus for objections, the North Tyne Valley Preservation Society was set up, with its President the former MP for Hexham from 1951 to 1966, Sir Rupert Speir. The main concerns were:

- Adverse effect on social structures of the North Tyne with 180 people displaced, largely from houses owned by the Forestry Commission
- Loss of agricultural land and young forestry plantations in the reservoir basin
- Potential change from a peaceful valley 'far from rush and bustle' to one with commercialised recreation and the noise of the motor car
- Adverse effect on the ecology and fishery of the North Tyne and Tyne
- The contention that alternative means of meeting the demands were available.

The Inspectors (and the promoters) acknowledged the disruption that the dam would cause to the community and to the ecology of the North Tyne valley. However, from 1969 to the completion of the second Kielder Inquiry in 1973, the main debate concerned the desirability of proceeding with a single large reservoir or with a staged development incorporating the Irthing site, which might ultimately cost more but would allow flexibility if the demand for water did not progress as rapidly as the NRA had forecast. Either choice involved risks, and costs and had to be based on predictions of an uncertain future. In hindsight the wrong choice was made; if Irthing had been built, no further reservoirs would have been needed.

The government decision took three years in the following stages:

Dec 1971	The Secretary of State gave notice that a Public Inquiry should be held.
Feb-Mar 1972	The first Public Inquiry was held
July 1972	The Inspector's report in favour of going ahead with the Scheme was submitted to the Secretary of State.
Dec 1972	The Secretary of State (the local MP Mr Geoffrey Rippon) informed the Authority that he needed further information before coming to a decision. He agreed with the need to augment water resources, but his remaining reservations were centred on whether staged development commencing with Irthing might yet prove preferable to Kielder.
June 1973	The Public Inquiry was reopened with a reduced brief.
Sep 1973	The Inspector submitted his report in favour of the Scheme.
Oct 1973	The Secretary of State decided in favour of Kielder but with certain modifications and conditions.
May 1974	The Kielder Order came into force allowing work to commence on the Scheme

After thirty years, we can review with unhindered hindsight to what extent the claims and forecasts of the Scheme's promoters have been fulfilled.

THE DEMAND FOR WATER

Water demand can be considered in two main categories: domestic consumption which is largely unmetered and industrial consumption, which is metered to individual establishments.

For the Public Inquiries the forecasts of the domestic consumption were based on combined trends in population growth and per capita consumption (Fig. 10.3). Up to 1981 a comparatively modest 10-year growth of 61 million litres per day (Mld) (18%) was forecast and the trend was continued to the end of the century. Given the inherent uncertainties, the forecast in growth of domestic

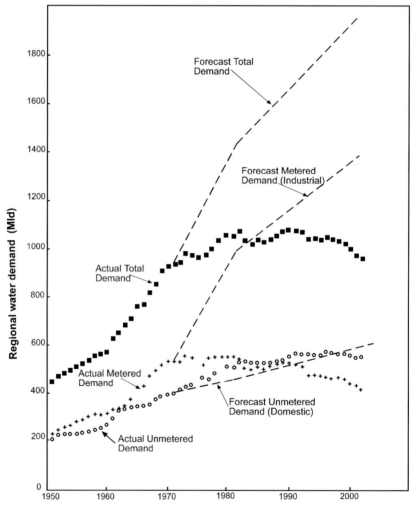

Fig 10.3 Comparison of the actual growth in regional demand for water with the forecast at the Kielder Public Inquiries 1972 and 1973

water demand can be considered a success. Actual domestic demand exceeded the forecast levels for the first part of the period and stood 11% above in 1981 but has subsequently remained steady, and in 2001 stood 9% below the forecast.

Industrial demand is much more difficult to forecast; it is sensitive to both local factors and to the more elusive state of national and global economies. Regional industrial demand was projected to grow at a base rate which maintained the relationship between domestic and industrial consumption, with additions for known expansion proposals and a further 10% for unforeseen expansion. This resulted in a projected growth of 87% in the decade to 1981, with an easing off to 20% in the following decades.

With respect to industrial demand, Northumbrian River Authority was entirely at the mercy of the industrialists and development planners, who made confident predictions about developments particularly on Teesside; these would provide thousands of new jobs and bring in investment that would put the Kielder investment in the shade. The evidence of Marshall for the British Steel Corporation (BSC) to the Second Inquiry was particularly telling:

> Teesside will have in the 1980s one of the largest and most modern steel complexes in Europe. The new works at Redcar will produce a further 7 million tonnes of steel and provide about 7500 new jobs. The cost of these works will total about £1 billion [compared with about £30 million for Kielder at 1973 prices]. It is no overstatement to say that this development is of critical importance to the Northeast as well as the Corporation. The plain fact is that without an assured supply of fresh water the projects cannot go ahead as planned, and if the Steel Corporation remains uncertain - as it is now - how much additional water is likely to be available in any year after 1977, there is a plain prospect that some or many developments will have to be postponed. The need for certainty of augmentation is urgent and is critical to the Redcar project.... The uncertainties in timing and quantity inherent in sequential schemes appear to spell disaster to our programme, grave disruption to our Teesside project, and social and economic consequences whose effects must be felt far beyond the northern region.

Such flamboyant optimism was cheap — for BSC did not have to put a penny towards the Kielder Scheme — but convincing. Without a basis for refuting these claims, how could the River Authority resist such arguments when thousands of jobs were at risk and the industrial prosperity of the region was at stake? Opinions on other industrial growth locations, such as Seal Sands, the oil industry in Teesside, and the Cambois Industrial Development Area in Northumberland, were affected by this same mood of optimism and significant future demands were included for each.

Even objectors to the Kielder Scheme, with a single exception, accepted the demand projections in principle. Thus Sir Rupert Speir's evidence concedes, "At no time have the Society or I questioned the need for increased water supplies to be made available for the Northeast". The exception was a young civil engineering lecturer at the University of Newcastle, Colin Marsh, who represented Tyneside Environmental Concern. In line with Alvin Toffler's recent book – *Future Shock*[11], he submitted that the rapid growth rates of the 1960s were unsustainable and would soon run into the buffers of environmental or resource constraints. Unfortunately, his evidence was considered inadmissible by the Inspector under the terms of reference of the Inquiry. Some time afterwards Colin Marsh left the engineering profession to pursue his prophetic vision in the Church.

However, it was only a couple of years before such views were more widely echoed in the water industry. In his presidential address to the Institution of Water Engineers and Scientists in 1975[12], C.A. Serpell, who was General Manager of the Sunderland and South Shields Water Company quoted Sir Eric Ashby[13] :

> "So the growth, which we have come to expect as normal, cannot go on for ever. Unless we end it in a deliberate and controlled manner, it will simply be halted by a confrontation with environmental limits."

Even then it was probably not too late to reconsider the decision, but the juggernaut had been set in motion, too much effort had been put into design and the planning process, too many reputations were at stake, and too many people still believed (as even today) that growth was desirable, inevitable and unstoppable.

The reality of demand for water has been rather different from the forecast (Fig. 10.3). It is ironic that industrial demand reached its peak in 1973, the year of the second Public Inquiry. The projected expansion of industry did not materialise, and demand has declined with the closure of industries and more efficient use of water. In 2001 the actual demand stood at 550 Mld which is only 40% of the forecast level.

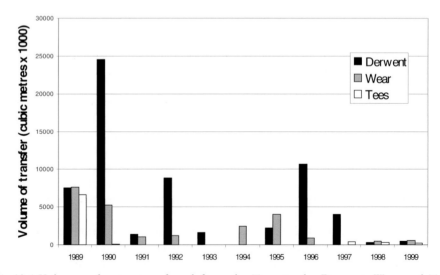

Fig 10.4 Volumes of water transferred from the Tyne to the Derwent, Wear and Tees

HOW MUCH WATER CAN KIELDER PROVIDE?

The extent to which Kielder or an alternative reservoir can meet the forecast demand, depends on a quantity referred to as 'reservoir yield', which has been defined as:

> The uniform rate at which water can be drawn from the reservoir throughout a dry period of specified severity without depleting the contents to such an extent that withdrawal at that site is no longer feasible

To the reader this may sound somewhat technical and indeed it has attracted the interest of statisticians concerned with risk and probability. However, it means that in order to provide an 'ample' supply of water to customers - as required by law - the supplier must design the system, not for the average year, but for a drought year (the dry period of specified severity). The dry period is typically a drought which will happen on average once in fifty years or may be based on an observed drought. In the case of Kielder, it was based on the drought of 1959, which was by far the most severe in the immediate period preceding the Inquiries. Hence, when it was stated at the Public Inquiries that demands would overtake present resources in, say 1976, the implication was not that the system would fail in 1976, but would fail only if a drought occurred in that year which was worse than the one for which the system was designed. To some this may seem to be over-egging the case for a new resource, but it is indeed the standard approach. The last three decades have brought an even greater emphasis on reliability and the necessity of avoiding restrictions in supply to customers which would occur if the design yield were exceeded by demand.

The yield of Kielder quoted in the Public Inquiries was 900 million litres per day. This figure should not be viewed as fixed for all time. The value depends on a wide range of assumptions including the choice of design drought. Since the yield calculation was carried out, there have been several prolonged and severe droughts in the Northeast — in the early 1970s culminating in 1976 and the recent extremes from 1989 to 1992 and again in 1995 - which are likely to be more critical for design than 1959. Other significant assumptions are the choice of compensation releases from the reservoir and the flows to be maintained in the lower reaches of the river, as well as the way in which the system as a whole is operated. If alternative assumptions had been chosen, the calculated yield might have been considerably higher or lower — both for Kielder and for the alternative sources.

One significant example is the effect of the choice of prescribed flows on the lower reaches of the Tyne, Wear and Tees selected to safeguard downstream river interests. Reservoir yield calculations for the Inquiries were based on two conditions:

1. A Minimum Maintained Flow (MMF), which is the flow value that would have to be maintained downstream from abstraction points whether or not releases are being made. In the case of the River Tyne this was 10% of the average daily flow (4.21 cumecs).

2. A 'Hands-Off Flow' (HOF), which is a value below which abstractions could not be made. That is, whilst abstractions were occurring, releases would have to be made to ensure that the flow stayed above that figure. In the case of the River Tyne this was 25% of the average daily flow (10.5 cumecs).

These conditions were seen by both the promoters and the objectors as an environmental benefit. The application of both conditions results in a much greater volume of release and transfers, than a 10% MMF condition only. For the design drought the HOF condition would result in 15–20% more water released from Kielder, and tunnel transfers at least four times greater than under MMF conditions only[4]. However, in giving his approval to the Kielder Scheme in 1973, the Secretary of State removed the necessity for a Hands-Off Flow, and at a stroke increased the potential yield of Kielder by an estimated 20% (180 Mld).

At this point there was no further opportunity to discuss the implication of the removal of the HOF condition on the choice of scheme. The judgment would have similarly increased the yield of smaller sources proposed by objectors and, had the option of reduced river support been fully and unambiguously discussed at the Public Inquiry, the principal alternative site of Irthing might well have proven more attractive. The objectors were lulled into seeing only the benefits of enhanced river flows downstream but did not see how assumptions of downstream conditions interacted with calculated yield or the choice of scheme.

Many of the issues concerning demand forecasting and assessment of yield are technically complex. If objectors to any proposed major scheme are to have any real chance of countering the arguments of the developer, they must have at their disposal technical expertise equal to or better than the developer.

HAS KIELDER BEEN USED?

From the outset, flexibility was recognized as a principal virtue of the Kielder Scheme; flexibility has proved to be a necessary virtue. At the Public Inquiry it was projected that 58% of new demand to 2001 would arise in the Tees, 20% in the Wear (including Derwent) and 22% in the Tyne area. The usage of the Scheme in support of water resources has been widely different from that envisaged at design. There are three basic categories of use:

1. Releases to support abstractions and prescribed flow conditions on the River Tyne
2. Transfers through the Kielder tunnel to Derwent, Wear and Tees
3. The use of cheaper local resources to a greater extent, on the understanding that Kielder is available as a back-up.

On the River Tyne, releases in support of abstractions and the statutory minimum flow have been made nearly every year, and in each of the drought years of 1989 and 1990 releases were made for periods of more than four months.

With respect to transfers through the tunnel, Fig. 10.4 illustrates the scale and the direction of Kielder support. Although it was the Teesside area which had by far the greatest forecast growth, the magnitude of transfers to the River Tees has been comparatively small. This was so even during the drought of 1989 when Selset Reservoir was emptied for remedial work and 17% of the Tees resource was unavailable.

In contrast, transfers to the Wear area have been much greater than anticipated, but the largest proportion has been to the Derwent catchment by means of a connection from the Kielder tunnel to Mosswood Treatment Works — as a substitute for the very depleted stocks in Derwent Reservoir. The amount transferred in 1990 was equivalent to half the capacity of the reservoir. This large unforeseen transfer to Derwent was primarily due to very low inflow into Derwent Reservoir in a drought much more severe than the design drought. However, the magnitude of the transfer had also been affected by a change in strategy for supplying mid-Durham and the coast, which resulted in more water than originally envisaged being taken from the Derwent system and less from alternative sources.

Probably the most critical condition occurred during the 1989 drought in the Bishop Auckland area, where the normal supply from Tunstall Reservoir would have been completely exhausted had it not been for another unforeseen use of the Kielder tunnel. As an emergency measure a submersible pump was dropped into a tunnel airshaft from its outlet on the moorland, and used to top up Tunstall Reservoir.

The benefits of a strategic resource are not only from transfer volumes but also from the ability to use local resources to a fuller extent and without restrictions, in the knowledge that support will be available if required. This may be illustrated by comparing response to the drought in 1976 with that of 1989. In the Wear area a sequence of drought measures in 1976 was initiated when Derwent Reservoir was 43% full, starting with a hosepipe ban and followed by reduction in compensation water discharges.. Since the construction of the Kielder Scheme no drought restrictions have been applied even though Derwent fell to 22% full in 1989.

Kielder-supported abstractions from the River Tyne have similarly permitted the extended use of local resources in Northumberland. Parts of southeast and mid-Northumberland are normally supplied from Font Reservoir, with dry weather support from Warkworth Treatment Works on the River Coquet. In the recent droughts Tyne supplies extended to areas, and by means, not anticipated in the Kielder proposals. Providing the main support in mid-Northumberland from the Tyne rather than the Coquet has enabled the supply from Warkworth Treatment Works to be reserved for meeting demand further north. So, by substitution, the benefits of the Kielder scheme have been felt as far north as Alnwick.

WHO IS PAYING FOR KIELDER?

The total cost of the Kielder Scheme, including dam and tunnel was £167 million. Part of this was paid for in grants (£62 million) from the European Regional Development Fund and the British Government under the local Employment

Act. The remaining £105 million was paid in loans on which interest and capital repayment was made during the 1980s.

In the run-up to privatisation in 1989, arrangements had to be made for ownership and responsibility for major water resources assets. This was done under Section 126 of the Water Resources Act 1989 and negotiations on an Operating Agreement were made on the Kielder Scheme between officers who were remaining with the privatised Northumbrian Water and those who were transferring to the regulator, the National Rivers Authority. The Operating Agreement was basically to enable the NRA to ensure the proper management of the Kielder Scheme by NW.

The Agreement was drafted for NRA to pay NW an annual sum equivalent to 7% of the outstanding debt of £105 million (£7.35 million in 1989), uprated annually by the Retail Price Index, in perpetuity. What the NRA were not told (until 1994) was that the debt for Kielder had been paid off by the Government at privatisation. There was no longer a debt. Operating agreements elsewhere in the country had been made on the basis of 2% of the asset value of resources including reservoirs. A similar arrangement for Kielder would have resulted in a charge of £2.1 million rather than £7.35. NW, with the help of the Government, had arranged an exceptionally good deal.

The National Rivers Authority, whilst in ignorance of the debt cancellation, were dissatisfied with other aspects of the Agreement and did not sign it. However, being placed in a position of weakness under privatisation, and intending to renegotiate later, NRA made the first annual payment to NW. By complying with the terms of the Agreement, they were legally regarded as having accepted it and had no further basis for a legal challenge.

It must be said that the £7.35 million (which by 2001 had grown to £11.5 million annually) is not a simple gift to NW. The NRA and, since 1995, the Environment Agency, have to recover the amount paid out in setting its license charges for abstractions. The largest abstractor is Northumbrian Water and it pays back the bulk of the charge. However, other abstractors in the Northeast were also foisted with exceptionally high unit charges — the highest in the country and more than twice those of neighbouring Yorkshire. Until 1995 this included North East Water which was thus placed at a competitive disadvantage. The merger of North East Water with Northumbrian Water has eliminated this inequity.

The answer to the question of who has paid/is paying for Kielder is thus not a simple one. Officially the debt has already been written off by the Government. Northumbrian Water is definitely not paying and at the very least, on the basis of clever negotiation, is receiving an annual sum which provides a cushion against the vagaries of the water business. Other private abstractors are paying a high surrogate charge which results from the Operating Agreement negotiated on the basis of Kielder debt repayment. The arrangement demonstrates some arcane aspects of corporate and government financing.

RELEASES FROM KIELDER

The impact of releases from Kielder to the River North Tyne were hardly mentioned amongst the concerns raised at the Public Inquiries. However, they have featured significantly in the issues raised by river users since the construction of the dam and particularly the impact of releases for hydropower — although one suspects that even without hydropower they would still have generated debate.

Although the Kielder Water Order of 1974 conferred powers on NW for the generation of electricity, there were no plans for hydropower in the original Scheme mainly because it was considered that the pattern of releases for the large forecast water supply demands would have made power generation uneconomic. With the downturn in demand, hydropower was reinvestigated and from 1982 to 1984 the power station was jointly built by Northumbrian Water and the Central Electricity Generating Board (now National Grid). Power is generated by two turbines; a smaller one, designed to use the continuous compensation water release of 1.3 cumecs generates 0.5 Megawatts and a larger turbine with a maximum throughflow of 14.1 cumecs generates 5.5 Megawatts. The power is transmitted to the National Grid at Spadeadam and the resulting revenue is accrued by the Environment Agency. The revenue is generally between £0.5 and £1 million per year.

When the dam and hydropower station were first completed, it was considered legitimate to draw up a release policy with the primary objective of maximising revenue from the sale of electrical energy whilst fulfilling their statutory obligations for other releases[14]. Two very sophisticated mathematical programs were written on the basis of historic inflow data to determine how much water to release each week and how the weekly releases should be distributed in time for maximum income[15]. The resulting release pattern (Fig. 10.5) depended more on the structure of the electricity tariff than on the natural river regime. In particular, releases took advantage of the brief period of peak electricity demand each day, during which the tariff nearly doubled. Short pulsed releases at the peak generating rate, lasting a few hours, were made each day except during the winter months when releases were more continuous. Water was mainly drawn through the scour valve from the lower levels of the reservoir as this gave better efficiency than drawing from surface water. In addition it was considered inefficient to operate the large turbine at anything less than its full discharge (14.1 cumecs). The flashy pulsed release was unnatural but drawing water from the bottom of the reservoir also raised questions about the effect of water quality, sediment and temperature on ecology and fisheries[16].

Two legislative measures in 1989 encouraged the reappraisal of the regulation policy. Firstly the National Rivers Authority, created alongside the privatised water companies, had a much stronger focus on conservation and amenity. Secondly the electricity companies, privatised under the Electricity Act (1989), were also given environmental duties. The Act introduced an obligation on the electricity companies to derive a proportion of their electricity from non-fossil sources — the non-fossil fuel obligation (NFFO). Subsidised tariff rates were provided to encourage power generation from renewable sources, and Kielder benefited from these from 1991 to 1998[17].

Significantly the NFFO tariff rate applied at a uniform rate daily and seasonally. There was no longer any financial benefit in making short pulsed

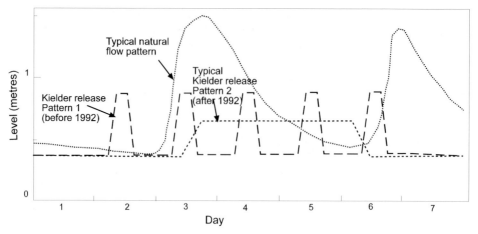

Fig 10.5 Release patterns from Kielder to the River North Tyne compared with natural flow patterns

releases. Instead of the daily pulse, releases were now made in blocks of three, five and seven-day duration, but at a flow less than the turbine maximum (Fig. 10.5). The time taken to raise the flow from the compensation level to full generation and back was increased from two to four hours to avoid risks to river users in rising levels, and to avoid stranding of fish and microbiota in falling levels. Large releases in excess of turbine capacity were made more consistently in November to encourage salmon migration upstream. Their timing also benefited canoeists. However, possibly the most important change made by the NRA was to discontinue the use of the water from the bottom levels of the reservoir through the scour valve and substitute water from the highest draw-off levels.

The NFFO tariff came to an end in 1998 and a variable tariff similar to the 1980s has returned, but the more benign release regime continues. Further adjustment may be possible as understanding improves on the relationship between flow regime and ecology and fisheries. However, irrespective of hydropower generation, river users must recognise that the release policy cannot mimic the natural flow regime completely — and they would probably protest if it did. Flow rates are limited by the capacity of pipes and valves. In particular, the absence of occasional very high flows in the reach below the dam has resulted locally in bed 'armouring' with interlocking stones making the bed less suitable for salmon spawning. On the positive side the absence of such high flows has significantly reduced flood risk downstream (Chapter 2). If the upward trend in the salmon catch in the Tyne can be regarded as a measure of the health of the salmon fishery and of the river ecosystem, then, at the very least, the Kielder release policy must be considered as not being seriously detrimental.

Sustainability has been a keyword in environmental policy over the last decade. Renewable energy from sun, wave, wind and water are seen as preferable to non-renewable and environmentally polluting sources from fossil fuel. Electricity generated at Kielder annually saves the emission of around 8000 tonnes of carbon dioxide, 100 tonnes of sulphur dioxide and 30 tonnes of nitrogen oxides from fossil fuel. However, renewable energy, from whatever source, also has environmental impacts; with respect to energy production there is no such thing as a 'free meal'. In developing an energy policy, government, developers and environmentalists must recognise that there is a fine balance to be struck between sustainable energy, sustainable water resources and river ecosystems.

WHITE ELEPHANT OR WHITE KNIGHT?

The optimism for growth of industry and its associated demand for water, for which Kielder was planned, has long since evaporated, but the droughts of 1989 and the 1990s demonstrated that existing sources were seriously deficient in locations not foreseen at the Kielder Inquiries. Kielder has thus saved the Northeast from serious water restrictions during these droughts. In hindsight a smaller reservoir such as the one proposed at Irthing would have been adequate. However, to achieve the necessary flexibility of the Kielder Scheme, the Tyne-Tees transfer tunnel, which consumed half of the overall costs of the Kielder Scheme, would still have had to be constructed.

Kielder has brought significant collateral benefits including the reduction in flood risk to vulnerable properties on the North Tyne and Tyne (Chapter 2). In addition, the recreational and amenity benefit of the lake is not to be sneezed at (Chapter 11). Kielder is the third largest tourist attraction in the Northeast with around 300,000 visitors per year. Whilst Sir Rupert Speir remarked at the Kielder Inquiry that the tough climate of the North Tyne was 'ideal for solitude and not for sailing', subsequent sympathetic development has shown that both interests can be satisfied (Plate 21). It would appear that most residents of the North Tyne are not only reconciled to Kielder Water, but positively welcome the contribution which it makes to amenity and employment.

REFERENCES

1. Pearce, F. (1982) *Watershed - The Water Crisis in Britain*. Junction Books, London.
2. Pearce, F. (1991) Pipe dreams to quench Britain's thirst, *New Scientist,* 16 Nov 1991.
3. Northumbrian River Authority (1973) *Report on Survey of Water Resources, Water Resources Act 1963, Section 14*, Northumbrian River Authority.
4. Brady, J.A. (1984) *Water Resources in the Northeast. The Kielder Water Scheme – A Decade of Change*. Northumbrian Water Authority.
5. Rennison, R.W. (1979) *Water to Tyneside: A History of the Newcastle and Gateshead Water Company*. Newcastle and Gateshead Water Company.
6. Smillie, J.F. (1897) *Tynemouth Water Supply*. Borough Surveyor's Office, Tynemouth
7. Sunderland and South Shields Water Company (1952) *Centenary 1852–1952*, S&SS Water Company.
8. Weaver, R (1944) Fluorosis and dental caries on Tyneside, *British Dental Journal*, **76**, 29–40
9. Water Resources Board (1967) *Interim Report on Water Resources in the North*, HMSO.

10. Burston, U.T., and Coats, D.J. (1975) Water resources in Northumbria with particular reference to the Kielder Water Scheme, *Journal of the Institution of Water Engineers and Scientists*, **29**, 226–251.
11. Toffler, A. (1970) *Future Shock,* Bantam Books.
12. Serpell, C.A. (1975) Inaugural Presidential Address, Institution of Water Engineers and Scientists, *JIWES,* **29**, 220–225.
13. Ashby, E. (1972) *Pollution: Nuisance or Nemesis? – A report on the control of pollution,* HMSO.
14. Johnson, P. (1988) River regulation; a regional perspective – Northumbrian Water Authority. *Regulated Rivers: Research and Management,* **2**, 233–255.
15. Johnson, P. and Sanderson, P.R. (1987) Control of Kielder hydropower generation. *Proc. of First National Hydrology Symposium,* 9.1–9.10, British Hydrological Society.
16. Haile, S.M., James, A. and Sear, D. (1989) The effects of Kielder Reservoir on the ecology of the River North Tyne, Northumbrian Water Authority.
17. Archer, D. and Williams, G. (1995) Resolving conflicts between sustainable energy and water resources in the regulation of the River Tyne, England, In *Modelling and Management of Sustainable Basin-scale Water Resources Systems.* Proceedings of a Boulder Symposium. IAHS Publication no. 231, p.3–14.

11. THE SPORTING TYNE

INTRODUCTION

Man has the strange propensity for adapting the activities of his livelihood such as hunting, boating and even ploughing to competitive sport. The British seem particularly adept at codifying and standardising the rules of the game, and sport associated with water is no exception The River Tyne has played an important part in the development of the sport of rowing, which through the middle of the nineteenth century, enjoyed a popularity on Tyneside at least as great as football today — with crowds of over 50,000 lining the riverside.

Nowadays, a wide range of watersports is available on the Tyne, including rowing, sailing and windsurfing, canoeing, water-skiing and power-boating. These take place in the estuary, on the freshwater river, and on Derwent Reservoir and Kielder Water. Within the scope of this short chapter it is not possible to do equal justice to all sports. So the main emphasis is on sports on the freshwater Tyne, upper estuary and reservoirs, whilst sports on the lower estuary or requiring motor power are considered more briefly. Contact addresses for all Tyne estuary watersports are available in the Watersports Directory[1].

Additionally, the River Tyne provides much opportunity for informal recreation and for the enjoyment of the environment of the river corridor. It is hoped that this book will provide material to enrich the appreciation of walkers and cyclists — and even those who are restricted to motor transport!

ROWING

Rowing, which originated as a means of transport and warfare, was practised by Egyptians, Greeks, Romans and Vikings. The first mention of competitive rowing is in Virgil's *Aeneid* just before the Christian era. Modern rowing grew out of the ordinary business of ferrying people and goods along rivers and estuaries in skiffs and wherries, propelled by watermen and wherrymen. River racing seems to have originated amongst the watermen of the Thames around 1700. The gentry placed bets on which oarsman would get them across the river in the shortest time, and professional rowing over the following 150 years continued to be organised on the basis of wagers by backers of each side. An annual race which was instituted on the River Thames in 1715 (the Doggett's coat and badge race) still takes place. It was originally rowed between two pubs along the Thames, reflecting the origin of the sport as a social pastime.

Developments on the Tyne were a little later, though perhaps much early activity went unreported. There is evidence that rowing had already become a recreation during the eighteenth century, based on a note in 1766 on the death of Richard Dawes, a retired headmaster of Newcastle Grammar School, whose retirement hobby was described as rowing on the Tyne. Boat racing on the

Tyne was undoubtedly underway in the 1820s, and by May 1830 a regatta formed part of the day's entertainment of horse racing and sideshows on King's Meadows Island. It was not until September 1834 that the first fully-fledged regatta was held on the Tyne. It was a society occasion, attended by 'fashionably attired ladies' arriving in carriages, and was opened by the Mayor of Newcastle, who arrived in a decorated barge. Thereafter it appears to have been an annual event. On the Thames, the Henley Regatta was not established until 1839.

Over the next forty years the Tyne was to become the northern centre of rowing excellence. Tyne men challenged and often defeated the champions of the Thames, which was (and is) the main river for boat racing in the south, and produced a crop of world champions. Three names stand out, those of Harry Clasper, Robert Chambers and James Renforth.

It might be well to explain at this point the variety of ways in which boats and rowers are arranged in competitive rowing. In sculling races each competitor has two oars and races singly, in a double scull (two rowers) or in a quad (four rowers). In sweep oar races each crew member has one oar and boats have two, four or eight oarsmen, plus a non-rowing coxswain (cox), who sits facing the rowers and the direction of movement and maintains the course and the rhythm of the team. Champion Tyne rowers of the nineteenth century competed mainly in single and double sculls and coxed fours. The cox was particularly necessary on the crowded Tyne of the nineteenth century for steering clear of other river traffic as well as floating debris. Nevertheless, it was not unusual for races to be decided when one or other competitor ran foul of river traffic; the professional foul on a competitor's boat, which added amusement for the highly partisan crowd of spectators, was also a common feature.

Tyneside heroes – Clasper, Chambers and Renforth

Harry Clasper was born in 1812, the son of Robert Clasper of Dunston (and later Jarrow). He had four brothers, Robert, William, Edward and Richard[3]. They were all keen oarsmen and rowed together as a team until 1845, when Harry's brother Edward died at the early age of 25. He had been a fine rower in spite of having a wooden leg. Edward's place was taken by his uncle, Ned Hawks, who rowed with the three brothers when they achieved their greatest triumph in 1845.

Harry's first attempt at boat racing was around 1837, when his four beat a Swalwell crew for a prize of £10. Over the next few years it was rare to see his crew defeated and they became undisputed Champions of the Tyne. Seeking new opposition in 1842 they challenged the Thames watermen, then undisputed national champions. For stakes of £150 they raced from Newcastle Bridge to Lemington. The race was won fairly easily by the London crew. Similarly in single sculls Harry was defeated by the Thames champion rower, Robert Coombes. Although Harry and his brothers had won all the local competitions, the greatest prize eluded them until 1845. For the prestigious event designated as World Championships held at the Thames regatta, Harry had built a new boat, the *Lord Ravensworth*. His crew competed in the finals against Robert Coombes' crew and another crack London crew, winning by one and a half lengths. The World Champions returned to Newcastle to an overwhelming reception accompanied by the pealing of church bells and firing of guns. Harry rounded off a successful year with wins in the sculls against top opposition from the Thames and Mersey.

He continued to race in sculls, pairs and fours until he was nearly fifty years old, often defeating opponents half his age, including the up-and-coming George Drewett in 1860. In later years his crew included his son, John Hawks Clasper, and his protégé, Robert Chambers, whom Harry had been coaching for several years.

Harry's deserved fame was not only for his rowing stamina and skill but also for his sportsmanship and dedication to all aspects of the sport, the craftsmanship of his boats and oars, as described below, and the development of a style which gave the Tyne oarsmen the edge over their competitors. He placed Tyneside on the world as well as the national map of rowing and when he died in 1870 the whole of Tyneside went into mourning. An estimated 100,000 to 130,000 witnessed his funeral as his coffin was taken over the championship course for the last time and then to Whickham cemetery, where his grave is marked by a striking memorial with a full sized-statue.

Robert (Bob) Chambers first came to national attention in 'the Great Race' of 1857 when he defeated five of the highest calibre London rowers by a margin of five lengths. In 1859 he beat Thomas White on the Tyne by upwards of 100 yards for the Championship of England, and later the same year defeated Kelley, the champion of the Thames, by 30 boat lengths. In 1863 he defeated his Australian adversary R.A.W. Green, for the Championship of the World on the Thames by a full five minutes. At his peak Chambers was almost unbeatable at sculls but eventually lost the title in 1865 to the persistent Harry Kelley, regained it in 1866 and finally, in failing health the following year, lost the title again to Kelley.

Robert Chambers died of tuberculosis in June 1868 aged only 37 years. He was described at the time as the greatest natural sculler the world had ever seen. In all he rowed in 109 races and won 89 — 34 out of 45 in sculls, 40 out of 45 in 4-oared races and 15 out of 19 in pairs.

With the failing health and passing of Bob Chambers, the Tyneside mantle fell on James Renforth, a man with natural sporting talent, who had served as a soldier in India and on return had commenced a sporting career as a swimmer. Entering his first boat race in 1867, he enjoyed uninterrupted success, having become champion in less time than any previous oarsman. He beat Kelley in a non-title bout, and again in a return match for the World title in 1868.

Renforth is best remembered as the lead oarsman in the Tyne four which in 1870 won the Championship of the World on the St Lawrence River near Montreal, defeating a Canadian crew by a wide margin for a stake of £1000.

The following year the team returned to America, strengthened by the old Thames oarsman Kelley. This time they were defending their title against the same Canadian crew, but this time on the Kennebecassis River in New Brunswick. After less than 200 yards the Tyne four had already pulled to a half-boat-length lead, when Renforth suddenly faltered. He continued an irregular stroke for some further distance, then collapsed into the arms of Harry Kelley. The crew abandoned the race and carried Renforth ashore where he died two hours later, with his last broken-hearted words, "What will they say in England?". It remains strange that a healthy young man of only 29 should suddenly keel over and die. In spite of the fact that Renforth was known to have suffered from epilepsy and the doctor's report that he died from 'heart strain', some suspicion remains that he was nobbled — more so in a sport in which the gambling stakes were high.

In his short and glorious career Renforth won 14 of his 17 sculls races, 7 out of 10 fours and 4 out of 8 pairs. He is also reported to have raced in two canoe races and, although defeated in both, appears to be the first Tynesider to attempt his skills at this discipline. After his death the Tyne never again achieved the same prominence in the world of rowing although, as described below, amateur oarsmen have continued the sporting tradition.

The body of Renforth was brought back to England and laid to rest in Gateshead East Cemetery. Amid public gloom at the untimely death of their third rowing hero in three years, his funeral was witnessed by nearly 100,000. A monumental tomb erected by public subscription shows a life-size figure of Renforth in the arms of the bearded Harry Kelley and now stands outside the Shipley Art Gallery in Gateshead (Fig. 11.1). The town of Renforth, New

Fig 11.1 Memorial to world champion James Renforth outside Shipley Art Gallery, Gateshead. A place of honour by the riverside might be a more appropriate location
(Photo: David Archer)

Fig 11.2 Sculling race between Elliott and Hanlan from the start at the High Level
Bridge to the finish at Scotswood Chainbridge around 1877

Brunswick was named in his honour, and to celebrate the town centenary in
1971, a Tyne crew was invited to compete again in a race on the Kennebecassis River.

Although no longer achieving international distinction over the following
decades, professional rowers continued to have strong popular support. Fig.
11.2 illustrates the enthusiastic crowds in a sculling race from the High Level
Bridge to the Chainbridge at Scotswood between the new local hero, Elliott,
and his Canadian rival Hanlan. Rowers also continued to attract the muse of
songwriters (Chapter 16). A major annual sculling event, the Tyne Christmas
Handicap, was established in 1876, and persisted with the exception of the years
of World War I until 1933. It was a knock-out event over a short distance and
attracted enough competitors to last from Christmas to the finals at New Year.
Gradually, however, the crowds dwindled; their loyalty was diverted to football.

Technical advances
Apart from the skill and physical stamina of the champions, the success of
oarsmen from the Tyne owed much to their ingenuity in creating lighter, faster
boats and devices that permitted more effective use of the oars. Not all the
inventions were successful however, and an early attempt in 1822 to build a 32-

foot iron boat was a signal failure. The following year a team using this boat was defeated in a race against a conventional wooden boat. Their failure was said to be due to "too much beer and too little ballast", but this seems unfair to the crew. Its unfortunate builder, James Smith, was in the process of redesigning the boat when he fell overboard and was drowned.

A more successful invention was the outrigger, which is the framework fitted to the boat's side to support the rowlocks and give the rower more leverage and control. The first outrigger was a rough wooden structure invented by Anthony Brown of Ouseburn, and the first iron outrigger appeared on the Tyne in 1830. This became the standard for racing boats on the Tyne and Wear but was not adopted at the Thames for another 15 years. Macfarlane-Grieve[2] notes that "London-based boats were found to be so inferior in speed to native outriggers that the latter were not allowed to compete in the same races". The invention came to be attributed to Harry Clasper who early adopted and perfected its use.

Harry Clasper had more innovations in store. He recognised the disadvantages of the heavy weight of his boat (the *St Agnes*), in which his Tyne crew lost to the London crew in 1842. His next boat (*The Five Brothers*) was revolutionary in its lightness. When it appeared in competition in 1844, it was the first time that outriggers had been used on the Thames. Within a year many of the London boatbuilders had copied the lines of Harry's boat. Another development generally attributed to Harry Clasper was the keel-less, smooth-bottomed boat of 1847, which gave a further advantage in reduced frictional resistance but was harder to control.

Clasper also experimented with the oars, in terms of their length and the shape of the blade, and developed the Newcastle oar with handles that overlapped on the draw, thus gaining a few centimetres in stroke length. His son, John Hawks Clasper, continuing the innovative tradition, invented and patented the fin keel to solve problems of steering in difficult conditions.

Finally, although the invention of the sliding seat is generally attributed to Babcock in New York in 1870, there are references to 'partial sliding' by oarsmen on the Tyne in 1857. This sliding may have simply been the greasing of leather breeches to achieve the same effect. However, it seems that it was Renforth's crew, who after his death developed a racing technique using sliding seats. By the mid-1870s the racing boat was little different in shape from its modern equivalent, although boats are now moulded in one piece and modern materials have further reduced the weight of the boat.

Amateur rowing on the Tyne
The popularity of professional rowing and the development of university rowing led to the rapid growth of amateur rowing on the Tyne. The Tyne Amateur Rowing Club was founded in December 1852 and is one of the oldest extant sporting clubs in the Northeast. It was intended for 'gentlemen', and besides restrictions on eligibility with respect to class and profession, the annual fee of one guinea would have put membership beyond the reach of the ordinary working man. Tensions between the socially exclusive and artisan oarsman,

between the gentleman amateur and the professional, remained a feature of the sport for at least a century[4].

The establishment of the Northern Rowing Club followed in the mid-1850s and there is a record of a club founded in 1865 named the 'Tatoe Wallopers'. By the turn of the century there were further clubs based at Hexham (established 1878), Ryton, Tynemouth and South Shields. However, all, except Tynemouth, Hexham, and the Tyne ARC (now simply the Tyne Rowing Club), had become extinct or dormant by the beginning of World War I in 1914. A number of clubs formed or reformed during the inter-war years and combined as Tyne United Rowing Club after World War II. That club mainly used the Elswick river reach, but finally succumbed around 1960 to the deteriorating condition of the river.

In 1853 the Tyne ARC organised an annual regatta and participated in competitions all over the north, particularly at Durham, which had also become a highly successful amateur rowing venue. Rowing on the Tyne appears to have waxed and waned over the last 150 years, with the Tyne ARC declining from over 100 members in 1864 to a mere three in 1891. Thereafter there was a rapid resurgence, warranting the building of a new clubhouse at Scotswood in 1893, and the first eight-oared races were held on the Tyne in the same year. The Tyne club won the Grand Challenge Cup at Durham (the premier trophy in the North of England) eight times between then and World War I, a success which it last achieved in 1938. The present clubhouse upstream from Newburn Bridge was opened in 1957 and extended in 1999.

The main event of the club calendar is the 'At Home' Regatta at the end of May with the premier trophy, the Joseph Cowen Challenge Cup, which in 1910 was presented to the club by Joseph Cowen, club member and editor of the Newcastle Chronicle. The Tyne Head race, which began in 1952, is an early spring event in which crews go off at regular intervals from the head of the rowing reach and race against the clock. It attracts over 120 crews of eights and fours.

As the club approaches its 150th anniversary, it has a healthy membership of 120 including 20 women. The gender barrier is gone along with the old social distinctions. The sight of sculls and eights cutting gracefully through the water at Newburn adds interest and colour on a summer evening and provides a reminder of the glory days of rowing on the Tyne. The Tyne at Newburn affords the best river rowing course in the country, with the possible exception of the Thames. There is ample room for four eights to compete abreast and, unlike many tidal courses, the uniformity of the tidal current across the section gives no unfair advantage on the basis of starting position.

Tynemouth Rowing Club, based at Priors Haven near the mouth of the Tyne, uses the harbour and river mouth.

The Newburn stretch of water is also used by school and university crews, including the Newcastle University Boat Club (Kings College before 1963) and the University of Northumbria Club, which is a successor to the successful Rutherford College Boat Club established in the 1960s. In recent years an annual Northern Universities boat race has been set up, using a mile course from

Dunston Staiths to Newcastle Quay. Whilst this is a popular event, it suffers from the lack of launch facilities in the reach, and boats have to be lowered from the Quayside by a mobile crane.

Rowing at schools depends very much on the enthusiasm and coaching skill of a member of the teaching staff. Currently, Ponteland High School is the only school rowing club using the Newburn reach. However, Queen Elizabeth High School at Hexham has established a very successful club in the river reach above Hexham Bridge under the coaching of Chris Grabham; both boys' and girls' crews have carried off national trophies. Matthew Wells, who learned to row at Hexham, became World Junior Champion at double sculls in 1997 and World under-23 World Champion in 2000; he also represented Britain in the Sydney Olympics in 2000. His brother Peter repeated Matthew's achievement to become world under-23 champion in 2002 as well as winning the Diamond Sculls at Henley. This Hexham school has had the unusual, if not unique, distinction of recently providing from the ranks of old boys and girls, a member of its club in each Great Britain team in 2001.

SAILING

Although there are long-established coastal sailing clubs at the mouth of the Tyne, the Northeast had little scope for inland sailing until the late 1960s. Within the Tyne basin, Greenlee Lough, adjacent to the Roman Wall at Housesteads, had the only sailing club and that was limited by the size of the lake to fifty boats. The upper reaches of the estuary at Ryton were also used during winter months. Beyond the Tyne, inland sailors had to travel to the Lake District or to the limited waters of Scaling Reservoir in North Yorkshire.

Derwent Reservoir

The opportunity for inland sailing improved dramatically with the completion of Derwent Reservoir by Sunderland & South Shields Water Company and the opening of Derwent Reservoir Sailing Club in 1967. The Club was enthusiastically promoted by Nigel Ruffle, then Engineer-in-Charge of the design and construction of the reservoir. Already a sailor at Greenlee Lough, he persuaded the General Manager, Andrew McClellan, to allow sailing on the new reservoir. Planning permission was obtained for a suitable sailing club site and concrete slipways were laid before the water rose. Press advertisement of the proposed sailing club demonstrated the public interest with nearly 700 questionnaires returned. A working party was formed in March 1966, under the chairmanship of John Sigmund, who later became the first club commodore. A government grant was obtained and a clubhouse and car and boat parks were completed in 1970.

Such a development at Derwent Reservoir was by no means inevitable. At one time water undertakers attempted to secure an unpolluted source of water and then to defend it against any kind of contamination, even excluding the public from gathering grounds[5]. By the early 1960s most undertakers realised that such a policy was neither practicable nor necessary and in 1963 a groundbreaking report by the Institution of Water Engineers[6] recommended an increase in planned recreational use of reservoirs and the provision of access and facilities. It favoured sailing and rowing but was opposed to canoeing, swimming and water skiing, which involved immersion and hence pollution by the participants. (This distinction seems somewhat inconsistent as sailors can hardly avoid being immersed occasionally in pursuit of their sport). Shortly afterwards a sailing club was established at the newly-constructed reservoir at Grafham Water in the East Midlands; Derwent Sailing Club's lease and rules were based on those developed at Grafham.

When full the reservoir covers an area of four square kilometres and has a length of 5.6 kilometres. The sailing area is typically reduced in summer and only a few of the lightest craft could be launched in the most drawn-down condition of the drought of 1989. Since then the Environment Agency and Northumbrian Water have agreed reservoir-operating rules which make drastic summer drawdown conditions much less likely.

The progress and success of the Sailing Club has fully justified the initial enthusiasm. It has nearly 1000 members and supports about 12 classes of boats, the most popular being GP14s, Flying 15s, Lasers and Mirrors, with Toppers and Optimists for the younger members (Plate 22). The club opens on weekends for sailing and windsurfing from April until November and on Wednesdays and Fridays from April to October, and there are regularly more than 50 boats on the water (Plate 22). There are competitive club, regional and national events throughout the year and Derwent RegattaWeek in May is an event which caters especially for families and children.

The club caters for all abilities and provides facilities for people with disabilities. It provides training courses for beginners and particularly encourages youth participation. In 1999 it attained the status of Royal Yachting Association Champion Club for promoting consistently high standards of coaching, competition, social activities and environmental awareness with respect to youth sailing. Visiting members from other accredited Royal Yacht Association clubs are welcomed as temporary members with their boats within the classes in use on the reservoir.

Throughout its life the Club has produced many national champions in various classes and members have competed successfully at international level although with no Olympic participants or medallists as yet. Whilst competition is strong, the club has focused also on the enjoyment of the open water and the social dimension of sailing.

Kielder Water

Amenity, recreation and sport were integral to the development of Kielder Water, but the emphasis in the Public Inquiry of 1972 was on passive recreation — sightseeing, walking, trekking, camping and bird-watching. Sir Frederick Gibberd, the landscape architect acting as consultant to the Northumbrian River Authority, said that active recreation which did not guarantee noise, particularly sailing and canoeing, should also be encouraged. The local authority supported such development.

By the time the reservoir had filled, the plans for recreation had expanded to

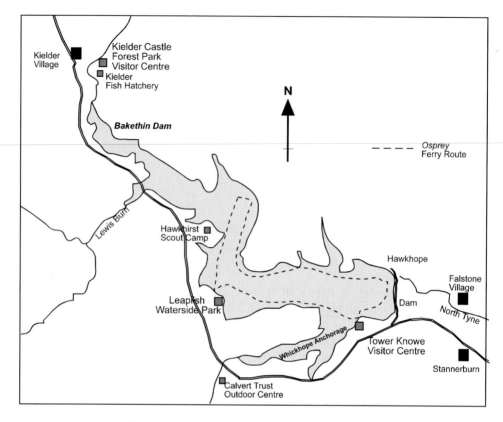

Fig 11.3 Kielder Water recreational facilities

include a wider range of activities — including some which generate engine noise[7]. However, the key active sport since inception has been sailing. Because of the reservoir size (10.9 square kilometres — more than double that of Derwent Reservoir) the range of acceptable craft has been much broader than at Derwent. The Kielder Water Sailing Club based at Tower Knowe (Fig 11.3) supports all classes of sailing dinghy and catamaran as well as windsurfers; the Kielder Yacht Club based at Whickhope mainly caters for motor cruisers, with a size limit of 28 feet and a speed limit of 9 knots. Membership is smaller than at Derwent, with about 200 Sailing Club members and 150 Yacht Club members. The Calvert Trust has a well-established centre for activity holidays for people with disabilities plus their family and friends, and provides opportunities for sailing, kayaking and canoeing as well as such land-based recreations as archery and abseiling.

The large and irregular size of the lake is a mixed blessing. The changing conditions of shelter and exposure provide a challenge to the sailor, but the spectator can quickly lose sight of the boats, especially on the Round the Lake Race which occurs once a month. The Kielder midge (the same species as the notorious Scottish midge) can also be a real problem for shore-based activities from late June until the end of the summer, especially in damp, humid weather. The midge appears not to venture more than 15 metres from the shore, so sailors escape their unwelcome attention (Chapter 5).

Kielder Water also supports water skiing but, to avoid conflict with other water users, three quite restricted areas have been designated, at which facilities and equipment are available for hire and for training. Jet skis (personal water craft) were briefly permitted during a trial period in 1987 but were found to be incompatible with other users and will not be reconsidered. Power boat racing has also occurred in special events of short duration, for which planning consent was required. Whilst such events remain an option, they are likely to be very infrequent due to the variable water level and limitations on easy access for such craft; the last such event was in 1990. For the less active visitor, the 86-passenger motor cruiser, *Osprey*, sails on a round-the-lake cruise three times a day from April until October.

In spite of the early reservations concerning the Scheme's impact on the environment and on community life, Kielder Water is now viewed by the majority of residents as a welcome asset. More than 30% of employment in the North Tyne valley is currently in tourism, including accommodation and a number of visitor attractions associated with Kielder Water or the Forest Park. The Visitor Centres register around 300,000 visitors per year, placing Kielder as third in rank behind Durham Cathedral and Hadrian's Wall amongst the tourist attractions of the Northeast.

Tyne Estuary Sailing
Dinghy and cruising yacht sailing is also a popular activity on the estuary, and the Tynemouth and South Shields Sailing Clubs in particular are long-established (Fig. 11.4). The emphasis is on sea sailing but use is also made of the river mouth between the piers, especially in stormy weather and in winter. Windsurfers also use the triangle of water within the piers on the south side. The 'Frostbite' challenge is organised by St Peter's Marina and occurs on Sundays for eight weeks in winter. It provides an opportunity for larger yachts to improve their skills at tacking within the confines of the estuary from St Anthony's to the City Centre area.

CANOEING
The open canoe and its sister the covered kayak originated amongst the native Indian and Inuit populations of North America, and the early development of canoeing for sport and recreation occurred on that side of the Atlantic. However, in Britain canoeing has seen a meteoric rise in participation during the last 50 years. The number of clubs affiliated to the British Canoe Union was 12 in 1948, 350 in 1969, and 577 (with 24,000 members) in 2001.

Canoeing is both a recreation and a sport. As a recreation it offers a unique mid-channel perspective of the river as a continuous thread rather than a series of bankside snapshots. For success and safety, the canoeist must 'read the river', harmonise with its currents and eddies, negotiate a safe way through rapids, and identify submerged hazards. There can be little outdoor pleasure greater

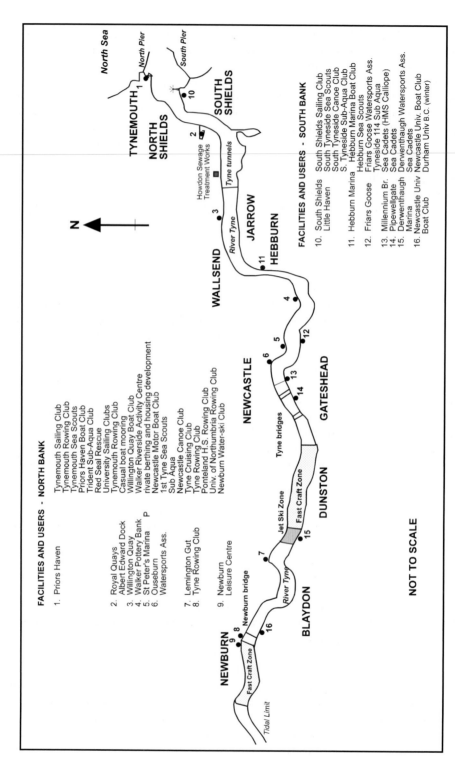

FACILITIES AND USERS - NORTH BANK

1. Priors Haven   Tynemouth Sailing Club
                   Tynemouth Rowing Club
                   Tynemouth Sea Scouts
                   Priors Haven Boat Club
                   Trident Sub-Aqua Club
                   Red Seal Rescue
                   University Sailing Clubs

2. Royal Quays   Tynemouth Rowing Club
  Albert Edward Dock Casual boat mooring
3. Willington Quay   Willington Quay Boat Club
4. Walker Pottery Bank Walker Riverside Activity Centre
5. St Peter's Marina P private berthing and housing development
6. Ouseburn   Newcastle Motor Boat Club
  Watersports Ass.   1st Tyne Sea Scouts
                   Sub Aqua
                   Newcastle Canoe Club
7. Lemington Gut   Tyne Cruising Club
8. Tyne Rowing Club   Tyne Rowing Club
                   Ponteland H.S. Rowing Club
                   Univ. of Northumbria Rowing Club
9. Newburn   Newburn Water-ski Club
  Leisure Centre

NOT TO SCALE

FACILITIES AND USERS - SOUTH BANK

10. South Shields   South Shields Sailing Club
    Little Haven   South Tyneside Sea Scouts
                  South Tyneside Canoe Club
                  S. Tyneside Sub-Aqua Club
11. Hebburn Marina Hebburn Marina Boat Club
                  Hebburn Sea Scouts
12. Friars Goose   Friars Goose Watersports Ass.
                  Tyneside 114 Sub Aqua
13. Millennium Br.   Sea Cadets (HMS Calliope)
14. Pipewellgate   Sea Cadets
15. Derwenthaugh   Derwenthaugh Watersports Ass.
    Marina   Sea Cadets
16. Newcastle Univ. Newcastle Univ. Boat Club
    Boat Club   Durham Univ B.C. (winter)

Fig 11.4 Sport and recreational organisations on the Tyne estuary

than gliding silently downstream on the North Tyne and glimpsing a family of otters playing by the bank or a kingfisher perched, sunlit and brilliant, on an overhanging branch. In contrast, the sporting canoeist jostles individually with the power of water or engages competitively in wildwater racing.

The Tyne offers opportunity for a wide range of canoeing activities for all levels of skill. For the beginner the reach from Haydon Bridge to Hexham provides a good introduction, whilst the North Tyne between Bellingham and Wark is also popular. Much more skill is required for the reach from Chollerford to Hexham, with the biggest section of white water on the Tyne at Warden Gorge. This is the scene of one or more competitions each year for wildwater racing specialists, and for a race which forms part of the 'Tyne Tour' on the first weekend of November (Plate 23). For this event about 1,000 paddlers converge on the river although only about 50 participate in the race. Experts seeking a special challenge use the River Allen in flood from Cupola Bridge to Ridley Hall, though suitable conditions tend to be short-lived and thus available only for local canoeists who keep a close watch on weather and river conditions.

Being comparative newcomers to the rivers of Britain, canoeists have had to address the fears of the long-established angling fraternity, that the fishery would be disturbed. Canoeists are also disadvantaged by having no legal right of access. However, experience has shown that canoeists and anglers can both enjoy their recreation without conflict as long as rules of access and timing are agreed. The Tyne has been a model in this respect with an access agreement, drawn up between the British Canoe Union and the Tyne Riparian Owners and Occupiers, to allow access to uninterrupted reaches.

Essentially canoeists have the run of the river during the winter months from November to March. In these months high water provides some of the best canoe conditions, during the period when fishing is either closed (November to January) or levels are too high for successful angling. From April to August canoeists are advised only to canoe when there is 'sufficient water', but they must leave the river entirely to the fishermen (irrespective of flow) in September and October. There are agreed access and egress points, and canoeists approaching anglers should stay close to the opposite bank and travel in groups of no more than six.

To sample the joys of canoeing it is best to join a club where members can make use of boats and gear for training. Casual hiring of canoes is not normally possible on the Tyne. There are two canoeing clubs on the freshwater Tyne, the Tyne Valley Canoe Club based at the Tyne Riverside Park at Low Prudhoe and the Hexham Canoe Club. These two each have a membership of about 100. Canoeists from many other northeastern clubs and further afield also use the Tyne.

WATER-BASED RECREATION ON THE ESTUARY
As already noted with respect to sailing and rowing, the tidal reach of the river Tyne plays host to a wide range of river-based sport and recreational activities (Fig. 11.4). Use of the tidal river is controlled by the Port of Tyne Authority (POT), whose main statutory duties are concerned with navigation by

commercial vessels, but it also has powers to control movement of recreational craft and the provision of moorings and slipways. In conjunction with the River Tyne Recreational Users Group, the POT gives written guidance to users in the form of a recreational rule book. The guide provides a basis for the co-ordination of the sometimes conflicting activities and for the apportioning of river reaches and timings to different users.

The zoning policy is particularly important in ensuring safe recreational use of the estuary. A general speed limit of six knots applies to vessels from the Low Lighthouse, North Shields to the limit of the POT's jurisdiction at Hedwin Streams, and 10 knots seaward of the Low Lighthouse. However, certain restricted reaches have been designated fast craft zones for the use of fast-moving craft and water skiers. These are:

❍ A waterski zone upstream from Newburn bridge
❍ A fast craft zone between Derwenthaugh and Dunston
❍ A zone specifically for personal watercraft (jetskis) adjacent to Derwenthaugh Marina

INFORMAL RECREATION

Whilst the Tyne provides the opportunity for active and competitive watersports, there is far greater participation in less taxing pursuits which use the river Tyne as a focus. These range from viewing the river from the comfort of a parked car, picnicking and birdwatching to walking and cycling on riverside routes.

Participation in informal recreation is one of the most significant developments of the post-war era; in 1990 an estimate suggested that 1,600 million trips are made annually to the countryside in England and Wales[8]. A significant proportion of these visits are made to waterside sites on river, lake and sea. With the regeneration of the Tyne riverside over the last two decades, the distinction between urban and rural river landscapes as a focus for leisure has diminished. River water quality of the estuary, once fetid and lifeless, is still not perfect but supports resident and migratory fish — and fishermen. Derelict industrial sites that blocked the view of the river have been transformed or removed to allow safe access to the river bank. River views are spectacular and in some cases breath-taking.

The admirable Sustrans, an environmental and transport charity, has created a network of joined-up cycle routes in association with local authorities. These routes, which are nearly all off-road, run along both banks of the estuary and as far west as Prudhoe. They can be and are widely used for walking, an activity now encouraged and sponsored by health authorities and the British Heart Association. Further long-distance cycle routes will traverse the Tyne catchment from north to south (Route 68 from Berwick to Appleby via Elsdon, Bellingham, Haltwhistle and Alston) and from east to west (Route 72 from Tyneside to Carlisle). A fair proportion of these routes are already available. Go, and see for yourself!

REFERENCES

1. Tyne and Wear Watersports Development Project (1993) Watersports Directory.
2. Macfarlane-Grieve, A.A. (1922) *A History of Durham Rowing*, Reid, Newcastle.
3. Clasper, D. (1990) *Harry Clasper, Hero of the North*, Gateshead Books.
4. Halladay, E. (1990) *Rowing in England: a social history. The amateur debate*, Manchester Univ. Press.
5. Willis, J.S.M. (1971) The recreational use of water; reservoirs and recreation, *Journ. Inst. of Water Engineers*, **25**, 96–101.
6. Institution of Water Engineers (1963) Draft report of the Council on the recreational use of Waterworks, *Journ. Inst. of Water Engineers*, **17**.
7. Coats, D.J. and Ruffle, N.J. (1982) The Kielder Water Scheme, *Proc. Instn. Civil Engrs., Part 1*, **72**, 149–176.
8. ASH Consulting Group (1994) *North of England Watersports Study: a consultation document*, Edinburgh

12. THE PORT OF TYNE

STAFFORD LINSLEY

INTRODUCTION

The River Tyne is naturally navigable within its tidal limit, and consequently its importance as an artery for Tyneside's trade for almost two thousand years cannot be overstated. The chief 'highway' in Britain, certainly from the medieval period onwards, was navigable water, the river and coastal trades being particularly important. The simple reason for the importance of water-borne carriage is that, until the twentieth century, such roads as existed were entirely inadequate for the carriage of heavy products. Packhorses could only manage relatively light loads. Furthermore the use of heavily laden waggons on our roads was restricted to the better months of summer. The overland carriage of high-bulk, low-value products like coal and stone was prohibitively expensive, but the carriage of such products over water was relatively cheap. Consequently the use of navigable rivers and coastal navigation for the carriage of high-bulk, low-value goods became essential for the development of the British economy before the coming of the railways.

THE ORIGINS OF THE PORT

Not surprisingly the Tyne's origins and development as a port remain unclear, although recent excavations on Newcastle's quayside have unravelled some of its medieval mysteries. That the Romans settled at Newcastle is now beyond doubt. Their forts at Benwell, Wallsend, and South Shields (the latter with 22 stone-built granaries), suggest the use of the river for navigation within its tidal stretches; it may be indeed that the Tyne was a significant port in the Roman period.

The Tyne also shared in the 'Golden Age of Northumbria' by virtue of the foundation of the monasteries of Jarrow and Tynemouth in the seventh century. To what extent the river saw traffic at that time and in the centuries leading up to the Norman Conquest can only remain a matter for conjecture. However, with the establishment of the Norman castle in 1068 on the site of the Roman fort in Newcastle, and the subsequent construction of a bridge over the Tyne below the castle by 1175, the future of the Tyne as a port became bound up with that of its major town. It might have been otherwise, for at the time of the conquest the settlement at Newburn, nearer the tidal limit where the Tyne was easily fordable, was probably the most important town on Tyneside. The construction of the Newcastle bridge was to have another long-lasting effect on the Tyne as a port, for the bridge and its eighteenth-century successor effectively limited navigation for all but keels and other small boats, to 'below-bridge'.

The 'Laws of Newcastle' of c.1140 gave the burgesses of the town monopoly trading powers including the sole right to trade in wool, hides, and cloth, and to purchase goods from ships at anchor at the mouth of the Tyne; these privileges established the Tyne as a port under the control of the burgesses of Newcastle. By 1203, the Tyne was ranked the eighth port in all England, and when King John authorised a merchant guild for the town 13 years later, the commercial structures were in place for further monopolistic enterprise. The burgesses continued to exercise their monopoly on payment of an annual rent of £100 to the Crown, but they easily recouped that rent, and more, out of dues that they could charge on all trade on the river.

It has been suggested that by the thirteenth century the river frontage at Newcastle had been provided with timber jetties, built out into the river to assist the loading and unloading of vessels. Over time the deliberate or wanton dumping of rubbish between the jetties raised up a continuous platform that contracted the river but at the same time provided additional flat and low lying land within the town walls. The building alignments of the present quayside with its chares and garths were created on this land. Much of this development had been achieved by 1300, by which time Newcastle had become the sixth most important wool port in England, was also shipping coal, and had further asserted its monopoly position over trade on the river. In 1258 for example, the town's burgesses persuaded the Bishop of Durham not to develop a fishing industry at South Shields. Moreover, the burgesses also acted to limit the development of Tynemouth and North Shields, which if allowed to proceed unchecked might have ruined Newcastle's trade and therefore reduced revenues to the Crown — or so the Newcastle men claimed. Their petition to Parliament was successful; the Prior of Tynemouth was forbidden from trading on the river, and his jetties were dismantled.

THE BEGINNINGS OF THE COAL TRADE

In such ways Newcastle defended and maintained its position of power over the Tyne. Although places like North Shields gained concessions much later, Newcastle dominated the trade and commerce on the river until the nineteenth century. There was however a change in its major article of export. By coincidence good quality coals, which are normally found at considerable depth in the Great Northern Coalfield were, by geological faulting and subsequent erosion, brought to the surface in the immediate vicinity of Newcastle — at Elswick, Benwell, Westerhope, and the Town Moor. On the south bank of the Tyne they outcropped in Gateshead and at Whickham. Long abandoned coal workings which outcropped on the steep river banks of the Tyne, only 50 yards from the water, were encountered during preliminary work for the Metro railway tunnels in Gateshead. Similarly, partially worked-out coal seams were also discovered only a few feet below ground level during more recent civil engineering projects at Scotswood and Westerhope. With such easy availability of good coals and with the river in their control, all the Newcastle burgesses needed to exploit the coal trade's great potential was a ready market and commercial acumen — neither of these seem to have been in short supply.

The impetus to expand the existing trade in coal came from two periods of acute trauma. Firstly, the repeated sieges of the town in the fourteenth century, accompanied by periodic devastation of the surrounding countryside, greatly interfered with established trading in hides and wool. Secondly, the Black Death plagues of 1349 and the immediately ensuing years carried off about half the population and devastated most branches of trade. Losing thereby so much of their established trades, the burgesses of Newcastle vigorously exploited the coal trade, in which they possessed considerable advantages over any other coalfield seeking to win the lucrative London market — good quality coals at shallow depths and very close to navigable water. Coal dominated the river's export trade by the end of the fourteenth century, and continued to do so until the second half of the twentieth century. Central to the commercial organisation of the coal trade in Newcastle were the 'Hostmen', their name derived from the medieval system of providing accommodation and commercial information to merchants visiting the town. Membership of the Hostmen was a privilege of wealth, and not unnaturally the Hostmen exercised considerable powers over the members of the Corporation of the town who were, in effect, the conservators of the River Tyne, although strictly speaking the conservancy of the Tyne was in the hands of the Crown until 1613. Thus the Tyne coal trade was not only important to Newcastle but also to the Crown and therefore to London and the nation. In 1368, the King reserved to himself a tax on coal sold overseas but allowed the Newcastle burgesses to levy a charge of 4d. per chaldron on all Tyne coal sold in Britain; at the same time he gave the burgesses permission to win coals outside the town walls.

Although coal dominated the trade of the Tyne a variety of exports also flourished. In the last three months of 1699 some 250 ships left with coal but others carried salt, lead, cinders, fish, corn, glass, iron, tallow, tobacco, nails, wool and stores. Of the 268 ships to arrive in the same period 232 vessels brought in only ballast while the rest brought corn, goods, fish, timber and tar. By that time some 500,000 tons of coal were being shipped yearly from the Tyne, mainly coastwise but some to foreign parts.

EARLY CHALLENGES TO NEWCASTLE'S SUPREMACY

Challenges to Newcastle's monopoly position persisted, with North Shields re-established as a fishing and victualling port in 1390. Disputes between the Corporation and the Bishops of Durham had also continued through the fourteenth century, but the time was opportune in 1530 for Newcastle to out-manoeuvre the bishop and his brother churchmen at Tynemouth, for the Reformation-minded government was certain to support the town against the clerics. It was decreed by Act that shipment or discharge of any goods on the Tyne, except salt, fish and ship's provisions, could only be made at Newcastle.

A charter of 1600 incorporated the Company of Hostmen and confirmed their exclusive right to the trading of all seacoal (meaning coal carried by sea), and grindstones on the river, except coal which was destined for the saltpans at Hartlepool; all ships should load or discharge at or near Newcastle unless they were physically unable to get there. This last provision was important since taking a sailing boat up-river to Newcastle could be hazardous in itself.

The poor state of the river encouraged support for shipping facilities at North and South Shields, both of which places had deep water near the mouth of the Tyne. As many as 200 ships might be seen at anchor in Shields harbour and quite naturally, it seemed to the people of Shields, this was a far better place than Newcastle to conduct trade; thus in 1625 some wharves were built at Shields in defiance of the powers granted to Newcastle. Matters came to a head around 1646 when Ralph Gardner of Chirton produced a pamphlet entitled 'England's Grievance Discovered' in support of the people of Shields who claimed that the dumping of ballast was blocking the river, that ships were often wrecked in sailing between Shields and Newcastle, and that it was only the greed of the Corporation and Hostmen of Newcastle that prevented the Shields developing as the main port for the Tyne. However, Newcastle continued to exert its granted powers although occasional compromises were made, for example when Newcastle gave license for the construction of ballast wharves at South Shields. The war of words, however, was to continue for more than two centuries.

PROPOSED EXTENSIONS TO THE NAVIGABLE LIMIT

At intervals throughout the eighteenth century some fruitless proposals were made to extend the navigable limits of the Tyne. Firstly, in 1705, there was a proposal to make the Tyne navigable from Newburn to Hexham, presumably by lateral cuts and canalised sections of the river. A petition for consideration by Parliament noted:[1]

> "Your Petitioners humbly conceive the making the River of Tine navigable from Newburne (the place to which it now flows) to Hexham ... would be of very great advantage and benefit to the inhabitants of Northumberland, in carrying their corne, lead, coles, and other the product of that part of the said County lyeing near the said River to the Towne and port of Newcastle ..." [etc.]

The proposal clearly failed to win sufficient support, as did a similar proposal of 1778. Two Tyne-Solway canal schemes were proposed 1794, one of which sought to follow the south bank of the Tyne to the Hexham-Haydon Bridge area, and the other the north bank. At a meeting held to stimulate support for one of the schemes, it was noted that:[1]

> "The present local trade from [Newcastle] to Carlisle, though very considerable might still be improved; and when to that we add the immense lead trade, the vast quantity of Limestone, Coal, Iron, Stone, Timber, hemp, flax, slate, glass etc. that will employ this Navigation, the ingenious mind, charmed with national improvement, dwells upon the picture before it with astonishment and delight, and seems to wonder that a scheme so pregnant with blessings to society should never before have been carried into execution."

But again, insufficient people felt that they needed such 'blessings to society' and the disputes that ensued between the respective protagonists for the north and south side canal schemes probably ensured that neither was built; neither side could raise the capital and the schemes were dropped. There were to be further canal proposals in the early nineteenth century, but these also failed to garner sufficient support.

STAITHS, KEELS AND KEELMEN

Because of the proximity of coal workings and the tidal river, special arrangements grew up on the Tyne for storage and transfer of coal from land carriage to water carriage. The coal staith was the handling device for transferring coal to keels and colliers. Initially the transfer was probably by barrow and plank, a simple system which could be accommodated to tidal variations especially above-bridge and which minimised coal breakage.

With the development of the horse-drawn waggonway the barrow and plank staith was modified to allow the coal to be transferred directly from waggons via a chute or 'spout' to a keel or collier (Fig. 12.1). These waggonway staiths had a hinged chute to allow for tidal variations but were still better suited to above-bridge conditions.

The new rope-worked or 'reciprocating' railway that emerged from about 1800 required staiths with greater handling capacity. The coal 'drop' which was developed consisted of a platform on to which a full waggon could be run. The platform was suspended from the end of a long pivoted lever-arm by which it could be lowered in an arc to reach the hold of a collier (Fig. 12.2) . The coal drop had the particular advantage that it could be located on the river bank but still reach out to deeper river water without excessive interference to shipping. It was better suited to direct loading into colliers rather than into keels.

Fig 12.1 A Thomas Bewick's engraving of a coal staith: This may be an invented scene, but one based on actual structures to be found by the Tyne, showing coal spouts (chutes), designed to allow horse-drawn coal waggons to be emptied via bottom doors, their coals being dropped into chutes which led to waiting colliers or keels. This illustration shows both type of vessel, the keel perhaps being used to finish loading the collier in deeper water. A glassworks is shown in the distance.

Consequently, the drop was ideal for the down-river locations favoured by the new reciprocating railways.

After 1852 the change from solid-ballasted sailing colliers to water-ballasted steam colliers, again required a new form of staith to make the best use of the potentially fast turnround time of the new colliers. The coal drop, which had served the coal trade well for half a century was designed for use by solid-ballasted sailing colliers whose turnround time was largely governed by the need to take on or remove the ballast and the need for constant hand trimming of solid ballast or coal whilst loading. However, since water ballast could be pumped out while coal was being loaded, the turnround time of the new colliers was now being limited by the coal drop with its batch loading and need for hand trimming. To maximise the potential of the new colliers, therefore, continuous loading, together with trimming spouts which could deposit the coal anywhere in the collier's hold were now essential; appropriate new spout staith designs were soon developed. The new coal chutes could be raised, lowered and trimmed. They were capable of dealing with the large tidal ranges experienced at down-river staiths and of handling much larger quantities of coal. These new designs, with small modifications and improvements, lasted until the end of the coal trade in the North East.

Keels and keelmen were peculiar to the harbours at Blyth, Hartley, Tyne, and Wear. They represented a key feature of the coal trade and were a distinctive aspect of river life up to the last quarter of the nineteenth century. And there were many of them. In 1799, for example, there were 320 keels on the Tyne, each of them crewed by four people. The keel boat, first mentioned in the fourteenth century, was mainly used to carry coal from above-bridge staiths to below-bridge colliers. It was a strong, wooden-built, flat-bottomed craft and, by the late eighteenth century, it was some 40 feet from prow to stern and about 19 feet in its beam amidships. It had a pointed stern, which made it easier to build and to handle, and could be propelled by a 22-foot long oar, and steered and partly sculled by a 25 foot 'swape' at the stern. Some, perhaps all, keels were also fitted with a single square sail which could be used when the wind was favourable. But the tide was the keel's prime mover, in both directions, and keels could not work beyond the Tyne's tidal limit. A loaded keel would be 'set' on the ebb tide and return on a flowing tide when empty.

The keel was so identified with the coal trade that it had become a unit of measure for coal at least by 1356. An Act of Parliament of 1421 required that all keel boats should carry 20 chaldrons of coal, and no more, and that every keel boat would have its carrying capacity ascertained and marked by the King's Commissioners with a 'Stock Nail Mark' at the bow and stern of the keel, so that when properly loaded the water came exactly to the mark. This was the earliest instance of a marked load-line in navigation.

It was only part of the keelman's job to carry the coal downriver from the staith, for the coal then had to be 'cast' into the waiting collier. Usually, it would seem, two keels tied up, one on either side of the collier, and the coals from each keel were simultaneously cast into the hold, thereby helping to maintain a level trim. Many of the early colliers were quite small, about 80 tons, and casting was fairly easy, the coals being simply shovelled up from the keel's gunwale to the collier hatch, a height of perhaps five to eight feet. However, as larger colliers were brought into service, casting up became more difficult, and the 1819 keelmen's strike was aimed at getting an extra shilling per keel cast, for every foot of the side of the ship above five feet. Thus, the keelmen could exercise considerable power, to the extent that they could halt the coal trade through strikes, riots, and the burning of staiths. Such industrial disputes were but a foretaste of the troubles that lay ahead for the keelmen, for the very technologies which were to transform the waggonways and the staiths led to their gradual extinction.

DISSATISFACTION WITH NEWCASTLE'S CONSERVANCY OF THE TYNE

The eighteenth century was to witness a return of the old rivalries between Newcastle and the river mouth settlements. The departure of the whaler *Swallow* from Shields in 1751 marked the beginning of a whaling industry which remained mainly based at Shields and lasted until the middle of the nineteenth century. But the Shields' shipowners continued to protest at the state of the river and at Newcastle's neglect of it, for theoretically they were still obliged to direct their vessels up to the town quays for discharge and shipment. In 1765 they petitioned the House of Commons with a devastating indictment of the river. Ballast dumping, they claimed, had shoaled up all previous loading and unloading places; large ships could only load at Shields and even here the river was shoaling up; only Newcastle had the power to levy port dues and improve the river but the heavy dues levied were being used for general municipal purposes rather than for river improvements. Not surprisingly, Newcastle counter-petitioned, and the House once more ignored the pleas of the Shields' shipowners. It is almost certainly true that the Corporation did regard its port dues as a very convenient source of municipal revenue and seems to have believed that its duties towards the Tyne were fulfilled if, at best, it was prevented from deteriorating.

Criticism of the Corporation could not be easily stifled since the river was becoming progressively worse for navigation. In 1774, Captain Phipps (later Lord Mulgrave) who was then a parliamentary candidate for Newcastle, noted that the Tyne could be one of the finest rivers in the world had not ignorance, inattention and avarice turned it into a 'cursed horsepond'; further that dealing with ballast on returning colliers would always be a problem, but the Corporation made matters much worse by charging such excessive rates for its discharge that ship's masters chose to dump their ballast just off the river mouth or indeed in the river itself, thereby aggravating the problem of riverbed shoals. Again these criticisms fell upon deaf ears. By 1800, when some 40,000 tons of shipping was owned in North and South Shields, the shipowners returned to the fray. They indicted Newcastle for obstructing 'the King's Highway of the Tyne' because shoals were not being removed. The Corporation were acquitted and no improvements followed. The Shields' shipowners then suggested that a representative Conservancy Commission should be placed in control of the river. Again nothing happened. New harbour leading lights were, however, constructed

Fig 12.2 The Coal Drops at Wallsend: The 'coal drops'enabled coal waggons to be lowered to the hold of collier brigs. Developed on the Tyne, this type of drop, with a few variants, came to be almost universally adopted in the Northeast, for it was ideally suited to the rope-worked and locomotive drawn railways. *(from: T.H. Hair: Sketches of the coal mines of Northumberland and Durham, 1839).*

in 1810 by Trinity House. Trinity House had established the river's first leading lights in *c.*1536.

In 1813, in a belated effort to prove that it did care about the state of the Tyne, the Corporation asked John Rennie, one of the most accomplished civil engineers of his day, to carry out a survey of the river and to prepare a report on its potential for improvement. Rennie seems to have worked at a pace which suited the Corporation, not producing his report until 1816. He recommended that the river be narrowed in some parts to give a better scouring by the tide, and widened in others, that some projecting points (such as Whitehill Point) be removed, that a south-side pier be built at the river mouth, and that masonry wharf walls be built where the river was to be narrowed. In all he made some twenty recommendations, with an estimated cost of £520,000. Prolonged discussions ensued, over several decades in fact, but almost nothing was done. Even so, by 1829, the Tyne had 202,379 registered merchant tonnage, and amongst English ports only the Port of London exceeded this figure.

The general situation was to change rapidly with the spread of steam-hauled railways after 1830, for no particular port could hold on to monopoly positions once the railways had demonstrated that coal could be carried cheaply and efficiently to the best, rather than the nearest port. Amble, West Hartlepool, and Middlesbrough were soon to take advantage of this fact, but Newcastle took much longer to recognise the inevitable — that railways were not only changing the whole pattern of inland communication, but were also bringing into question the continued suitability of the historic ports. This realisation seems to have briefly descended upon the collective minds of the Newcastle Corporation, for it did flirt with a number of railway companies, holding shares for example in the Newcastle & Carlisle and the Brandling Junction railway companies. Yet whilst it recognised that railways might increase trade on the river, and therefore also increase the Corporation's revenues, it still remained reluctant to improve the river.

Agitation from the Shields' interests now gained momentum. They proposed converting the tide mill dam at Mill Dam, South Shields, into a wet dock, as first suggested by John Smeaton in 1769, but Newcastle's response was to fill it in with ballast. Small-minded blocking tactics seemed to have succeeded again. Matters did improve slightly after the 1835 Municipal Corporations Reform Act required the election of councillors, and expenditure on the river was increased a little. The Corporation continued to regard the Tyne as simply a navigable river leading to its principal quay at Newcastle. As long as ships could actually get to Newcastle, no matter what the difficulties in so doing, the Corporation seemed satisfied that it was discharging its proper responsibilities. One man's view of the Newcastle Corporation at this time may well give a valuable insight into the governance of the town and the river. John Fife was a leading Newcastle surgeon and mayor of the town when he claimed, after the Whigs had taken control of the Corporation from the Tories:[2]

> The constituency of this town is of a very mixed character: one third
> may be called reformers — another third is made up of Whigs and a set

of trimming wavering and vacillating shabbies — the remaining third consisting of wealthy fools and the rich order of tradesmen, this latter class being the most ignorant and besotted of the three, and as destitute of political principle as of political information.

Nevertheless, the reformed council did appoint an engineer to oversee developments on the river, but his allocated budget was so small that he could never do much more than tinker with the manifest problems. The Corporation seems to have been oblivious to the port and harbour developments taking place elsewhere in the country, and indeed in the region, and remained largely content to avoid any progressive undertakings. For example, when the Stanhope & Tyne Railroad Company, which had opened to South Shields in 1835, was shipping some 400,000 tons of coal per annum from riverside coal drops by 1838, there were, understandably, renewed calls for docks. The Corporation was reluctant to embark on such a venture itself but did at least indicate that it would not be averse to the Stanhope & Tyne Company providing such facilities. However, when the railway company began to experience the financial difficulties which were to lead to its demise, the Corporation refused to come to its aid. This lack of imagination and foresight, and the continued unwillingness of the Corporation to spend harbour dues on river improvements, was seen by many as a scandal which should not pass unnoticed. In 1841, for example, petitions were available for signature by anyone who felt that the Corporation was guilty of a 'Misappropriation of the River Funds' (Fig 12.3).

THE TURN OF THE TIDE FOR CONTROL OF THE RIVER

In such ways, the critics of the Corporation maintained their attacks, and they were to receive a major fillip to their campaign from the Commissioners for Tidal Harbours who, in a report of 1846, noted that the Tyne had:[3]

"... coasted upwards of two million tons of coal per annum for the last quarter of a century. Her foreign trade has risen to half-a-million tons yearly; and the revenue derived from the river, and paid to the City Corporation, by charter, as conservators of the port, amounts to £19,000 a year; exclusive of £6000 annually levied by the Trinity Board for primeage, buoyage, etc. Where all seems so prosperous, it is an ungrateful task to point out that such a state of things may be deceitful; yet so it will certainly prove to be in the Tyne, if the river be much longer abandoned to itself, as, generally speaking, it has been until the last few years. The improvements proposed by Mr. Rennie, 30 years since, have, with the exception of a quay at Newcastle been left unexecuted. The width of the river remains extremely irregular, in some places the channel being only 60 yards wide; sharp angles increase the difficulty of navigation; upwards of ten acres of sandbank, dry at low water, still disfigure the bed of the stream; Newcastle bridge ... almost acts as a mill dam ... coal staiths are projected irregularly into the stream; and no dock accommodation has been provided, while Shields harbour, the daily

MISAPPROPRIATION

OF THE

RIVER FUNDS

BY THE

NEWCATLE

Corporation.

PETITIONS

TO BOTH

Houses of Parliament

LIE HERE

FOR

SIGNATURE.

April 1841

Fig 12.3 Petition to Parliament in 1841 against Newcastle Corporation's 'Misappropriation of the River Funds'

resort of hundreds of colliers, is so inconveniently crowded that damage frequently occurs."

There were at this time about 19,000 sailings per year from the Tyne, that is, an average of 52 sailings per day throughout the year. In addition there were also perhaps 150 keel boats permanently in the river. It really was a congested river, and it really was unimproved (Fig. 12.4). The Tidal Commissioners' report was another clear indictment of the Corporation's failings as conservators of the Tyne, and with such strongly worded support from an independent, government-appointed body, the Shields' interests now confidently pressed home their claim to become a separate Port of Custom.

In 1847, the Corporation confirmed that the Port of Tyne should remain undivided, but it did agree that auxiliary Custom Houses could be established at North and South Shields. The Shields' interests regarded this as an insufficient gesture and agitated for totally separate Custom Houses, gaining a partial victory in 1848 when Shields harbour was constituted as a separate Port of Custom. A Custom House was established at North Shields in the same year, but this did not satisfy the good people of South Shields who continued a vigorous campaign for their own Custom House, and achieved success some 17 years later. The Shields' interests, aided and abetted by above-bridge allies such as Joseph Cowen Snr., attempted to execute a *coup de gras* during 1848 by holding meetings in North and South Shields aimed at drawing up plans for a Tyne Conservancy Bill to be presented to Parliament. Newcastle Council objected strongly and unanimously to the very idea, but without any convincing arguments. The promoters of the Bill, on the other hand, had plenty of ammunition and did not

Fig 12.4 Shields in 1835: A very busy scene near the mouth of the Tyne, but not an unusual one at the time. It is easy to see why the merchants of Shields sought release from the controlling powers of the Corporation of Newcastle as conservators of the Tyne, and for Shields to be declared a port in its own right. *(By permission: Beamish, the North of England Open Air Museum)*

hesitate to fire. They claimed that the Corporation had received a total of £958,000 in shipping dues between 1808 and 1848, and that although £400,000 had nominally been spent on the river, only about £40,000 had gone on 'real improvements'. They further stated that more than 800 acres of sand banks lay dry at low tide between Shields and Newcastle, and that at such times the best parts of the river only had 2 feet 4 inches of water. It was even possible, they said, to walk across the river-mouth bar at low tide. A broadsheet war was declared. On New Years Day 1849 'A Faithful Son of Father Tyne' published a broadsheet which noted that:[4]

> "During the past fifty years, to my certain knowledge, many hundredweights of tobacco have been smoked over this grievance in North and South Shields, under cover of which smoke tremendous volleys of imprecations have been discharged against the Town Council of Newcastle. Endless smoking — infinite cursing — but now, my friends, is it not time to lay down our pipes and fall to business."

Getting down to business quite simply meant getting rid of the Corporation as conservators of the Tyne; they only exercised their barbaric control over the river by virtue of the 'old tyrant, Henry the Eighth', who granted it. The 'faithful son' passionately believed that the present conservators could not possibly be the best people for the job, for they had private interests which ran counter to the general good. He was certainly ready for a fight, one based on moral certitude as much as on business imperatives:

> "It inspires one with as much sorrow as indignation to look at this waste of life and wealth, and to know that all the evil that is done, and the good that is left undone, is the inevitable result of a dishonest system. Shall we any longer submit to it? Is not the time arrived for a vigorous effort?... During half a century there has been an incessant growling over this grievance, breaking at intervals into an outcry - but no regularly organized attempt like the present. It is time the question was settled. If the dues are public dues, let us know it; if they are private dues, let us know it; and then we will be at or wits' end, and waste no more time in grumbling."

Later in January a meeting was held in the Town Hall, South Shields, which unanimously supported the Bill. Captain John Washington RN carried out a preliminary inquiry for parliament, and his report of May 1849, was scathing in its criticisms. The report concluded that it:[5]

> "... must be manifest that the several duties usually attached to the conservancy of a harbour have not been attended to on the Tyne; that the most ordinary duties of river engineering, such as regulating and deepening the channel, cutting off projecting points, dredging away or otherwise removing the shoals, so as to produce a uniform bed of the

river, have all but been entirely omitted; that sufficient quay accommodation for the traffic has not been provided; that no attempt has been made to improve the bar, or to get rid of the obstruction to the tide by the piers and starlings of Tyne Bridge; that the casting of ballast close to the entrance, and to a large extent in Shields harbour, had not been prevented."

Even so the Bill was withdrawn, but only through lack of time. The Newcastle Corporation had stared defeat in the face, and the Bill's withdrawal was merely a postponement of what must now have seemed inevitable. The Tyne Improvement Act, enabling the formation of the Tyne Improvement Commission (TIC), was passed in 1850. The Commission would have control of the entire river within its tidal limit, except for Newcastle's Corporation Quay, but it would only be allowed to collect three-eighths of the river's coal dues while the Corporation would take the remainder. The Corporation had asked for three-quarters of the dues, but in truth there was little justification other than historical precedence for their stance, and the five-eighths of the dues which they were allowed to take was generous. Even so it was not until 1870 that the TIC took the entire coal dues, but only on condition that they paid appropriate compensation to the Corporation.

THE WORK OF THE TYNE IMPROVEMENT COMMISSION

The TIC took over a river 'much as nature had left it' and, if the Tyne were to compete with other northeastern ports which had improvements well underway, it had much catching up to do. Moreover, the railways were in a strong competitive position *vis á vis* the coastal carriage of coal by 1850. The sailing colliers were now too slow, and the manifest success of the railways led some to believe that the coastal trade might be doomed. However, as discussed in Chapter 13 the successful performance of Charles Mark Palmer's *John Bowes* steam-powered water-ballasted screw collier of 1852 began to tilt the balance away from the railways and towards the new colliers.

While the provision of 'wet docks' was an important development at British ports and harbours, beginning in the 1770s, they appeared much later in the North East. The 'wet dock' was an artificial deep-water basin, surrounded by quays, which could give permanent and sheltered deep water for sea-going vessels. Although small wooden sailing colliers had little need for deep water for loading or unloading, the swing to larger steam-powered iron colliers with screw propulsion greatly increased the potential usefulness of wet docks in the coal trade. Sunderland had built its first wet dock in 1837, Hartlepool built two wet docks in the 1840s, and Middlesbrough Dock opened in 1842, all being served by up-to-date railways. The Port of Tyne was falling behind its neighbours in improved port provision, but the creation of the TIC provided the opportunity to reinforce the dominant position of the Tyne. The TIC moved quite quickly and professionally.

The TIC commenced the building of river-mouth piers in 1855. The Northumberland Dock was opened at Howdon in 1857 to serve coal-carrying railways from several collieries in Northumberland, while Tyne Dock was opened by the North Eastern Railway at South Shields in 1859. These were the first substantial improvements ever made to the Port of Tyne. So the first decade of conservancy by the Tyne Improvement Commission saw considerable strides forward, but revenues were quite low largely because the river itself was still as the Commissioners had inherited it. Mr John Francis Ure, their engineer, reported in 1860 that:

- Sailing vessels sometimes had to wait two months at the bar before they could get into the river.
- Only small vessels could reach Newcastle.
- One-third of the total traffic on the river was still carried in keels.
- Even the keels had navigation difficulties above bridge.
- The new docks could not therefore be fully utilised.
- Shifting sands gave uncertain water depths at the coal staiths such that many of the new coal drops could no longer be used.
- The larger vessels were deserting the Tyne in favour of the improved River Wear.

In that year three large American vessels had been unable to cross the Tyne Bar, while ships of a similar size could easily have entered the Wear. Ure believed that extensive river bed dredging was a prerequisite for truly effective improvement of the Tyne. This was soon put in hand, with 2.5 M tons dredged from the river in 1863, 4.2 M tons in 1864, 4.5 M tons in 1865, and 5.3 M tons in 1866. It has been said that more material has been dredged from the Tyne than was excavated to create the Suez Canal. Ure also advocated the removal of the river bar (carried out in 1863), extensions to the piers, the replacement of the Tyne Bridge by a swing bridge (first suggested in 1851 but not carried out until 1876), followed by dredging above bridge and the removal of King's Meadows Island, and the straightening of the river in the Lemington–Stella area to give deeper water at Blaydon (carried out c.1880). Ure was aided and abetted in all this by Joseph Cowen Snr, until just before Cowen's death in 1873. Cowen had participated on behalf of the above-bridge communities and industrial concerns in the earlier attempts to wrest control of the Tyne from the Corporation. He was made a life Commissioner when the TIC was created and was Chairman of the TIC by 1853 remaining so until his death.

The replacement of the eighteenth-century stone arch bridge at Newcastle by the Tyne Swing Bridge and the subsequent dredging and straightening of the river above-bridge had exactly the impact so eagerly anticipated. The river was opened up as far as Blaydon to sea-going vessels, allowing expansion of above-bridge industrial concerns. Indeed, the terms 'above-bridge' and 'below-bridge' had now lost any real meaning in respect of navigation on the river. However, the still quickening pace of some aspects of the Industrial Revolution, in particular the increasing size of ships, was to make the old distinction a reality again within a few decades, but without greatly damaging consequences. For a while the above-bridge improvements together with the creation of the

Scotswood, Newburn, & Wylam Railway, led to consideration of the creation of docks at Blaydon and Scotswood; wisely perhaps, these did not proceed. However, the TIC constructed the Albert Edward Dock near North Shields in the 1880s; this dock was designed for coal exports and general cargo imports and could take larger vessels than the Northumberland Dock. The river had been sufficiently dredged above-bridge to enable the Armstrong Works at Elswick to commence shipbuilding by 1887, the North Eastern Railway rebuilt Tyne Dock in 1890 and created Dunston staiths in 1893, and the Consett Iron Works built the Derwenthaugh staiths in 1900. All these endeavours gave new or improved shipping points between Shields and Blaydon, thereby maintaining the economy of water transport. Nor were the lesser Tyne industries forgotten, for the North Shields Fish Quay was constructed in 1886–7.

Meanwhile work had been progressing somewhat erratically on the river-mouth piers. Work on the north pier had begun in 1855 and on the south pier in the following year, but well before they were completed their design was altered to provide longer piers reaching out into deeper water. These plans were further altered in 1862–3, before stormy seas caused considerable damage to the uncompleted piers in 1867. Repairs went ahead, but a decision to lengthen the intended piers still further was made by 1887. More storms were to cause damage during construction, but the piers and their terminal lighthouses were completed in 1895, only for the north pier to be severely damaged in the following year. The outer part of this pier was completely reconstructed on a different alignment, but this was not finally completed until 1915.

The growth of the nation's railway system had led to increasing amounts of coal being carried to London by rail. Some of this coal was from the North East, but the competition from coal carried from the coalfields of the Midlands and Derbyshire was strong because of the shorter distances involved. In 1865 only 8.9% of the coal reaching London by rail had originated in the North East, and by 1877 that figure had fallen to 5%. The new breed of collier, based on the *John Bowes*, had enabled the North East's rail companies to meet some of the competition in the London coal trade by a combination of railways leading to well equipped northeastern ports, and the cheap coastal trade now offered by the new colliers. It was partly to ensure such trade, that the North Eastern Railway Company was often at loggerheads with the public and private bodies which owned port facilities in the region, and this conflict in turn had led the railway company to take Hartlepool docks under its ownership and to build Tyne Dock and coal staiths at Dunston on Tyne and elsewhere. But there was also another reason for the North Eastern Railway's interest in port development for it was but a short step from steam colliers in the coastal trade to steam colliers in the export trade, and such trades would be open to any railway company with good access to good ports. The whole development of steam shipping, on a global scale, with its voracious need for bunker coal, brought new opportunities to the North East. By 1913, around 70% of northeastern coal went in exports and foreign bunkering, and almost all of this export trade was being fed to its ports by railways. The plan had worked, but just in time, for the railways were now carrying more coal than the coastal collier fleets.

THE YEARS OF DECLINE

Even so, within a couple of decades northeastern coal outputs began their remorseless decline. In 1923, 22M tonnes coal were shipped from the Tyne, but that figure had fallen to 2M by 1995. The annual number of openings of the Swing Bridge (Fig. 12.5) tracks the rise and fall of above-bridge traffic. Tyne Dock, which once shipped 7M tons of coal in a single year, shipped its last coal in the 1960s. Along with that decline in the coal trade went an equivalent decline in the importance of the Port of Tyne; port operations have always been something of a barometer of economic activity.

Some port developments took place during these difficult years. The Tyne Commission Quay fronting the Albert Edward Dock opened in 1928; new coaling staiths were built at Jarrow in 1936 and at Whitehill Point in 1954; a large iron ore import facility to serve the Consett Ironworks was opened at Tyne Dock in 1953, only for these imports to cease in 1974; Jarrow Slake, a large area of tidal mudflats, from part of which Tyne Dock had been created, was reclaimed during the years 1974–78 for port uses such as the Nissan Car, Tyne Grain, and Tyne Coal terminals.

The misfortunes of the Port of Tyne in the twentieth century were not simply

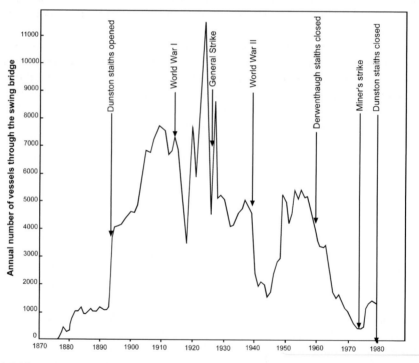

Fig 12.5 The annual number of Tyne Swing Bridge openings (up and down) 1876–1980 indicating the fluctuating trade 'above bridge' after the opening of the Swing Bridge; it thereby also illustrates the varying fortunes of the Tyne, often under the influence of significant national events.

a result of the falling coal trade, for there was also a decline in engineering, shipbuilding, and general manufactures from around the middle of the twentieth century. In parallel with the decline in the coal trade there has been a fall in other traffic, albeit less striking. In 1970, some 4M tonnes of traffic other than coal went through the Port of Tyne, but by 1995 only about 2M. On average twelve ships entered the Tyne in 1970, but only four or five by 1995. In the meantime the TIC was formally dissolved in 1968 and the 'Port of Tyne Authority' constituted.

As a consequence of these changes, coal staiths have been demolished, some docks filled in or converted to 'marina villages', and former industrial sites such as Armstrong's at Elswick converted to business parks. Some 'new' industrial activities are in evidence; for example, offshore industries to some extent replaced shipbuilding (which may yet return). While the Tyne is clearly still a viable port, the signs of a new age seem unmistakable. Perhaps that new age began with the Tall Ships Race of 1986 and then the deployment of Dunston staiths as a focus for the 1990 Gateshead National Garden Festival. More recently the Newcastle and Gateshead quaysides have undergone, or are undergoing, a fundamental transformation from industrial commerce to leisure pursuits. If that is now the way to achieve economic rejuvenation on Tyneside, then the River Tyne is clearly integral to it, but it will be a development which could never have been foreseen by generations of river users over the past two millennia.

On the other hand, as traditional port activities have gradually focused nearer the river's mouth, it may come to be believed that the Prior of Tynemouth was justified in his actions in the thirteenth century, and that the Corporation and its successors as conservators of the Port of Tyne have unwittingly obstructed the inevitable for 700 years.

REFERENCES

1. Mackenzie, E, (1825) *An Historical, Topographical, and Descriptive view of the County of Northumberland*, Vol. 1, 2nd Edn., Newcastle.
2. John Fife, *Newcastle Journal*, 30 July 1836.
3. Tidal Harbour Commission (1846) Second Report, HMSO, London.
4. A Faithful Son of Father Tyne, 'To the Shipowners and Inhabitants of Shields' Broadsheet, (New Years Day, 1849).
5. J. Washington, 'River Tyne Conservancy Bill: Report of the Admiralty Inspectors', House of Commons, 4 May 1849.

13. TYNE INDUSTRIES

STAFFORD LINSLEY

INTRODUCTION

The Tyne has a reputation as an industrial river especially in its tidal reach, and indeed this was true for several centuries. Many of the industries have now gone, overtaken by technological, social, economic and sometimes political forces, largely but not exclusively beyond their control. The river and its banks have been transformed in the post-industrial era, but an appreciation of the type and scale of industry on the Tyne is essential to understand and interpret the past in the present landscape. Industries can be classified according to the ways in which they used the river.

○ For import and export in the navigable section of the Tyne, in particular the coal trade but also the pottery, glass, chemical and grindstone trades.

○ As a source of power to drive waterwheels for corn, woollen, paper, and lead mills, mainly above the tidal limit.

○ To serve waterborne transport in the maritime industries, especially shipbuilding but also rope making, sailmaking, paint manufacture etc.

○ For the river water itself, used for steam raising and cooling, for water supply and as a means of disposal of waste (largely dealt with in other chapters).

○ For the animal life of the river in the once famous Tyne salmon industry (Chapter 6)

Although the oldest of these human activities was fishing for food, and the second oldest the milling of corn, the most important industrial activity on the Tyne from at least the twelfth century onwards was undoubtedly the coal trade.

THE TYNE COAL TRADE

The origins of the coal trade in the North East are unclear, but there is archaeological evidence for the use of coal by the Romans, and documentary evidence for the trade from the thirteenth century. For example, complaints were made in 1256 concerning the dangers posed to travellers approaching Newcastle by the derelict or unfenced coal workings which surrounded it. A ship belonging to the Prior of Tynemouth, together with its cargo of coals, was seized in 1269, and 'Newcastle' coal was certainly available in London by 1270. Coal would soon be the country's major article of coastal trade, as in the succeeding centuries the tonnage of northeastern coal carried round its coasts exceeded that of all other commodities put together.

Although there was probably some activity on almost all UK coalfields from the thirteenth century, the northeastern coalfield dominated until 1913. There were several reasons for this. Firstly, until the development of rail systems, the transport of high-bulk, low-value commodities like coal for more than three or four miles overland was prohibitively expensive, but their transport over navigable water was relatively cheap. For example, the cost of carrying coal four miles overland was about the same as carrying it over water from the Tyne to the Thames. Thus an early and important advantage enjoyed by the North East over other coalfields was the fact that many of its mines operated within a couple of miles of the tidal waters of the Tyne, the tidewater pits, close enough to make pack-horse or cart carriage of coal to the river economically viable. Moreover, some of its best coals lay very near the surface, indeed they outcropped around Newcastle and Gateshead. In addition, the North East was handily placed for export to London, always the dominant market for coal and many other commodities, and there was clearly a local willingness to exploit this and other markets. Finally, well-organised trading procedures and networks were developed at an early period in the industry's history.

The Tyne coal trade came to assume crucial importance in the national economy, and yet its early organisation lay entirely in the hands of a small group of Tyneside landowning and merchanting families whose continued prosperity and conspicuous consumption astonished many. The Newcastle Hostmen (Chapter 12) controlled the coal trade of the river at least from the fourteenth century to the eighteenth century, and through their influence over the Newcastle Corporation, they effectively held responsibility for the river itself. They were also aided and abetted by the 'Guild of Pilots and Mariners' who purchased a property in Newcastle's Broad Chare in 1492 — the beginnings of Trinity House and its responsibility for pilotage and lighthouses on the Tyne.

An Act of Parliament of 1600 incorporated the Hostmen and codified their responsibilities in the regulation of the Tyne coal trade. The 'Regulation of the Vend' became their most important function and this enabled them to stipulate the coal output and pithead price at each Tyneside pit, thereby determining coal importation into London. Coalowners could only sell their coals through intermediaries employed by the Hostmen called 'Fitters', who then transacted the sale of the coal to the ships' masters operating on behalf of the shipowners. Hostmen and their Fitters generally owned the keels which were necessary for transhipment from above-bridge staiths because the headroom at the Tyne Bridge denied passage of sailing colliers further upriver. They also employed the keelmen on a yearly bond.

Although of uncertain origin, wooden-built collier brigs carried Tyne coal to numerous destinations, mainly to the east and south coasts of England, but also to Scotland as far as the Shetlands, to France, Spain, Scandinavia, the Baltic, and on to Russia. The collier represented Britain's first specialised trading vessel, distinctive in build and rig, and it so proved its sea-worthiness over the centuries that Captain Cook, a north country man, chose a second-hand and suitably converted north country collier for his great expeditions. His ship *Endeavour* had sailed for four years in the coal trade before being taken by the navy in 1768. They were highly-regarded boats, as John Ruskin testified:[1]

191

"But most assuredly, nothing that ever swung at the quay sides of Carthage, or glowed with crusaders' shields above the bays of Syria, could give to any contemporary human creature such an idea of the meaning of the word Boat, as may be now gained by any mortal happy enough to behold as much as a Newcastle Collier beating against the wind."

Colliery waggonways and pumping engines

Many tidewater mines seem to have been exhausted above the water table by about 1650, leaving only two options for the continued viability of the trade. Mine shafts could be deepened to below the water table, but subsequent coal working would require more powerful pumps than were then available, as well as winding from greater depths than ever before. Alternatively, new shallow and easily drained mines could be sunk further afield, but such pits would only be able to enter the trade if the cost of overland carriage by pack-horse or cart could be significantly reduced. This latter option was the first to become available through the agency of the horse-drawn wooden waggonway, the progenitor of the railway, first brought from Nottingham to the North East in c.1605. Waggonways reduced the cost of overland transport by about 50% and thereby enabled pits up to eight miles from navigable water to enter the trade. To perform economically, waggonways were obliged to take the shortest available route to navigable water, consistent with topography and wayleave agreements, and many led to above-bridge coal staiths from which keel transhipment was required. For reasons connected with coalfield stratigraphy, it was these above-bridge collieries which now came to dominate the trade.

However, a lifebelt was at hand for the tidewater pits by the early eighteenth century in the shape of the Newcomen atmospheric pumping engine, first used at a Warwickshire colliery in 1712. Three such 'fire engines' were at work in the North East by c.1715, and many more were to follow, enabling some flooded tidewater pits to be reopened and sunk to deeper seams. Many of these were below-bridge pits with no need for keel transhipment, and by 1770 they had usurped the formerly dominant above-bridge pits.

The organisation of the trade had changed irrevocably since the beginning of the eighteenth century as a cartel of powerful coalowners who, not being freemen of Newcastle were denied access to the Company of Hostmen, successfully formed an organisation in opposition to the Hostmen. Fitters were now to be contracted to the coalowners, acting as their servants rather than, as formerly, their masters.

New forms of colliery railway

Although London's domestic needs still dominated the market for coal, industrial demand was rising towards the end of the eighteenth century. The Napoleonic wars were to have a major impact on the country, and on the overland haulage of coal in the North East, as the horse-drawn waggonways gave way to more economical forms of railway. In part the impetus to change was a period of high prices for horse feed and timber, with a simultaneous fall in the price of iron, stimulating attempts to improve the horse's effectiveness and ultimately to replace it. The result was firstly a new breed of coal-carrying railway sometimes called the 'reciprocating railway', and subsequently the steam-hauled freight and passenger railway inaugurated by the Liverpool & Manchester line of 1830.

The new reciprocating railways were worked by combinations of fixed and locomotive engines, rope-worked inclined planes, and horses running on iron rails and stone sleeper blocks. They were economic over much greater distances than the waggonways, and so did not need to take the shortest available routes to navigable water. Consequently, they could achieve further economies in coal carriage by heading for staiths nearer the river's mouth, thereby avoiding keel transhipment and ensuring more certain shipments.

The Tyne tug
Irrespective of the inadequacy of the Corporation of Newcastle as conservators of the Tyne, and indeed perhaps because of this inadequacy, some other developments were to improve the lot of the coal shippers. The problem of navigating a collier brig up or down the river grew progressively more acute in the early nineteenth century, but the immediate solution to this problem was to lie in the development of the steam tug rather than in river improvement. The origins of the steam tug are somewhat unusual. In 1814, a wooden-built steam-powered ferry, the *Perseverance*, was working on the Tyne (believed to be the first steam boat to appear on an English waterway), but for some reason that venture failed. However, in *c.*1818, *Perseverance* successfully towed a vessel across the Tyne bar, a manoeuvre which had never been tried before. It must have been immediately apparent that the same trick could be used to assist the entry and exit of colliers to and from the Tyne, and indeed to haul them up or down river, whatever the wind or weather, thereby offering a more certain trade and faster turnround times. The steam-powered paddle tug soon became an integral feature of the Tyne trade and it was soon to be claimed that tugs enabled vessels of 400 tons register to be brought up to Newcastle, whereas previously the maximum was 240 tons. Vessels which once only averaged eight voyages a year between Tyne and Thames could now manage thirteen.

When the Tyne Improvement Commission took over control of the river in 1850, the collier fleet was still a sailing fleet, carrying some 4M tons of coal per annum. On some days up to 1,500 vessels would throng the river. The river really was unimproved and congested, and trade was being lost to neighbouring ports. Perhaps more importantly, steam-hauled railways could now compete with the coastal trade, such that Midlands' coal could now be carried to London by rail as cheaply, and possibly cheaper, than north-east coal carried by sea. The Tyne Commissioners could hardly be expected to counter this threat to the North East's coastal coal trade, for their task was long-term improvement, but this potentially bleak situation was rescued by the development of a new and revolutionary kind of collier.

Ballast and the John Bowes *screw collier*

Collier brigs with no return cargo (and this was normally the case in the coal trade), needed ballast for the return journey if they were to remain stable at sea. From the very beginnings of the coal trade the need for stability meant the part-loading of the ship's hold with solid materials, most of which were of little value to the North East, although certain industries came to depend on them. Perhaps the earliest account of the unloading of ballast is that given by William Gray in 1649:[2]

> "Below east [of Sandgate, Newcastle] is the Ballist Hill, where women upon their heads carried ballist, which was taken forth of small ships which came empty for coales; which place was the first ballist shoare out of the toune: since which time, the trade of coals increasing, there is many ballist shoares made below the water, on both sides of the river."

Some 900,000 tons of ballast were being brought to the Tyne annually by the mid-nineteenth century, and the very contours of the banks of the Tyne below-bridge were being massively altered by the dumping of 'foreign' materials. But attempts in the 1840s to use water instead of solid ballast culminated in the launch of the *John Bowes* from Palmer's shipyard at Jarrow. This vessel was the first unequivocally successful sea-going, iron-built, steam-powered, screw-propelled, water-ballasted collier, although she was also rigged as a three-masted topsail schooner just in case. Palmer's yard must have been confident of success, for a considerable celebration was arranged for the launch in June 1852:[3]

> "A splendid iron screw steamer, constructed ... at Jarrow, and the first vessel of that description ... built for the London coal trade, was launched in the presence of a numerous and influential concourse of spectators ... The vessel [of] 465 tons register, was calculated to carry thirty keels of coals, and to make thirty trips per annum between Newcastle and London. It was ballasted with water ..."

John Bowes commenced her first journey from the Tyne to London on 29 July, reaching the West India Dock in 48 hours, an unprecedented journey time. A rapid turnround was effected by unloading about 630 tons of coal in 18 hours while simultaneously taking on water ballast, and she was back on the Tyne by 3 August after an 18-hour passage. She had cost the equivalent of three collier brigs to build, but she could do in five days what three brigs would take at least a month to perform. At the time of her launch an even larger collier, the *James Dixon*, was already on the stocks at Jarrow. She was to carry 1,200 tons of coal with a crew of 21 men, the equivalent of sixteen collier brigs with a total complement of 144 men. Soon Palmers were building 'colliers by the mile', and the phrase 'steam boat regularity' entered the lexicon of the coal trade. There was hardly a sailing collier to be seen by 1873.

Outputs from the northeast coalfield continued to expand into the twentieth century, from about 15M tons per annum in 1860 to a peak of 56M tons, of which Tyne shipments contributed 20.5M tons in 1911. There were some new colliery sinkings in the early part of the twentieth century, such as at Westoe in c.1909, still mainly feeding their coals onto navigable water, but as these pits were being sunk, others were closing. Even the 'new' pits were being closed down towards the end of the twentieth century, Westoe colliery ceasing production in c.1985.

The Coke trade

Many if not most local collieries produced large amounts of 'small' coal, for which there was only a very limited market, for example in the local salt and glass works. However, by 1764, some of this small coal was being sintered to form coke, often referred to simply as 'cinder', (but 'dephlogisticated coal' by the French!). There were many more uses for coke in a range of industries which were expanding by the late eighteenth century, and by 1825 there were substantial coke works on Tyneside at Wylam, South Shore, Derwenthaugh and St Anthonys. Early coke-making methods were unsuited to the recovery of by-products such as gas and tar, both of which had been the focus of experimentation in the late eighteenth century, but later methods allowed the recovery of several by-products. A tar works by the Blaydon Burn gained the distinction of being the first in the world to produce petrol from coal — 'Blaydon Benzole'. Liquid waste from coke works provided the source of some of the worst pollutants to the Tyne estuary (Chapter 8).

THE BALLAST INDUSTRIES

Although most of the solid ballast brought to the Tyne on the returning colliers was merely dumped, some ballast materials found uses in local industries, and indeed became essential to their continued viability; such industries were most conveniently located on tidewater sites. The *John Bowes* and her descendants were a blessing to the coal trade, but often spelled the death knell to the ballast-dependent industries.

Pottery Manufacture

The earliest pottery in the region was not located on a tidewater site, but in the unlikely setting of Newbottle in County Durham in c.1720. But John Warburton established the first of many potteries near the tidal river Tyne, in Pandon Dene in c.1730. More potteries followed, mainly in the semi-urban tidewater industrial areas of Tyneside, such as those at St Anthony's, Stepney Bank, and by the Ouseburn. The North East had some 25 potteries by 1863. Cheaply imported ballasted raw materials were vital to the Tyneside industry, enabling it to compete with the Staffordshire potteries. For example, in the 1860s, clay was being imported to the North East at 5s. per ton compared with its cost of 13s. per ton in Staffordshire, while flints were being imported at 4s. 6d. per ton to the North East compared with 19s. to Staffordshire. However, the steady introduction of water ballasting eliminated much of Tyneside's transport advantage and, the firm of Malings apart, the local potteries began an inevitable decline.

Glass Manufacture

The early seventeenth century saw the emergence of glass making as a large-scale industry on Tyneside, partly because of the unlimited amount of cheap coal in the area, and partly because some materials like sand could be imported cheaply as ballast on colliers returning from the Kings Lynn area. There were numerous glassworks on Tyneside by the end of the eighteenth century, all located on tidewater sites and all below-bridge except for that at Lemington. The region had become the chief centre of the nation's glass production, a position which it was to hold until the middle years of the nineteenth century. The decline of the local glass industry was apparent by the 1860s. Tyneside's former advantages became less significant as gas came to be preferred to coal for glass manufacture and as the cost of raw materials increased due to the introduction of water ballast. As in the case of other declining northeastern industries, local manufacturers believed that they could still rely on their traditional strengths. They simply refused to give up the use of cheap coal furnaces for the more efficient and clean gas furnaces.

The Chemical Works

An essential raw material in glass manufacture was alkali, traditionally provided in the form of kelp, the ashes of burnt seaweed. Demand for kelp for the local glass industries seems to have outstripped supply by the late eighteenth century, for efforts were being made to find a non-organic substitute. Given the importance of the local glass industry, it was perhaps not surprising that the North East should take the initial lead in this development. In 1790 Archibald Cochrane, the 9th Earl of Dundonald, together with John Losh of Woodside, Cumberland, attempted to produce alkali from common salt. After initial trials, they carried out larger scale experiments at Bell's Close, near Scotswood on Tyne, where Dundonald already owned a coal tar distillery, and there they produced the country's first synthetic alkali, colloquially called 'soda', on a commercial scale. They moved to Walker on Tyne in 1798, and the Walker Alkali Works gave Tyneside a flying start in the art of synthetic alkali manufacture. However, soon after production commenced at Walker, French chemists developed the much simpler Leblanc Process for synthetic alkali, and this process was introduced at Walker by 1806, its first use in Britain. It was quite a complex process, and it required the import to the Tyne of sulphur from Sicily, sodium and potassium nitrate from Peru, pyrites from Ireland, Cornwall, Germany, Spain and Scandinavia, salt from Cheshire, and limestone as ballast from London and France. But the most important requirement was for large quantities of coal, needed both as a source of fuel and as an ingredient in the chemical process; consequently the Leblanc alkali industry was best situated on tidewater sites near supplies of cheap coal. Tyneside was an ideal location, and some twenty-three works were established, mainly along the south bank of the Tyne between Gateshead and South Shields, making Tyneside the seat of the nation's chemical industry (Fig. 13.2). The local output of synthetic alkali increased from zero in 1800, to 120,000 tons per annum by 1870. However, it was not all good news, for the process released vast quantities of hydrochloric

Fig 13.1 Industry at Scotswood which was home to coal mines, paper works, and most famously of all, the Adamsez Works, to be seen at centre right. The successful export trade of this firm meant that the legend 'Made at Scotswood-on-Tyne' could be read in public toilets in all the world's seafaring countries. The railway bridge, for the Newcastle to Carlisle railway but now disused, is the third on this site, opening in 1871.

Fig 13.2 Allhusen's chemical works commenced at Saltmeadows, Gateshead in 1840, its river frontage being particularly important for import and export, as well as for effluent disposal. Eventually the works comprised some 50 acres of buildings, making it one of the largest such works in the country. However, the entire Tyneside chemical industry was to decline from the 1880s, Allhusen's closing in 1926.

acid gas into the atmosphere, about 60,000 tons per year by 1863, plus large amounts of mainly sulphurous waste materials piled up in heaps adjacent to the works. Some mourned the arrival of these alkali works which so dominated the banks of the Tyne:[4]

> Baith sides of the Tyne, aw remember,
> Were covered wi' bonny green fields.
> But now there is nought but big furnaces,
> Down frae Newcastle to Shields.
> And what wi' their sulphur and brimstone,
> Their vapour, their smoke and their steam,
> The grass is all gaen, and the farmers
> Can nowther get butter or cream.

The industry was soon to enter a sharp decline. Firstly, the increasing use of water ballast militated against the local industry, and secondly, the new and simpler Solvay process was developed in 1872. This process needed very few raw materials, much less coal than the Leblanc process, and was better suited to locations where brine, rather than coal, was readily and cheaply accessible. The northeastern chemical works owners were unwilling to change their ways, perhaps in the mistaken belief that the Leblanc process could hold its own and indeed win out over the Solvay process, or possibly that its by-products would keep the Leblanc industry going. But in failing to move with the times, the local alkali industry disappeared almost without trace, and became concentrated on Teesside and South Lancashire. The increased use of water ballast after 1851 had brought problems to several ballast-dependent industries, and they were never to have the same importance again. Chemical manufacture did, however, return to the Tyne, albeit briefly, when the Prudhoe works was established by government as an emergency plant to produce synthetic ammonia during World War II. It was operated by ICI, and produced large quantities of sulphate of ammonia, which in 1949 was said to provide 'what is probably the most valuable of Newcastle's exports'.[5] The plant closed in 1967.

THE WATER-POWERED INDUSTRIES
The first major use for water power was in corn milling, but waterwheels were subsequently crucial to a wide range of other local industries, for example in the textile, paper, mining, metal and quarrying industries. Waterwheels were also used in numerous other lesser industrial and agricultural activities such as the colour, oil, naphtha, charcoal, blacklead, clay, flint, woad and threshing mills. The need for water power often drew these industries to rural areas, although such locations could face difficulties in transporting raw materials and finished products. The mills were not generally powered from the waters of the Tyne itself, because of the danger of flood and the expense of building large weirs. Rather the tributaries were used, for example at Bardon Mill and Haltwhistle which had corn and textile mills, and the river Derwent which had a variety of mills and forges.

It was especially difficult but not impossible to establish water-powered industries along the tidal stretches of the Tyne, for a corn mill at Mill Dam, South Shields was powered by water collected at high tide and released via a waterwheel at low tide. Those industries which needed water power from tributary streams, but also tidewater locations for import or export, faced a particular problem. However, certain key locations had both, for example on the lower but non-tidal reaches of the Ouseburn where imported flint ballast was ground for use in nearby potteries. Similarly, the Crowley ironworks at Swalwell were heavily dependent on imported iron from Sweden in particular, but also from Russia and North America, and on the export of its products to as far as the West Indies. Hence the works were located beside the short tidal section of the Derwent and therefore accessible by keels, but the water needed to power its waterwheels was channelled from above the tidal limit of the Derwent.

Corn mills
The earliest known watermills in Great Britain were built by the Romans, one of them at Haltwhistle Burn Head, Northumberland, and there were numerous water-powered corn mills on the Tyne's tributaries by the early medieval period; the vast majority of these continued well into the nineteenth century. Many suffered a precarious existence over the centuries, not least at times of border warfare and of severe flood, but it was changing technologies and transport economics which brought about their decline in the nineteenth century. The development of the rotative steam engine offered the possibility of corn milling without the need for water power. Secondly, the growing importation of cereals, made increasingly economic through cheaper ocean transport in the nineteenth century, favoured port-based mills. Thirdly, roller milling came to replace the stone milling of grains. The inevitable consequence of these changes was the establishment of large, port-based, steam-powered roller mills, and the slow decline of the country water corn mills. This development may have been particularly early on Tyneside, with the building of a steam mill at Willington in *c*.1801, said to be the largest and most complete of its kind north of London. Another renowned Tyneside steam mill was the 1854 'Phoenix Mill' in the Close, Newcastle, which processed corn from various parts of England, but also from the Baltic, Australia, India and America — all brought by sea and river direct to its own wharf. The trend to large port-based mills continued into the twentieth century, with electrically-driven mills such as Spillers in Newcastle (1938), and the Baltic Mill in Gateshead (1949).

Tyne paper mills
The fate of the Tyne's paper mills was rather similar to that of the corn mills, although less dramatic for there were fewer of them. Some of the earliest paper mills associated with the Tyne and its tributaries were at Chopwell, founded by 1697, Gibside (1728), Felling Shore (*c*.1750s), Fourstones (1762), and Haughton Castle (1788). These were all water-powered mills for the manufacture of hand-made paper, a process which also required large quantities of clean water for

pulping purposes. However, paper-making machines were introduced in the first decade of the nineteenth century. Combined with the use of stationary steam engines they allowed the industry to free itself from the need of water for power, but not for pulping.

Later, the use of imported raw materials, like esparto grass after 1862, made tidewater sites the favoured location for new paper mills. The Tyne could import esparto grass from the east coast of Spain almost free of transport charges, for ships carrying coal and coke to Spain would bring back heavy mineral ores plus a near-full hold of the very light esparto grass freighted on top of the minerals. New northeastern paper mills were established for esparto grass paper, for example in the Team Valley and at Swalwell, while some of the older paper mills also swung to esparto grass, as at Jarrow, Shotley Bridge and Lintzford. Paper making had now virtually ceased to be a rural industry, except for odd exceptions such as the Fourstones mill, which was no doubt able to survive because of its location alongside the Newcastle & Carlisle Railway. Only a few new paper mills were established in the twentieth century; Kimberly Clark was in part attracted to Prudhoe in 1971 by plentiful water supplies from the Tyne. But overall, paper mill closures were more common in the twentieth century, as at Shotley Bridge which was about 12 miles from navigable water and insufficiently close to a railway.

Woollen mills

As early as 1296 there were weavers and a fuller and a dyer of woollen cloth at Corbridge, a fuller at Newburn, and fullers and dyers plus several wool merchants at Newcastle. Newcastle was a significant raw wool exporter by 1342; indeed it was the chief wool exporting port for the whole of the north of England, drawing some of its supplies from the west coast of England and from across the Irish Sea. However, there was a period of recession in the late sixteenth century for the northern sheep farmers, spinners, weavers and fullers, although some important wool merchants remained active in Newcastle. The Tyne remained an important exporter of woollen cloth over the first 40 years of the seventeenth century. With extensive exports to the Baltic and the Netherlands, it ranked third in importance in this trade, after London and Hull. The somewhat more settled times of the second half of the seventeenth century, *vis a vis* the English and the Scots, probably saw a consolidation of the local wool industry, especially in Northumberland, and perhaps even expansion, as agriculture was slowly improved in some areas. Thus a French visitor to Tyneside noted in 1672 that Gateshead was:[6]

> "... inhabited by divers manufacturers, employed in making cloth and worsted stockings in great quantity, which are here very cheap; wherefore they are sent all over Europe, even to Paris ..."

By the early eighteenth century and perhaps much earlier, water-powered fulling mills were in operation at Bywell, Cocklaw, Stocksfield and Bardon Mill, all on Tyne tributaries. A fulling mill was set up by the Haltwhistle Burn in

1749, and the manufacture of coarse baize was established there in 1762 — the beginning of a long period of textile manufacture in the town, with the Haltwhistle Burn providing the necessary power. A mill to process and spin imported flax was established beside the Ouseburn in the early years of the nineteenth century, another speculative venture encouraged by the presence of the river Tyne for import and export, but also by the Ouseburn as a source of water power. In 1836 the mill was severely damaged by fire in spite of seven fire engines "speedily on the spot, and a plentiful supply of water being at hand".[7] Clearly the Tyne and some of its tributaries supported a range of small-scale textile industries, but equally clearly the North East did not become another West Riding of Yorkshire.

THE LEAD INDUSTRY

The region's lead industry was centred on the North Pennine Orefield, and field evidence for its heavy dependence on water is ubiquitous. All we can say about the origins of lead mining activity in the North Pennines is that any evidence for Roman involvement is entirely circumstantial, but lead ore was being mined and smelted by 1130. It was an important regional industry by the fifteenth century and dominated occupations in the North Pennines for the following four centuries. Its eventual collapse was brought about by the nineteenth century rise of the Spanish industry and the concomitant decline of indigenous reserves. Although very little lead ore was won from the North Pennines in the twentieth century, some associated minerals, formerly deemed useless, had gained a commercial value, so that a few mines were able to switch to the extraction of fluorspar, barytes, witherite, and zinc ore. Such activities declined from the late 1970s and there is now no commercial mining within the orefield.

However, the Tyne and several of its tributaries witnessed the lead industry on their banks over many centuries, water being utilised in many aspects of mining, in washing and dressing (the separation of ore from waste materials), and in smelting. For example, water was used both for surface prospecting and in a form of opencast mining known as 'hushing'. This involved the collection of large quantities of water in hill-side or hill-top reservoirs, which were periodically released along the lines of known veins to scour away the earth's drift material and to expose or exploit veins of lead ore. The lighter materials were washed down into adjacent streams and rivers and the denser materials, like lead ores, were left behind.

Water power was also sometimes used to assist underground ore mining, for example to power waterwheel-driven drainage pumps, as at the lead mines by the Derwent south of Blanchland. But of equal importance, substantial quantities of water were needed for waterwheel-driven crushing devices as a first stage of ore separation and to provide the medium for ore washing and its gravity separation from wastes. Thus, a common problem faced in conventional forms of ore mining was an excess of water below ground and an insufficiency for the many processing activities carried out at the surface. Waterwheels were also used at the smelt mills to drive the bellows for hearths and furnaces.

Those who were responsible for engineering these applications of water power, such as John T. Bewick, chief engineer to the Blackett-Beaumont's W.B. Lead Co. in the mid-nineteenth century, could take legitimate pride in their endeavours. Bewick described his water power arrangements in the East Allen valley in enthusiastic tones in 1869:[8]

> "The most notable instance of the application of hydraulic machinery is at the W.B. Lead Mines, where the utilization of the water is carried to great perfection ... In one instance in the vale of Allen the water is used in driving no less than 18 different water wheels or hydraulic engines in a distance of less than eight miles [being] applied in the various operations of pumping, winding, crushing, dressing, and smelting."

Whilst water for these various purposes was frequently collected on upland fells, the tributaries of the river Tyne were a crucial asset to the lead industry; large smelting mills, with their attendant toxic discharges, were to be found in the valleys of the South Tyne, the Devils Water, the Derwent and the East and West Allen. A smelt mill, which soon became a refinery for the extraction of silver from lead, was also established at Blaydon on Tyne in 1696. However, it was another 100 years before the urban areas of Tyneside witnessed a further development of the industry in the form of the lead works which specialised in the manufacture of products such as white and red lead, and also in lead piping, sheet and shot. A concomitant development was the establishment of Tyneside paint works, particularly for anti-corrosion and anti-fouling paints. These works were mainly located alongside tidal stretches of the Tyne for ease of export.

SALT

The early salt industry in the North East, based on the forced evaporation of seawater, was not particularly centred on the coalfield. However, as coal fuel came into more general use in salt-making, coalowners saw salt manufacture as a profitable way of using their otherwise unsaleable small coal, and the salt industry became concentrated at the mouths of the coal exporting rivers, especially at North and South Shields. Salt-making at the Shields was an extensive and expanding industry by the end the sixteenth century, and Sir William Brereton was astonished at its scale in 1635:[9]

> "Here I viewed the salt-workes wherein is more salt workes and more salt made then in any part of England that I know ... here att the Shields are the vastest saltworkes I have seen, and by reason of the conveniencye of coale, and cheapness thereof."

Many keelmen were involved in carrying the coal from up-river pits to the pans at Shields, for the industry was based on an apparently extravagant consumption of inferior coals, about 8½ tons of 'pan coal' per ton of salt produced. Brereton could not fail to notice the atmospheric pollution caused by some 250 salt pans burning these huge quantities of coal — "Here is such a cloud of smoake ... you cannott see to walke". Almost a century later Daniel Defoe watched the smoke of the Shields saltpans "ascend in Clouds over the Hills" from four miles south of Durham city and also from the summit of Cheviot.[10] By 1714 about 20,000 tons of salt were being produced each year in the North East, but output began to fall from the 1740s and declined rapidly after 1760 to 1,000 tons per year in 1791. There were a number of reasons for this collapse, including the rise of salt making from the rock salts of Cheshire, and the likelihood that many northeastern coalowners found new and more profitable uses for small coal in glass making and in cinder production for export to London. The industry had a lingering death, but it would seem to have ended when a few pans which had been dissolving imported Cheshire rock salt in sea-water and then re-crystallising the salt closed in the 1860s.

TYNE MARITIME INDUSTRIES

Many Tyne industries sprang from the needs of maritime activity, notably shipbuilding, but also rope, sail and net making, paint, marine instrument and winch manufacture. Only two of these are briefly considered here.

Shipbuilding

Shipbuilding on Tyneside has a very long and important history, to which justice cannot be done within the present confines. Some developments such as the collier and the steam tug have already been noted, and only a few more examples of innovation in shipbuilding will be noted here. Daniel Defoe penned one of the earliest appreciations of shipbuilding on the Tyne *c*.1722, noting that:[10]

> "They build here ships to perfection, I mean as to strength, and firmness, and to bear the sea; and as the coal trade occasions a great demand for such strong ships, a great many are built here. This gives an addition to the merchants Business, in requiring a supply of all sorts of naval stores to fit out these ships."

Shipbuilding continued throughout the eighteenth century, but it was in the nineteenth century that local shipbuilders made innovations and broke records with monotonous regularity, as can be demonstrated by considering just a few examples. The first oil tanker in the world, the sailing ship *Atlantic*, was built on Tyneside in 1863, and just nine years later Palmer's yard built the world's first steam-powered oil tanker. Then, in 1886, the Tyne witnessed the launch of the world's first modern type of oil tanker, in which the hull of the ship was used as the oil-holding tank. The opening of the Tyne Swing Bridge and subsequent up-river dredging enabled the Armstrong works to create a naval shipyard at Elswick; the first battleship built there was the HMS *Victoria*. At the time of her launching in 1887, she was the biggest and most expensive vessel ever constructed on the Tyne, which might explain why hundreds of spectators on the river bank were soaked by the wave created. Ten years later, Charles Parsons demonstrated the steam turbine-powered *Turbinia* at the Spithead Naval Review; this was the first time that form of propulsion had been used. Its success

Fig 13.3 SS *Mauretania*: Following the success of Charles Parson's *Turbinia* the marine steam turbine engine was rapidly adopted for battleships and passenger liners. Only ten years later the *Mauretania*, then the largest liner ever built, steamed out of the Tyne powered by steam turbines. *(Photo by permission: Beamish, the North of England Open Air Museum)*

eventually led to the adoption of the marine steam turbine engine for warships and for passenger liners. Only 10 years later the Tyneside-built *Mauretania*, then the largest liner ever built, steamed out of the Tyne powered by steam turbines (Fig. 13.3). But innovation was not always on the grand scale. Inspired by the loss of the sailing ship *Adventure* with all hands in 1787, the first self-righting lifeboat was developed on Tyneside by two South Shields men, William Wouldhave and Henry Greathead, together with Lionel Lukin, a London coachbuilder.

Rope-making

The manufacture of rope, principally for the coal mining and shipping industries, has existed on Tyneside for centuries, ropemaking being one of the 'nine mysteries' of Newcastle. The earliest plans of Newcastle and South Shields show long 'rope-walks' where, prior to the mechanisation of the industry at the end of the eighteenth century, hempen ropes were manually spun. The main sources of hemp were St Petersburg, Riga and Archangel, and consequently there was a considerable advantage in locating ropewalks on tidewater sites (Fig. 14.3). But there was another reason: those roperies which specialised in the very large cables needed by warships had to be close to the river, for these cables might be up to 24 inches in circumference and weigh up to 15 tons. They could not be coiled into lifting coils, but had to be run 'on end' from the works into river craft which conveyed them to the ships for winding on. Any such ropery which was not located immediately by the river's edge would normally possess rights of way over the intervening property, to enable the cables to be run out.

The swing to mechanised rope manufacture and the introduction of wire rope were embraced by the larger Tyneside works, although many works combined the manufacture of hemp and wire ropes. Tyneside became recognised as the national centre of wire rope production, and while prestigious commissions such as the wire rope for the Niagara suspension bridge were welcome, the mining and shipbuilding industries remained the main customers.

SERVICE INDUSTRIES AND THE TYNE

The development of service industries was central if not crucial to the Industrial Revolution. The service industries provided water and powered the engines of manufacture. By providing more accessible sources of energy for lighting, heating and cooking, they also enabled householders to be freed from the squalor and drudgery which had typified the slums of Tyneside in the first half of the nineteenth century (Chapter 8). The provision of water for domestic and industrial use is described in Chapter 10 with emphasis on the Kielder Scheme. More comprehensive early histories of water supply are provided by Rennison[11] and Northumbrian Water[12].

The gas industry
Newcastle's Mosley Street was lit by gas in 1818, seemingly the first street in the world to be so illuminated, and almost every large town in the United Kingdom was lit by coal gas by the mid-nineteenth century. The early gas works in Newcastle were quite small and were located on constricted sites in Forth Street (1817), Manors (1818) and Sandgate (1831), all established by different companies. These companies had all been combined by 1838, together with another in Gateshead, to form the 'Newcastle & Gateshead Union Gas Co.' As demand for gas grew — fifteen-fold from 1829-1860 — the constricted nature of the works sites became a handicap, and in 1859 the company commenced a new and much larger works at Elswick, followed by an even larger one at Redheugh in 1876. Both works were rail served, and located on tidewater sites for the easy export of by-product coke.

Electricity supply
The decades which straddled the turn of the twentieth century saw the electricity supply industry become a hugely important element within the industrial structure of Tyneside. The development was rapid. Newcastle's first power station was operating in 1889, yet by 1910 all the great industrial concerns on the north bank of the river, along with the North Eastern Railway and the Tyneside Tramways & Tramroads Company, were major electricity consumers.

Electricity power stations needed water for steam-raising and cooling purposes, and most of them were drawn to tidewater sites for easy access to coal. All but one of Tyneside's power stations took their water from the Tyne; for example the Newcastle Forth Power Station of 1889 took its water from the Tyne via a

100-yard brick tunnel. Similarly, the Newcastle Tramways Power Station in Melbourne Street obtained its water via a pumping station on the Tyne about 400 yards away. All subsequent Tyneside stations had river frontages, and Carville Station (1904), was provided with a tunnel under the Tyne for the supply of customers south of the river. Later power stations at Dunston and Stella followed the same pattern of location on tidewater sites, although their upriver locations may in part reflect concerns about water quality.

All these power stations by the Tyne are now closed. They have gone for much the same reason as so many earlier Tyne industries. Coal has been carried to Newcastle! Water power no longer has any significance, commercial navigation is largely confined to the last three or four miles of the river, the maritime industries are much reduced and few if any activities use the river water for steam raising or cooling purposes. Pollution from industry is much reduced; it is a cleaner river, but in many ways a less interesting one.

REFERENCES

1. Ruskin, John (1856) *The Harbours of England*, London, p12.
2. Gray, W. (1649) *Chorographia: or a Survey of Newcastle upon Tyne*, Newcastle upon Tyne, p95.
3. Sykes, J., Latimer, J., & Fordyce, T. (1867) *Local Records ...*, Vol. 3, Newcastle upon Tyne.
4. Campbell, W.A. (*c.*1961) *The Old Tyneside Chemical Trade*, Newcastle upon Tyne, p48.
5. Hill, B. P., & Clemo, G. R. (1949) 'Chemicals', in *Scientific Survey of North-East England* British Association for the Advancement of Science, Durham, p163.
6. Jorewin de Rocheford - see Manders, F. (1973) *A History of Gateshead*, Gateshead, p51, quoting F Grose (ed) *The Antiquarian Repertory*, **4** (1807), 611.
7. Sykes, J., Latimer, J., & Fordyce, T. (1867) *Local Records ...*, Vol. 3, Newcastle upon Tyne.
8. Bewick, T. J., (1868-69) 'On Mining in the Mountain Limestone of the North of England', *Trans. North of England Inst. of Mining Engineers*, **18**, 163–182, Newcastle upon Tyne, discussion in Vol. 19 (1869–70), 92–111.
9. Brereton, Sir W., *The Journal of Sir William Brereton: 1635*, Surtees Society No. 124, Durham, 1914, 17–18.
10. Defoe, Daniel, (1723-5) *A Tour through the Whole Island of Great Britain*, London.
11. Rennison, R.W. (1979) *Water to Tyneside: A History of the Newcastle and Gateshead Water Company*. Newcastle & Gateshead Water Company.
12. Lyonnaise des Eaux Dumez (Undated *c.*1999) *Water Reflections – A short history of four water companies*, Granta Editions, Cambridge.

Plate 13.
Alien invaders at Ovingham; the towering flower heads of Giant hogweed (*Heraculeum mantegazzianum*) with a lower level cover of Himalayan balsam *(Impatiens glandulifera),* not yet in flower. *(Photo: David Archer)*

Plate 14.
A fisherman leans his rod against a dense thicket of Japanese knotweed *(Fallopia japonica)* which overhangs the river bank at Wylam. Wylam bridge is in the background. *(Photo: David Archer)*

Plate 15.
That well-known fisherman, Jack Charlton, holds a fine spring salmon caught at Broomhaugh on the Bywell Syndicate Waters. *(Photo: Aidan Pollard)*

Plate 16.
A fresh-run 12 lb salmon caught at Bardon Mill on Tyneside Anglers Syndicate waters on the South Tyne on 31 May 1999. David Hetherington is photographed with his fish before returning it to the river. *(Photo: David Carrick)*

Plate 17. The Howdon treatment works, looking west. The original primary treatment works is in the rectangular block to the right (N) of the jetty, with primary settlement in the eight striped-roof buildings and four sludge holding tanks nearer the river. Secondary treatment is now carried out in the white rectangular plant in the middle distance and the process completed in the 16 circular sedimentation tanks.*(Photo: AirFotos Ltd)*

Plate 18. The 1986 Tall Ships Race – a pivotal point in the attitude of Tynesiders to the river *(Photo: Richard Pelmea, by courtesy of Graham Hancock, Robertsons of Gosforth)*

Plate 19. The straggling 'dragon' arms of Kielder Water show where the lower reaches of tributary burns have been flooded *(Photo: Northumbrian Water)*.

Plate 20. Kielder dam with scour valve releasing its maximum flow of 44 cumeecs during tests in December 1981.

Plate 21. A peaceful summer's evening by the lake *(Photo: David Archer)*

Plate 22. Sailing at Derwent Reservoir. The start at the Flying Fifteen class UK Inland Championship, May 1998. *(Photo: Robin Jefferson)*

Plate 23. Canoeing on the North Tyne. Shooting the rapids at Barrasford during The Tyne Tour, 1994. *(Photo: Barbara Pike)*

Plate 24. The picturesque and secluded bridge over the Rede, about one mile northeast of West Woodburn and known as East Woodburn bridge, lies on what was a highway leading from Hexham to Elsdon. The flattish main arch of 62 feet span, is the result of a partial rebuilding in 1832.
(Photo: David Archer)

Plate 25. West Wylam Railway Bridge, known locally as 'The Points Bridge'. This single-span wrought-iron arch railway bridge of 1876, built for the former Scotswood, Newburn & Wylam Railway, is now part of the popular Riverside Park route for walkers and cyclists between Prudhoe and Newburn.
(Photo: David Archer)

14. GETTING ACROSS THE TYNE

STAFFORD LINSLEY

INTRODUCTION

Rivers have always presented both obstacles to and opportunities for human movement; getting across larger rivers safely and economically at all times has challenged the ingenuity of mankind. The past and present crossings of the river Tyne and its tributaries, illustrate the evolution of the means by which such obstacles have been overcome. During the past 10,000 years, fords, ferries, bridges and tunnels, have all been used in getting from one side of the Tyne to the other. All are still employed today, although fords and ferries have declined in their use, as bridges and more recently tunnels have replaced them. As we shall see, such technological progress was sometimes hard-won.

Simple bridging structures, like logs over streams or stepping stones augmented by logs, may have been the first 'engineering' structures devised by mankind. Perhaps it is not surprising therefore, that bridges and bridge-building have entered the domain of myth, of which the most persistent seems to have been that 'every bridge demands a life', either in its construction or in its subsequent use. But bridge building eventually came to be seen as a human conquest over nature, rather than one over the supernatural, and as an activity blessed with economic and social benefit, rather than one damned by vengeful gods.

Few people fail to be impressed by the bridgescape over the tidal Tyne between Gateshead and Newcastle (Plate 2), essentially because of the variations in the forms of bridge built along a few hundred yards of river, all but two bridging a considerable gorge at a high level. This variation in bridge form stems from differing functions, materials, building techniques and site constraints. Since the 1870s the requirement to maintain full navigational clearance has also been an important determining factor in the design of bridges between Gateshead and Newcastle. But even above the Tyne's tidal limit, its bridges display a considerable variety. The bridges at Wylam, Corbridge, Hexham, Ridley Hall, etc. are all very different, and the main reason for these differences lies in the very nature of bridge building.

Most bridges over the Tyne and its tributaries are stone-built arch bridges (Plate 24). The Tyne is not unusual in this respect; the stone-arch bridge has been the norm in Europe for centuries. Many building stones are hard-wearing and particularly resistive to compressive stresses, making them ideal structural materials for arch bridges, and since stone is a widely available building material, it has been used for thousands of years. Consequently, the oldest extant bridges throughout the world are of the stone-arch type, and the stonemason's skills in bridge building have been long established. However, stone-arch bridge design and building have rarely, if ever, been an exact science, no matter what some designers might have claimed. A hallmark of scientific endeavour and experiment is that results must be reproducible, but almost every stone-arch river bridge was custom designed and built; reproducibility was never really a facet of bridge building.

Bridge design is partly dependent on whether the bridge is intended for road, rail or pedestrian traffic, but the main controlling factors are the site conditions of the river crossing and the variability of river flow (hydrological regime – Chapter 1). Site conditions include the channel and floodplain width, the steepness of the valley sides, and the strength and stability of the materials underlying the bed and banks. The expected flood magnitude is particularly important in design, and in the past such predictions were often based on the doubtful recollections of the oldest inhabitant — with unfortunate consequences.

In this context it must be appreciated that stone-arch bridges are not 'fastened down' but simply stand on their foundations. They are designed to be stable to vertical loadings such as the passage of humans, animals and vehicles, but not necessarily to horizontal loadings such as wind, and more particularly flowing water. Thus, once successfully constructed, the greatest threat to a stone-arch bridge is fast-flowing flood water. If a flood is sufficiently high and fast, and lasts for a sufficient period of time, no stone-arch bridge will withstand it. Either it will simply be pushed over or, unless properly designed against scour, its piers will be undermined.

Thus every stone-arch river bridge presents its designers and builders with a different set of choices: the precise location; the number of spans; the form of foundations, arches and piers; the materials of construction; the building sequence. The large number of variables involved in building a stone-arch river bridge ensures that each is unique. Indeed, bridge building has often been seen as more of an art than a science. John Smeaton, the most influential British civil engineer of the eighteenth century, claimed that he was prepared to "risk his credit as an Artist" on a particular bridge designed to cross the Tyne at Hexham; as it happens, much of Smeaton's 'credit' as engineer or artist was lost when that bridge failed.

Some of the above considerations apply equally to other bridge forms, each with its own design criteria to facilitate its intended purpose. The optimum form of bridge for any particular river crossing has changed over time, partly because of new challenges and partly through developments in bridge building materials and techniques. As a consequence, bridges reflect the *zeitgeist* as well as, and often better than, other structures, for bridges have only rarely been subject to architectural fashions and pretensions.

TYNE FORDS AND FERRIES
In the past fords and ferries played an important role in crossing the Tyne and indeed some remain in use today. Fords especially could be very dangerous. William Hutchinson found the ford of the South Tyne at Haltwhistle a daunting experience when he crossed in *c*.1776.[1]

"... we were obliged to pass the ford, which is broad and deep, with a bottom of very large stones, over which a horse, breast deep in the water, unaccustomed to the passage, incessantly faulters or stumbles. Those circumstances would have been greatly aggravated by our ignorance of the place, had we not met with a person to conduct us — instances of well applied charity characterize this age: it would not be one of the least, to give a stipend to an attendant at such fords as these, by which many valuable lives would be saved."

Equally dangerous were the fords at Hexham, about which Wallis observed in 1769:[2]

"... the floods after rains and sudden thaws of snow, sometimes come down so hastily, that they surprise and drown the passenger at an instant, or else, which sometimes happens, force him to take refuge on an islet where he is at leisure to lament his situation til the danger is over."

Nine years later, witnesses informed a House of Commons Committee that two men had drowned in 1776 while trying to cross the Hexham Low Ford during daytime, and that:[3]

"The Ford ... is extremely dangerous at Times of Floods, which frequently happen after Rains; that, at such Times, the Bottom of the ... Ford is shifted by the Violence of the Current, which renders the Passage through it always uncertain, and frequently in practicable."

There was also a ferry across the Tyne at Hexham, at least from 1356, for in that year it was let to Archbishop Thoresby on condition that he did "no harm or wrong" to its users! By 1608, the ferry was known as the East Boat Ferry, for there was also a West Boat Ferry at Warden 1½ mile west of Hexham. The East Boat ferry then belonged to the Hermitage Estate on the north bank of the Tyne and, apart from a few brief and sorrowful interludes, it was the only dry way to cross the Tyne at Hexham until 1793.

Most of the Tyne's ferries were located within the tidal stretch, where one still operates, but a long-lasting ferry operated at Haughton on the North Tyne (Fig 14.1). It may have been established as early as the twelfth century, but was certainly there by 1272 and it continued until the 1930s. Temporary ferries were often introduced after a bridge had collapsed or became otherwise unusable, as in 1698, when a ferry was set up at Chollerford. Similarly, a ferry was installed at Haydon Bridge in 1722, and at Newcastle after the Old Tyne Bridge was destroyed in the 1771 flood. Using ferries could also be dangerous; ten passengers were lost in 1760 when a small but overloaded ferryboat sank between North and South Shields.

TYNE BRIDGES UP TO THE SIXTEENTH CENTURY
The Romans built Tyne bridges at several places, notably at Newcastle,

Fig 14.1 Haughton Ferry across the North Tyne around 1906. The illustration shows a simple form of rope ferry where the ferryman (standing), hauled his boat across the river by hand. There were, of course, times when the ferry could not be operated when the river was in flood, or more rarely when the river was frozen and people simply walked or cycled across. *(Photo by permission: Beamish, the North of England Open Air Museum)*

Corbridge and Chollerford, as part of their overland network of trading and strategic routes. However, Roman bridge building techniques seem not to have survived the loss of Roman involvement in the area, with the result that that fords, and perhaps a few ferries, were used thereafter until the twelfth century. The two or three centuries following the Norman conquest saw the first flourishing of bridge building in the area when, under the influence of the church, the maintenance of roads and bridges came to be regarded as an act of piety. Thus, the great monastic foundations, while mainly charged with saying prayers, teaching, or giving alms, came to see bridge building and road repair as a religious duty, one as meritorious before God as visiting the sick or caring for the poor. Quite how this came about is not known, but it may be that travellers on the country's roads had come to be regarded as poor unfortunates in dire need of Christian charity.

Early Tyne bridges seem to have existed at Newcastle by 1175, at Bellingham by some time in the twelfth century, at Corbridge by 1225, at Hexham by 1263, at Haydon by 1309, and at Chollerford by 1333 — the Tyne Gap transport route was clearly important at that time. It is known that the Newcastle and

Bellingham bridges were essentially of timber, perhaps supported on stone piers, and it may be that others were similarly built, but as such they were prey to fire, flood, wear and tear. Other bridges which may date from this early period are at Prudhoe Castle and in the grounds of Hexham Abbey, while a long-gone medieval bridge once stood at Dilston.

There is little available information on these early bridges, and such as there is often merely points to their decay or destruction. For example in 1304 a commission was appointed to inquire into a failure to repair the bridge at Corbridge 'which is so broken down that men wishing to cross it have been drowned'. It was presumably repaired and certainly continued to be used through much of the fourteenth century, but John Leland's account of the bridge in c.1540, suggests that it had been replaced by another:[4]

The stone bridge which now crosses the Tyne at Corbridge is large, but has been built a little downstream of the old bridge.

NEWCASTLE'S OLD TYNE BRIDGE

The most famous of the early medieval Tyne bridges was undoubtedly that between Gateshead and Newcastle — the 'Old Tyne Bridge'. The town of Newcastle grew around the bridging point first used in the Roman period when the Emperor Ælius Hadrian built the bridge which gave Newcastle its earliest name - *Pons Ælius*. The Roman bridge, either a timber superstructure on masonry piers or a masonry bridge, must have decayed in the post-Roman period, and perhaps fords and ferries sufficed thereafter until the Normans arrived. The first post-Roman bridge, probably of timber and probably built close to the site of the Roman bridge but not necessarily on its foundations, appears to have been built by 1175. This bridge was said to have been destroyed, along with much of the town in a fire of 1248, but was replaced by one of stone. This rebuilding seems to have been a collaborative exercise by the corporation of Newcastle and the Bishop of Durham, possibly because the Bishops had accepted the responsibility to maintain one-third of the earlier bridge. The new bridge was 'financed', as was common at the time, by the granting of indulgences to all those who would assist in the rebuilding by attending in person, by sending others in lieu, or by money donations.

The work of rebuilding must have commenced soon after 1248 but, given that the bridge was built in tidal waters, it may not have been completed until c.1270 or even later. It was a twelve-arched stone bridge, with 23 feet thick piers surrounded by oak-piled starlings. These piers clearly presented a considerable obstruction in the river, for less than one-half of its natural width was available for water flow. It is perhaps surprising, therefore, that the bridge withstood the river for so long. The roadway was some 15 feet wide between the parapets but, as with the old London Bridge, houses, shops, workshops and other structures built on the bridge, reduced the effective road width to some eight feet. Part of the bridge was said to have been carried away by a flood in August 1339, at which time between 120 and 167 people were believed to have drowned.[5] An ongoing battle between bridge and river had clearly been joined.

Although the bridge had been built with twelve arches, Leland noted c.1540 that it had ten arches. It would appear that some northern arches had been incorporated into cellaring during the building of Newcastle's quays out into the river; one such ribbed and pointed arch, with a 22-foot span, can still be seen beneath buildings at the north end of the Swing Bridge. Later the bridge only had nine visible arches, after the southern arch was covered by quay extensions in Gateshead.

By this time the Bishop of Durham owned and maintained one-third of the bridge, while the Burgesses of Newcastle owned and maintained two-thirds, implying that they shared responsibility for the fourth pier from the Gateshead end, the boundary being marked by the 'Blue Stone'. The Bishop and the Corporation also collected their respective rents from the buildings erected on the bridge, and it may or may not be significant that most of these were crowded thickly at the Bishop's end. James Oliphant's house, at the extreme southwestern end of the bridge, as described in 1768, may have been typical:

"It had four floors, viz. cellar, shop, kitchen and parlour, and attics. The cellar, (if so it may be called) hung down in the arch over which the house had been erected. It [the cellar] had half-doors (upper and lower) looking out upon the river, which rose to within a few inches of the floor, so that goods could be received and shipped."

In the following year the Bishop of Durham asked John Smeaton to advise on the condition of the bridge, and the Corporation of Newcastle did likewise in 1771. Smeaton, the most important engineer of his generation, advised that the bridge was in a very poor state of repair and could fall at any time. He therefore recommended the building of a new bridge on an adjacent site. In the event, a few trifling repairs were made in May of 1771, and the ancient bridge was destroyed six months later in the great flood. A replacement bridge of nine arches, designed by Robert Mylne, opened in 1781.

TYNE BRIDGES FROM THE SIXTEENTH CENTURY TO THE END OF THE EIGHTEENTH CENTURY

There was a decline in the church's involvement in bridge building and maintenance during the years leading up to the dissolution of the monasteries in 1536–39; Hexham's bridge seems to have fallen into disuse, possibly in the fourteenth century, and was replaced by ferries, while Bywell Bridge was in ruins by 1540. In an attempt to replace this particularly useful aspect of religious fervour, Government passed the Statute of Bridges in 1531, which placed certain responsibilities for bridge building and road maintenance on the laity. For example, the onus for the repair of bridges in towns was placed upon their citizens, and in the country on the county authorities (the county Justices of the Peace), except where other liability could be proven. Then the General Highways Act of 1555 allowed each county to appoint two bridge surveyors and to raise revenues for the repair of bridges. The surveyors were required to report on the condition of the bridges within the county. The JPs were also empowered to levy a bridge rate (cess) on all the inhabitants of their county, to be disbursed on the salaries and expenses of their surveyors, and on the repair of bridges. Northumberland is thought to have been the first county to appoint a surveyor in *c.*1684, when one George Barkas was made Surveyor of Highways at £20 per annum.

An eventual result of such Statutes was that several new bridges were built over the Tyne and its tributaries in the seventeenth and early eighteenth centuries, for example at Corbridge in 1674, Linnels before 1694 (rebuilt in 1698), Alston before 1697, and Chollerford by 1717. All these bridges were owned by the county authorities and known as 'County Bridges'. By 1742 the county of Northumberland was already responsible for bridges over the Tyne and its tributaries at Allensford, Dilston, Erring, Featherstone, Haydon, Little Shotley, Newburn, Ponteland, Sandyford, Salters (Gosforth), Shotley, Three Mile (Gosforth), and Wolsington.

The greatest period of bridge building in Britain, however, was undoubtedly that which we might loosely call the Industrial Revolution when turnpikes, canals, and then railways were developed to support and foster an expanding overland trade. The North East did not wholly fit the national pattern, firstly because no canals were ever built in the region, and secondly because of the necessary great bridge rebuilding after the 1771 flood.

CROSSING THE TYNE AND ITS TRIBUTARIES IN THE TURNPIKE ERA
By the early eighteenth century the creation of turnpike trusts was seen as a remedy for the poor condition of the country's parish-maintained roads, at least for the main routes, since the turnpikes embodied the then novel principle that road users should pay tolls for road upkeep.

Turnpike trusts were first created in the home counties, but the principle gradually spread through the rest of the country. The first turnpike trusts in the North East were associated with the Great North Road, all established under local Acts passed in the 1740s and '50s. The Military Road turnpike of 1751 ran along the north side of the Tyne valley, while the Glenwelt turnpike of 1752 branched off the Military Road turnpike above Aydon and passed through Corbridge, Hexham, Haydon Bridge and Haltwhistle before rejoining the Military Road at Glenwelt (Greenhead). The Alemouth turnpike, also of 1752, ran from Hexham to Alnmouth via Rothbury, while other turnpikes to impinge on the Tyne valley were the Gateshead to Dilston Bar (1777), the Hexham to Alston (1778), the West Auckland to Elishaw (near Otterburn) via Corbridge (1792), and the Alston Roads Turnpike (1824). Few of these turnpikes required the building of substantial bridges, for they could use existing county bridges at the major river crossings. For example, the Military Road Turnpike crossed the North Tyne using the county's Chollerford bridge, the Glenwelt turnpike used county bridges at Corbridge and Haydon, and the Hexham to Alnmouth turnpike used county bridges at Chollerton, Rothbury, and Hawkhill; there was, however, no bridge over the Tyne at Hexham at this time.

The unprecedented floods of 1771 and 1782 tested both the stability of bridges and the stoicism of bridge builders on the Tyne. Reputations were ruined and pockets were severely strained. The role of the county in bridge repair, and the havoc wreaked by the Tyne — a flood-prone river — can be illustrated by considering the cases of the Ridley Hall and Hexham bridges.

Although some points remain unclear, the following is the likely story of successive reconstructions of Ridley Hall bridge. Ridley Hall lies less than half a mile south of the South Tyne, and the bridge was probably inspired by the building of the Glenwelt turnpike along the north bank of the river. William Lowes of Ridley Hall wished to secure a more direct route between his home and the new turnpike, rather than use the ford at Bardon Mill, about 1½ miles to the west. In *c.*1756, the county offered him £300 towards the building of a stone bridge. The bridge must have been completed during 1757, but it was swept away by flood waters in November 1761. Apparently undeterred, Lowes came to a similar arrangement with the county in 1762, and he also agreed to maintain this replacement bridge for seven years following its completion, after which it would become a county bridge. This bridge was certified complete in January 1764 and thus became the responsibility of the county in January 1771, only for it to be swept away ten months later by the great flood, together with every other bridge on the Tyne except that at Corbridge.

This time there seems to have been less hurry to replace it, perhaps because it did not form part of an important route. However, Jonathan Pickernell, the county's bridge surveyor, had designed a new bridge by March 1780, which seems to have been completed according to schedule by the first day of May 1781. It was not a propitious time, and this bridge was also thrown down by flood waters in March 1782.

The county now called in Robert Mylne, whose bridge design skills were well-known in the area. Mylne inspected the "ruins, situations, materials, foundations, etc. for a new design" early in October 1785, but it was not until a year later that he was able to send "his design and 4 drawings and 2 long writings, for rebuilding Ridley Hall bridge, and laying the foundations". Work on the replacement bridge was begun in 1787 under the direction of Robert Thompson, a county bridge surveyor, and the bridge was officially opened in 1792. This bridge, the fourth at Ridley Hall in less than 40 years, had cost the county about £4,000, but it stands today more or less as built some 200 years ago. Its story illustrates the fact that a stone-arch bridge is only as strong as its foundations and that the greatest skill a bridge builder could demonstrate, especially where a volatile river like the Tyne was concerned, was in an adequate formation of the pier foundations and the abutments; once these were secure, any competent stonemason could build, and even design, the bridge's superstructure. As John Smeaton put it:

> "The principal strength of a bridge consists in its foundation ... this being well secured, the superstructure ... seldom fails."

It is indeed ironic that one of his bridges came to grief at Hexham because of the insecurity of its foundations. Smeaton had first designed a Tyne bridge for Hexham in 1756 but it was never built, and the absence of such provision continued to disadvantage travellers on the Hexham to Alnmouth turnpike.

The turnpike trustees had not sought powers to build a Tyne bridge, preferring instead to let others take any risks involved. However, a prominent trustee, Sir Walter Blackett, agreed with the county in 1767 to bridge the Tyne at Hexham at an estimated cost of £3,459. The county would contribute £1,000 towards the new bridge on the usual conditions, that Blackett would maintain and repair it for seven years after its completion against a bond of £3,000; thereafter the county would take responsibility for the bridge.

Blackett's bridge, built to a design by William Gott, opened in September 1770, but was destroyed in the flood of November 1771. Its pier foundations can still be seen about a mile west of the present bridge, exposed by the ravages of gravel extraction in the twentieth century (Chapter 4). Blackett forfeited his bond rather than attempt to rebuild the bridge, and believing that such a flood could neither have been foreseen, nor designed against, he absolved Gott and his assistant George Brown of Cambo from any blame. Brown's role in this and subsequent events is rather interesting. He was already a County Bridge Surveyor as well as being clerk, treasurer and surveyor to the Hexham to Alnmouth turnpike, and he had the no doubt melancholy task of reporting on all of the destroyed bridges in the south of the county.

The county had, in effect, made a profit of £2,000 on this failed venture at Hexham, and they engaged John Wooler to progress a replacement bridge in 1774. George Brown carried out some test borings in the bed of the Tyne and became convinced that a stratum of clay, about 50 yards upstream of the failed bridge, would be entirely appropriate for bridge pier foundations. Wooler designed a bridge to be built at Brown's site, but found quicksands at a depth of four feet below the river bed soon after work had commenced on the first pier foundation.

Wooler was somewhat distressed at this turn of events and pronounced his plan for a bridge to be impossible. Brown must have been equally unsettled over the outcome, for he declined to continue as County Bridge Surveyor and was replaced by Wooler's assistant, Jonathan Pickernell. The County Justices had spent £3,500 on preliminary works and materials for this latest attempt and were reluctant to see the entire project abandoned. Consequently, Pickernell carried out more test borings of the river bed and found what he believed was a suitable site for a bridge near Henry Errington's Sandhoe estate, about three-quarters of a mile down-river from the failed Blackett bridge. Errington now engaged John Smeaton to build a new bridge.

Smeaton had accrued a considerable portfolio of successful civil engineering works, including the bridges at Coldstream (1767), Perth (1771) and Banff (1779), all of which still carry traffic, and he based his new Hexham design on these. Some flood problems arose during its construction under Pickernell as resident engineer, but the bridge opened in January 1781. Pickernell retired as County Bridge Surveyor just as the bridge was being completed, presumably in the belief that he had just completed one of his greatest works. After a while:[7]

"... even the Gilligate people ... ceased their visits, who before had constantly after every flood, come to inspect, in hopes of finding

215

something correspondent to their prayers and wishes for the downfall of the bridge."

They should have kept coming, for had they been there on the morning of 11 March 1782, they would have seen Smeaton's bridge collapse swiftly in flood. Errington had made the customary agreement with the county to maintain the bridge for seven years after its completion and, after much vexatious litigation, he was forced to stump up his bond of £4,000 in compensation for failing to keep his bridge in repair for the required period.

The county had engaged Robert Mylne as their expert witness in their case against Errington, and therefore against Smeaton, but Mylne advised that the bridge could be rebuilt, provided that the piers were provided with much better foundations. The county accepted this recommendation and the present bridge was built under the direction of the County Bridge Surveyors William Johnson and Robert Thompson, probably commencing in 1789, partially opened during 1793, and completed two years later, its superstructure being to Smeaton's design and dimensions within inches (Plates 11 and 12).

Smeaton had "risked his credit as an Artist" on his Hexham bridge, and its collapse shattered his self-confidence. He claimed that he had neither appreciated nor been warned of the degree of violence that the river was capable of, and that he had "the Horrors of the River Tyne painted upon his imagination". He died in October 1792, and so did not live long enough to witness a significant development in bridge building which had the potential to allay such worries.

THE SUSPENSION BRIDGE

The turnpike era witnessed this important development in bridge building - the creation of suspension bridges capable of carrying wheeled vehicles. It is worth noting that Europe's first permanent foot suspension bridge is widely believed to have been the Winch Bridge over the Tees, first built in *c.*1741, while a similar bridge spanned the river Derwent at Blackhall Mill by 1754. However, for the inception of the vehicular suspension bridge we turn to Captain Samuel Brown (no relation to George Brown) and to Tweedside. Brown made a major leap in suspension bridge design with his successful Union Bridge over the Tweed near Cornhill, which opened in 1820. It had the largest single span of any bridge in the western world, some 437 feet between its towers, and was the world's first suspension bridge for vehicular traffic. As such it marked the beginning of the long-span vehicular suspension bridge, and it remains in use — the oldest suspension bridge in the world still carrying vehicular traffic. It significance was appreciated soon after its completion:[8]

"Its security has now been satisfactorily tried; and as bridges of this description can be erected where those of stone cannot, and as they cost much less, it is to be expected that many of them will arise throughout the empire."

This form of suspension bridge, with no river piers and no bank-side

Fig 14.2 The West Boat Chain Bridge over the South Tyne at Warden was built to replace the West Boat Ferry with the intention to be part of a new turnpike from Cupola Bridge at Whitfield to Bellingham. It was designed and financed by Capt. Samuel Brown and opened in 1826. The turnpike was never built, but the tolls taken at the tollhouse shown in the illustration must have helped to reimburse Brown.

abutments, must have seemed the ideal bridge for crossing the troubled waters of the Tyne, for it was the very nature of stone-arch bridge design that made them so vulnerable to the unprecedented, and as it happens un-repeated, Tyne floods of the second half of the eighteenth century.

An early opportunity to utilise the benefits of the suspension bridge in crossing the Tyne followed J. L. McAdam's recommendations to the Commissioners of the Greenwich Hospital, in or about 1823 to improve the roads in the North Pennine area. One element of his plan required a new route from Bellingham to Whitfield Cupola Bridge, with a new bridge to replace the West Boat ferry over the South Tyne at Warden, and another new bridge at Bellingham over the North Tyne. With thoughts of the 1771 and 1782 Tyne floods still sufficiently fresh in the collective memory, it was decided that the new Warden bridge should be a single span suspension bridge (Fig. 14.2). It opened in 1825-6 and was not replaced until 1903. Bellingham did not receive its new bridge until 1835, a conventional masonry bridge of four spans being deemed sufficient for the calmer waters of the upper North Tyne. The road between the two bridges seems never to have been turnpiked.

Samuel Brown spent many years promoting his suspension bridge design all over the country, although not all of his proposals were accepted. In 1825, for example, he proposed crossing the Tyne between North and South Shields with a three-span suspension bridge whose main span would be 780 feet, carried at 100 feet above high water. Although the plan was turned down, probably on account of the estimated cost of £100,000, the mere fact of its proposal indicates the extent to which the suspension bridge allowed a serious consideration of bridge spans never before contemplated. In fact the next, and the last vehicular suspension bridge to be built over the Tyne was at Scotswood (Fig. 11.2). Its promoters were no doubt influenced by the rapidity with which a suspension bridge could be built, but also by the relatively low costs involved and the immunity it would offer from any occurrence of high floods.

The design of the Scotswood bridge was entrusted to John & Benjamin Green who proposed a suspension bridge "as being the cheapest durable structure and possessing advantages over every other kind in such a situation". Building of the Scotswood 'Chain Bridge', whose main span was 370 feet, began in July 1829, and it opened in April 1831. Although ostensibly designed by John Green, the bridge was almost pure Samuel Brown in concept. When formally opened its strength was immediately put to a severe test which, unlike the infamous millennium bridge over the Thames in London, it passed with flying colours.[9]

"... crowds of people ... rushed with thoughtless impetuosity on the bridge, in the centre of which they were soon collected into so dense a mass as to be incapable of moving, and putting the bridge to a severe trial. No fewer than 3,000 persons were collected between the points of suspension, making, with those on the ends, a crowd of between 5,000 and 6,000 persons."

CROSSING THE TYNE IN THE RAILWAY ERA

At the time the Scotswood Chain Bridge was opened, the Stockton & Darlington Railway had been running for nearly six years, and construction of the Newcastle & Carlisle Railway was underway. The railway revolution was in full sway and thousands of new bridges would soon be built throughout the length and breadth of the land. It should, however, be noted that the building of horse-drawn waggonways had begun in the North East in the first decade of the seventeenth century. Causey Arch, built for the Tanfield waggonway of 1727 over a tributary of the Tyne, demonstrates that the art of building large bridges was not confined to the development of road transport systems. It was the largest single-span bridge in the United Kingdom at the time of its construction and remained so for the next 30 years. Successive improvements to the horse-drawn waggonways led to the steam-hauled railway of the nineteenth century and the massive bridge building programmes which this development initiated.

Perhaps it was not surprising that the suspension bridge was considered a candidate for railway use, but its first trial, on an 1830 extension to the Stockton & Darlington Railway over the Tees, was so unsuccessful that it seems to have put British railway bridge designers off the idea for ever. So although the Tyne and its tributaries were now to witness a rash of railway bridges, beginning with those of the Newcastle & Carlisle Railway, these were largely of conventional form. The Newcastle & Carlisle line was opened between Carlisle and Redheugh (Gateshead) in 1836, and Redheugh was to remain the eastern terminus until the Scotswood railway bridge of 1838 enabled the line to be taken into Newcastle. Although the bridges and viaducts on this railway were mostly conventional, the Scotswood and Warden railway bridges were multi-span bridges with timber-truss superstructures carried on clusters of braced timber piles at Scotswood, but on masonry piers at Warden. These designs by John Blackmore were said to be novel, but probably arose out of the need to produce inexpensive bridges which would not present too much obstruction to river flows. Ironically, the first Scotswood railway bridge burned down in 1860 during a Board of Trade inspection.

Other early wooden railway bridges worthy of note were those on the Newcastle & North Shields Railway, for which John Green designed two splendid laminated timber viaducts to cross the valleys of the Ouseburn and the Willington Gut; both were built in 1837–39, but reconstructed in wrought iron in 1869 (Fig. 14.3), while still retaining the basic outline of the originals. Green actually produced a laminated timber-arch bridge design to take a railway at high level between Gateshead and Newcastle, but it was Robert Stephenson's design which was ultimately chosen for the High Level Bridge.

The only bridges between Newcastle and Gateshead from the time of the Romans had been the Old Tyne Bridge and its replacement by Mylne. However, change was at hand as the obstacle posed by the Tyne was about to be overcome by a succession of new bridges. Rails connected London and Darlington via Leeds by 1841, and three years later Gateshead was connected to Darlington, albeit via a circuitous route through County Durham using George Hudson's 'Newcastle and Darlington Junction Railway'. Concurrently, the Scottish North British Railway was building a route south from Edinburgh. Although their original intention had only been for a line to Dunbar, Hudson agreed with the North British that if they would continue to Berwick, then he would back a Newcastle to Berwick line, thereby completing rail links between the capitals of the two countries. Hudson's line was opened between Newcastle and Tweedmouth in July 1847, and on the first day of that month the Edinburgh to London mail coach made its last journey through Gateshead carrying a flag surmounted by black crepe. However, the Tyne had not yet been bridged, for questions surrounding the precise location and nature of the Tyne crossing had dragged on. Should it be achieved by a low-level or a high-level bridge and, given that three separate railway companies were intending to cross the Tyne, how many railway bridges should there be?

Eventually, the decision was taken to build a combined road and rail bridge at 120 feet above low water, leading to a single central station at high level in Newcastle, both of which could be used by the otherwise competing railway companies. The design was entrusted to Robert Stephenson and the bridge opened in 1849. There were now two bridges between Gateshead and Newcastle, but that number would rise to five in the 80 years which followed.

Many more railway bridges were built over the Tyne and its tributaries as the railway system spread. When the Alston Branch railway (from Haltwhistle)

Fig 14.3 Willington Viaduct and Ropery: The Willington Viaduct was built in 1837-39 to the design of John and Benjamin Green, of Newcastle. The unusual arches of laminated timber were replaced in wrought iron in 1869. Rope-making at Willington, by the tidal Willington Burn, goes back to 1789, and as the hemp needed to make the ropes was imported from St Petersburg, Riga, and Archangel, a riverside location was a considerable advantage. Ownership of the works passed to Haggie Brothers of Gateshead in the nineteenth century.

opened in 1851–2, it boasted three major viaducts over the South Tyne and six lesser viaducts and bridges. The most spectacular of these works was the nine-arched Lambley viaduct, but Burnstones viaduct, although less impressive, is a most unusual double-skew viaduct over road and river, while that at Haltwhistle is a single-skew viaduct whose piers are pierced with arched openings, apparently intended for a foot bridge.

A North Tyne railway, the Border Counties Railway, was projected in 1853, and it opened from Hexham to Riccarton in 1862 under the North British Railway. The engineers for the line were Robert Nicholson, who died in 1856, and his nephew John Furness Tone who was ultimately responsible for the bridges and viaducts. Of the major viaducts, the 'Border Counties Bridge' at the crossing of the Tyne just west of Hexham was built of iron on masonry piers, while all the others were of stone. The original Act decreed that a single-track line should be built, but the main bridges and viaducts were designed to take double tracks, a precaution taken in anticipation of increased traffic levels which never arose. Building the Border Counties Bridge presented familiar problems, for its temporary works were completely washed away in flood, but it was completed early in 1858. The Kielder viaduct presented difficulties of a slightly different order, for it would be within sight of the Duke of Northumberland's hunting lodge — he let it be known that it would need to be suitably embellished, and so it was.

Further east the Scotswood, Newburn & Wylam Railway opened in 1876, and the only significant engineering feature on this line was again a Tyne crossing - the West Wylam railway bridge (Plate 25). Its design was by William George Laws, consulting engineer to the railway company and later engineer to the corporation of Newcastle. The original intention had been to have a four-span bridge, but that design was abandoned in favour of a single-span bridge because of uncertainty about the nature of coal workings under the bed of the river, and the fact that coalowners were concerned that water might flood into their workings while foundation strata were being sought for the river piers. It was a rather unusual bridge for a railway at the time, its 240 feet single arch span of wrought iron, carrying a suspended rail deck. Although the line closed to rail traffic in 1968, the bridge remains available for walkers and cyclists.

URBAN DEVELOPMENT AND TYNE IMPROVEMENT

From the middle of the 1830s up to the 1860s, most new bridges over the Tyne and its tributaries were railway bridges, although there were exceptions such as at Bywell (1838) and Falstone (1843). However, the expanding urban areas of Newcastle and Gateshead and the need to improve navigation on the Tyne, brought significant new road bridges over the tidal reaches of the river. The first of these was the Redheugh bridge, in some ways the most interesting of the Tyne bridges in the Newcastle–Gateshead area. The Redheugh Bridge Company was formed in 1865 with the aim of building a Tyne bridge which would make the Redheugh Estate more attractive to developers. It would also provide a means of carrying gas and water mains across the Tyne from the north side, and would allow an easier route over the Tyne between Redheugh and Elswick than the

Fig 14.4 The Tyne Swing Bridge is shown closing after the passage of a vessel. Its replacement of a multiple-arched stone bridge on the same site enabled large sea-going vessels to pass 'above bridge', so opening the higher reaches of the tidal Tyne to more extensive industrial development. The Tyne Bridge had not yet been built at the time of this photograph in 1925. *(Photo by permission: Beamish, the North of England Open Air Museum)*

existing High Level Bridge and the hilly Windmill Hills route through Gateshead. The Bridge Company was supported in their efforts by the Newcastle and Gateshead gas and water companies, who would lose their mains over Mylne's Tyne bridge, which was due to be replaced by the Tyne Swing Bridge. This involvement of the utility companies was to have an unusual impact on the design of the bridge.

The Chief Engineer for the new toll bridge was Thomas Bouch, a designer of many splendid bridges, but regrettably best known for his involvement with the infamous Tay Bridge in Scotland. His design consisted of lattice girder main spans in which gas mains formed the top booms while water mains were carried in the trough girders which supported the road deck. Thus, the gas mains were not merely appendages, but were integral components of the girder structures. Seemingly at the request of the Tyne Improvement Commission (TIC), the bridge was designed to allow full navigational clearance in anticipation of the river being dredged above-bridge and opened to all vessels after the construction of the Swing Bridge (Fig. 14.4). Consequently, at 87 feet above high water, the underside of the bridge deck was four feet higher than that of the High Level Bridge under which any vessel bound upriver would have to pass before reaching the Redheugh. Work commenced in July 1868, and the bridge was opened in June 1871.

Bouch's Tay Bridge had opened in 1878, but collapsed in the following year; Bouch died the year after that, no doubt amidst public worries about the safety of his other bridges. The Redheugh Bridge Company sought assurances that its bridge was perfectly safe and was advised, in 1880, that:

> "The opinion of most eminent railway Engineers [is] that the bridge was of the most undoubted stability - that there was not the slightest comparison to be made between it and the Tay Bridge."

However, a report of 1895 noted that the bridge was 'dangerously defective' and would have to be either re-constructed or replaced. Consequently, a new bridge was built in the years 1897–1901, exactly on the same alignment as the old. Minimum interruption to traffic and water and gas supplies on the old bridge was achieved by building the new bridge around the old. This second Redheugh bridge lasted until it was replaced by the present bridge in 1983.

By the second half of the nineteenth century, several above-bridge industrial concerns stood greatly to benefit if the Tyne could be made fully navigable to their works, but for that to be made possible, Mylne's bridge would have to be removed or replaced and the river upstream would have to be dredged. Shortly after the opening of the High Level Bridge, control of the Tyne had passed from the Corporation of Newcastle to the TIC (Chapter 12). In 1860 John Francis Ure, the TIC engineer, outlined the problems caused by the Mylne's bridge, and recommended its replacement by a new low-level bridge, but one which could be swung about its centre to allow large vessels to pass upriver.

The TIC obtained Parliamentary permission to build an appropriate bridge, and the contract was awarded to the Armstrong Works at Elswick, probably the only concern in the world then capable of carrying out such work. Armstrong's, design was for the largest centre-swing, hydraulically-powered bridge ever contemplated. It provided for four river channels, spaced to coincide with the openings of the existing High Level Bridge, and two land arches. Work on the new bridge began in 1868 and was concluded in 1876 (Fig. 14.4). It was built on exactly the same alignment as Mylne's bridge. The preparations for the formal opening were considerable. The Italian transport ship *Europa* was standing by downstream ready for the first opening, as were the TIC steam launch and Sir William Armstrong's steam wherry. However, an ordinary workaday coal wherry hove into view just before the bridge opened, and it beat all other contenders to be the first vessel through the opened bridge, albeit broadside on!

Two significant bridges were built over tributaries of the Tyne during the next five years, Newcastle's Armstrong Bridge of 1878 over the Ouseburn in Jesmond Dene and the Byker road bridge further downstream in the same year. Then two more were built over the Tyne itself, the spindly Ovingham Tyne toll bridge of 1883, to replace an ancient ferry, and the Newburn toll bridge of 1893, to replace equally ancient fords and ferries. The Newburn bridge was designed to be capable of carrying heavier traffic than the High Level and Redheugh bridges, but also of interest is the fact that its design owed something to the over-arching ambitions of the Tyne Improvement Commission. Although no commercial craft used that shallow section of the river, it did fall within the TIC's jurisdiction. Consequently the bridge was made 100 feet wider at its abutments than the actual river width to allow for an intended widening and deepening of the river, while its road deck gave a 21-feet headway clearance. The only vessels to benefit from these specifications seem to have been pleasure boats heading for Ryton Willows.

The next large bridge to be built between Gateshead and Newcastle, the King Edward rail bridge of 1906, was constructed to allow through running of trains on the east-coast route by providing an additional rail crossing parallel to the existing High Level Bridge; ultimately it allowed the running of non-stop trains between Edinburgh and London.

These bridges, built over the Tyne during the nineteenth and early twentieth century, all in some way reflected the developing industrialisation of the North East, but the next significant bridge, the Newcastle Tyne Bridge of 1928, was built at a time of industrial depression. By the 1920s the High Level Bridge was being used by some 3 to 4 million people per year, while the Swing Bridge was opening about 30 times every day, each opening causing a 15 minute delay to road traffic. There was therefore a need to augment the existing road bridges between Newcastle and Gateshead, preferably at a high level, for both towns had now firmly left behind their traditional commercial centres on their quaysides. But two further considerations informed the decision to go ahead with another bridge, firstly the expectation of a 65% government grant towards the bridge's construction, and secondly the hope that its construction would help alleviate chronic unemployment in certain areas of Tyneside.

Of course the TIC was involved, insisting that the bridge should have no river piers and should allow full navigational clearance throughout its construction and also after its opening. It was implicit in the TIC's requirements, and later made explicit, that no materials were to be raised from the river during the bridge's construction. These requirements ensured that the design of the bridge would be dramatic and the manner of its construction bold. Work commenced in August 1925, and progress was remarkable as the largest single-span bridge in Britain rapidly took shape. The arch was closed in February 1928, and the formal opening took place in October with some elements of the bridge not quite completed. Although the new bridge had substantially increased river crossing capacity, there was unprecedented traffic chaos in the first days after its opening, as former users of the High Level bridge deserted that route to avoid the payment of toll.

There was to be little in the way of further new bridges over the Tyne until the decaying Scotswood Chain Bridge was replaced by an unloved and initially unreliable steel arch bridge in 1967. The Tyneside Metro rail system resulted in two new large bridges, the Byker Viaduct of 1979, and the Tyne Metro Bridge of 1981. The growth of the motorway system resulted in the Blaydon (western bypass) bridge of 1990.

The redevelopment of the Gateshead and Newcastle quayside areas is being facilitated by the splendid 2001 Gateshead Millennium Bridge for pedestrians and cyclists (Plate 2). The Tyne's bridges continue to reflect the *zeitgeist*, and in the Millennium Bridge we see a bridge essentially created to serve leisure purposes - certainly the first large bridge to be so designed in the region. Yet curiously, as a moveable bridge capable of being rotated to allow the same navigational headroom as the Tyne Bridge, it harks back to long-gone days when the river Tyne, from its mouth to Lemington, was one of the busiest rivers in the world.

REFERENCES

1. Hutchinson. W. (1776) *Northumberland,* Vol. 1, Newcastle.
2. Wallis J. (1769) *The Natural History and Antiquities of Northumberland and North Durham,* London.
3. House of Commons Jnls., Vol. **36**
4. Leland, J. (c.1540) *Itinerary,* Edited by J. Chandler (Alan Sutton Publishing, 1993).
5. Brand, J. (1789) *History and Antiquities of the Town and County of the Town of Newcastle upon Tyne,* 2 Vols., London.
6. Bruce J. C. (1872–85) 'The Three Bridges over the Tyne at Newcastle', *Archaeologia Aeliana,* NS X.
7. Smith, D. (1974) The professional correspondence of John Smeaton, an eighteenth century consulting engineering practice, *Trans. Newcomen Soc.* Vol **47**.
8. 'A Tourist' (1826) *A Border Tour.*
9. Sykes, J. (1833) *Local Records or Historical Register of Remarkable Events from the Earliest Period of Authentic Record to the Present Time,* Newcastle upon Tyne.

15. THE ART OF CROSSING THE TYNE

Thomas Bewick, born in 1753 at Cherryburn below the village of Mickley, was undoubtedly the most distinguished artist of Tynedale. Yet his 'canvas', the woodcut, is miniature, generally encompassed within a space no more than two inches in diameter. Bewick raised the art of wood engraving from obscurity, and by technical innovation, mastery of his craft and pure artistic genius brought it to perfection. The innovation was to use as his medium the hard end grain of the boxwood, which was far more sensitive than the same wood cut along the grain. This 'plank style' engraving had previously been used to produce much coarser illustrations. By judicious use of his graving tools he achieved remarkable effects of light and shade, depth and distance.

His art is deeply rooted in nature. Bewick is best known for his *General History of Quadrupeds*[1] published in 1790 and for his *History of British Birds*[2,3] published in two volumes in 1797 and 1804. These books containing Bewick's engravings introduced generations of British readers to the joys of the countryside, not only through his illustrations of wildlife but also through the delights of his tail-pieces, with which he brought each chapter to a close. His art was appreciated by naturalists like Audubon and also by writers like Charlotte Bronte, Ruskin and Wordsworth, who wrote in his *Lyrical Ballads* "O that the genius of Bewick were mine".

From the beginning his life was intimately engaged with the River Tyne[4]. Cherryburn House (now the Bewick Museum) is only a quarter of a mile from the river. From 1763 to 1767 (aged 10 to 14), Bewick crossed the Tyne daily to attend school at the Ovingham parsonage under the tutelage of Revd. Christopher Gregson. He would have used the ferry at Eltringham, or perhaps at Ovingham, as there was no bridge at that time between Newcastle and Corbridge. He would have seen the river in all its moods, the summer low flow with exposed gravel banks, the turbid autumn flood carrying logs and branches, the covering of ice thick enough to cross — for these were still the bitter winters of the Little Ice Age. No doubt he was occasionally stranded on the wrong side when the river rose too quickly. Bewick recounts an incident when he played truant and waded or swam across the Tyne, still strewn with ice floes after a winter flood; on another occasion he broke in a horse by swimming him in the river. As a child he already had an artist's eye but also a robust constitution and a playful humour.

His recollections of running free in the fields and woods and by the river bring a nostalgic tear to those of us given similar freedom in a more recent generation, and sad regret that children of the present time cannot be left alone to foster the same intimate appreciation of nature.

From an early age Bewick was an angler. His years were marked by the beginning and end of the fishing season.

"As soon as the bushes and trees began to put forth their buds and made the face of nature look gay — this was the signal for the Angler to prepare his fishing tackle and in doing this I was not behind hand with any of them in making my own all ready — fishing rods, set gads and night lines were all made fit for use and with them late and early I had a busy time of it during the summer months until the frosts of autumn forbid me to proceed."

At the age of 14, Bewick was sent away to be apprenticed to Ralph Beilby the engraver in Newcastle. We sense the depth of his despondency in being parted both from his beloved home and the familiar rural scene.

"The eventful day arrived at last, and a most grievous day it was to me — I liked my master, I liked the business, but to part from the country and to leave all its beauties behind me, with which I had all my life been charmed to an extreme degree and in a way I cannot describe — I can only say my heart was like to break, and as we passed away — I inwardly bid farewell to the whinney wilds — to Mickley Bank and the Stob Cross hill, to the water banks, the woods and to particular trees and even to the large hollow old elm which had lain (perhaps) for centuries past in the haugh near the ford we were about to pass and had sheltered the salmon fishers while at work there, from many a bitter blast — this old tree was swept away by a great flood of 17 November 1771."

After he completed his apprenticeship in 1774, Bewick returned for two years to Cherryburn where he re-established his links with the countryside and returned to angling with zest. After a walking holiday in Scotland and a visit to London he returned to Newcastle in 1777 in partnership with his former employer. For the next eight years, sometimes accompanied by his younger brother John, who became his apprentice, he paid weekly visits to Cherryburn. It was fourteen miles each way.

"On setting out upon my weekly pedestrian flights up the Tyne I never looked out to see whether it was a good day or a bad one — the worst that ever fell from the sky never deterred me from undertaking my journey – on setting out I always waded through the first pool I met and had sometimes the River to wade through at the far end. I never changed my cloaths however they might be soaked with wet and though they might be stiffened by the frost, on returning home at night until I went to bed. ......My travelling expenses for the day was commonly only a penny or two for crossing the water. ....I often called in, almost every Sunday for my glass [at Crawcrook] while my rout lay on that side of the river and until being quized for visiting 'Maggy Hay's bonney lasses' — I then left off and walked up the north side of the Tyne and crossed at

Wylam, Ovingham or Eltringham Boat and now only sometimes at Scotchwood when I had occasion to visit my friends in Hedley — but indeed I varied my roundabout ways in these Journeys pursuing the one I had haunted myself to for perhaps a quarter of a year to an end before I left off and thus became known to most of the villages on both sides of the Tyne — and as nothing can pass unnoticed in Villages — so they noticed me and set me down for granted that I was sweethearting some pretty female on the way."

Thus did Bewick learn every pool and riffle of the lower reaches of the Tyne and his artistic memory inspired his drawings for the rest of his life. For after 1785, when his mother, sister and father all died, he left off his walks to Cherryburn, a place now only of 'sorrowful reflections'.

Many of Bewick's tailpieces are scenes of the river and this chapter is dedicated to those showing the crossing of the river by ordinary and fanciful means. His miniatures are models of precision — every leaf, every shadow, every ripple a perfect model of nature. His compositions are superbly balanced and we can tell the demeanour of his figures by their posture even when the face is obscured. Some have a humorous tale to tell with the anticipation of a mildly unpleasant denouement. Although not many of his scenes can be matched with a particular place, he has undeniably distilled the essence of Tyne.

During his life, Bewick had many apprentices who produced work in a similar vein under his supervision. Some such as Clennell, Nesbit and Harvey were highly talented in their own right. Some of the illustrations below may be from hands other than Bewick, but I have not attempted to distinguish the artist.

1. Wading the river[2] A simple scene but the resolute stepping-out of both figures suggests a commonplace journey that holds no fears.

2. Wading the river[1] The slight figure of a peddler is carrying his wife,
a small child and a full basket. He looks stressed!

3. Stepping stones[5] You can sense the weight of the load on the young man's back. He
can hardly raise his head sufficiently to see the stones in front of him. Will he or will
he not make it to the other side without dropping his burden.

4. Crossing on stilts[5] The traveller with his bag and dog have chosen the smoother
path of the ford to attempt the crossing dry shod. The path with the tracks of carts
leads down to the river. In the background water is spilling over the overshot mill
wheel.

5. Crossing on the ice[1] A winter scene with the old man and the dog crossing gingerly on the ice. He carries a heavy load of sticks; his axe stowed in the tie-rope adds a touch of realism. Their shadows on the ice heighten the sensation of slipperiness. The church tower is reminiscent of Ryton.

6. Four pole stilts!![2] Was this really a mode of crossing the river or was it a flight of Bewick's imagination. The back stilts are conventional but the front ones are like crutches with forks fitting under the arms. It is not a normal crossing point and a cautious companion is waiting at the gate to see if the crossing is successful.

7. The pole vault[6] Having skilfully placed his bag and stick on the far bank, the vaulter seems to have judged his leap perfectly, but a crumbling bank or a slippery sod could easily precipitate an unhappy ending.

230

8. Pontoon boots!![4] The poacher, shod with pontoon boots covering his feet up to the ankles, is punting himself across with his vicious forked leister. It looks an entirely unstable method of crossing with a serious risk of the feet being forced apart in the current, and the consequent soaking seems imminent.

9. Ferry crossing with horse[6] Hatted ladies sit comfortably at the front of the boat. The horse stands firmly in the middle to keep the balance. We hope the horse stays calm on the crossing but the barking dog on the bank is not much help.

10. Saving the bridge toll[4] The farmer is holding the cow's tail as he drives it across the river. He has avoided the bridge toll but lost his hat on the way. The bridge is reminiscent of the old bridge at Haydon Bridge.

11. The tree branch crossing[1] The traveller has thrown his bag and stick to the far bank and is following precariously on a moss-covered branch. Will he make it without plunging into the pool below?

12. Hurray he's made it![4] Or has he? The last step is the most dangerous.

13. The last crossing[1] This was said by Bewick's daughter Jane to be her father's last woodcut. It shows the funeral party making its way down to the Tyne from cottages reminiscent of his birthplace at Cherryburn. The Eltringham ferry waits to cross to the Ovingham churchyard where Bewick is buried.

DEDICATION

This chapter is dedicated to the memory of good friend and neighbour Douglas Mennear, who died in September 2002. Douglas's infectious enthusiasm for Thomas Bewick (amongst many enthusiasms) inspired this chapter, but more significantly provided the spark for the establishment of the Bewick Trust which acquired and restored Bewick's birthplace at Cherryburn, now a National Trust Visitor Centre

REFERENCES

1. Bewick, T. (1790) *General History of Quadrupeds – with figures engraved on wood.* Reprinted by Windward, 1980
2,3. Bewick T (1797 and 1804) *History of British Birds,* Vol. 1 *Land Birds* and Vol. 2 *Water Birds,* Reprinted by Frank Graham, Newcastle upon Tyne, 1971 and 1972 (a facsimile of the 6th Edition 1826)
4. Bewick, T. (1862) *A Memoir of Thomas Bewick written by himself* (published posthumously) Reprinted and edited with an introduction by I. Bain, Oxford University Press, 1975.
5. Cirker, B (Editor) (1961) *800 woodcuts by Thomas Bewick and his school,* Dover Pictorial Archive Series.
6. Bain, I (Editor) (1981) *The Watercolours and Drawings of Thomas Bewick and his Working Apprentices,* 2 Vols. Gordon Fraser, London

16. THE TYNE IN MUSIC, SONG AND VERSE

PAUL L. YOUNGER

'CHANNELLING MUSICAL CREATIVITY': THE IMPULSE TO CELEBRATE RIVERS WITH WORDS AND TUNES

Singing the praises of a river is nothing new. Much has been written in the English language praising the grandeur of rivers, or else using them as metaphors for some of life's poignancies[1]. Amongst the many celebrated rivers of Britain, few have received more lyrical attention than the Tyne, which, as we shall see, can boast mentions in balladry dating back as far as 600 A.D. Although a substantial canon of songs concerning the Tyne remain popular with local singers, many more have fallen silent. Nevertheless, a large number of these unfashionable songs await possible resurrection from the pages of various books which appeared from the late 1700s onwards. The course of local history has greatly influenced the emphases in local literary and musical endeavours, so that many of the songs that have come down to us now serve not just as entertainment but as vivid illustrations of past life along the banks of Tyne.

This chapter examines the musical, poetical and lyrical heritage of the River Tyne. It is **not** meant as an exhaustive, academic study; rather it is intended to convey in plain words a little of the delight and historical insights which the tunes, poems and songs of Tyneside have brought to many. The account which follows opens with the instrumental tunes which celebrate the river (overwhelmingly conserved in the rural areas of upper Tynedale), through local examples of universal genres, such as ballads and love songs, to the distinctive dialect songs of industrial Tyneside. In this manner, the flow of the material roughly follows the Tyne itself from source to sea, albeit with a few turbulent eddies here and there. The music, songs and poems considered here all have a direct connection with the River Tyne. As such, the chapter does not consider wider aspects of Tyneside culture, such as mining songs or songs concerning general social life; one unfortunate consequence is that the chapter makes scant reference to the works of the two finest Tyneside songwriters, Joe Wilson and Tommy Armstrong.

'BONNY NORTH TYNE': PIPE AND FIDDLE TUNES

Few other rivers have been as extensively celebrated by dedications of instrumental music as has the River Tyne. The proliferation of tunes which describe the river or its life is in no small part due to the existence and continued popularity of the Northumbrian Smallpipes. This engaging chamber instrument has the distinction of being not only the peculiar folk instrument of Northumberland, but is in fact the only extant indigenous English instrument. The Northumbrian Smallpipes resemble most other kinds of bagpipe, save that they have:

- a bag which is inflated using bellows (a feature they share with the Irish *uillean* pipes)
- tuneable drones
- a chanter which is closed at the end, so that no air leaves the chanter when all holes are covered. Fingers are lifted and replaced one at a time, producing a distinctive staccato sound
- typically a much wider range than other bagpipes, by virtue of being fitted with many keys (as many as 23 on some sets), which can be so numerous as to render the instrument fully chromatic over two octaves.

Most importantly of all, the Northumbrian Smallpipes are relatively quiet and sweet in tone. The repertoire for the Smallpipes is essentially traditional Northumbrian country dance music, which is also frequently rendered on more common instruments such as the fiddle, accordion, flute, etc. This repertoire includes slow airs, reels, jigs, marches and waltzes, as in other British and Irish musical traditions, but has two particularly distinctive attributes:

- A distinctive local tune format, known as the "rant", which may be described as a "slowed-down reel", or more flatteringly as a "syncopated dotted polka', depending on whom you ask.
- An unusually large number of distinctively local hornpipes. Northumbrian folk musicians tend to know far more hornpipes than their peers from adjoining areas of England and Scotland. Given the well-known affection which sailors have traditionally held for hornpipes, it is interesting to speculate whether the presence of the Port of Tyne is in itself an explanation for the prevalence of hornpipes locally. More controversially, it could be argued that the shipping of coals from Newcastle carried the local enthusiasm for hornpipes to other parts of Britain and to Ireland, where hornpipes never enjoyed quite the same popularity as in their 'native' Tyneside.

Quite a number of very old Northumbrian tunes of unknown authorship bear titles which reflect an appreciation of the River Tyne. Two meditative slow airs spring immediately to mind: "Bonny Tyneside" and "Sweet Hesleyside" (the latter referring to the seat of the Charlton family in North Tynedale, west of Bellingham). More upbeat tunes include the popular hornpipe 'Lads of North Tyne' (which is also known elsewhere in Britain and Ireland under the title 'Boys of the Blue Hills'), the 'Whittle Dene Hornpipe', the jigs 'Keelman Ower the Land' and 'The New Tyne Bridge'. The march tune entitled 'Salmon Tails up the Water' is ever-popular at ceilidhs in the region. The sustained popularity of this tune belies the fact that salmon were all but absent from the Tyne itself for almost a century, until the Tyneside interceptor sewer scheme of the 1970s made the tidal reaches passable once more to migratory fish. Now the inspiring sight of 'salmon tailing up the water' of Tyne against a powerful autumnal current is a fairly common spectacle once more, restoring to us a pleasure which several generations were denied.

A considerably greater number of traditional-style tunes of **known authorship** refer to the Tyne, such as W. Ballantyne's 'Bonny North Tyne', and Winham's 'New High Level' and 'Warksburn Waltz'. A number of tunes of persistent popularity were composed by James Hill, a fiddler who frequented the Gateshead and Newcastle Quaysides in the mid nineteenth century. Amongst the jigs and hornpipes he composed are five which are named with reference to the River Tyne: 'The Redesdale Hornpipe', 'The Quayside', 'The Champion Hornpipe' which commemorates the great Tyne oarsman Harry Clasper, 'The High Level Hornpipe', 'The South Shore' and 'The Steamboat'. Arguably a Tyneside invention, the steamboat was a modern marvel in Hill's time. Along with Hill's other well-known compositions, especially 'Random Notes' and 'The Hawk', all of these tunes remain firm favourites amongst northeastern musicians.

The melodies for all of the tunes mentioned above may be readily accessed in the two Northumbrian Pipers' Tune Books[2] and the Northumbrian Minstrelsy[3], with Hill's extant repertoire having been collated by Dixon[4]. In addition to these tunes, many of the melodies of Northumbrian songs are also played as instrumental pieces on the Smallpipes and other folk instruments.

'NAE MAIR ALANG THE BANKS O' TYNE': BALLADS AND ROMANTIC SONGS

The bardic or ballad-creating tradition has very deep roots in Tynedale. Besides giving rise to so many poems and songs in the English language, or at least in its Northumbrian variant, the valley has a legitimate claim also to the oldest extant poem in *Cymraeg* (Welsh). Britain's oldest heroic poem, *Y Gododdin,* arose from the *Gŵyr y Gogledd,* or 'Men of the North', who were the indigenous, Welsh-speaking inhabitants of present-day southern Scotland and Northumberland. *Y Gododdin* is an elegy for warriors who fell at the battle of *Catraeth* (Catterick) in around 600 A.D., at which the Celtic armies were routed by Angles advancing northwards from *Deira* (present day East Yorkshire) to fortify the recently-established Anglian kingdom of *Bernicia* (now Durham and Northumberland). Line 1010 of *Y Gododdin*[5] reflects nostalgically on the childhood of one of the warriors, Dinogad, who was evidently raised in the Tyne valley, growing strong on the proceeds of his father's success as a hunter and fishermen:

> *'Pan elai dy dad di i fynydd*
> *dyddgai ef pen iwrch,*
> *pen gwythwch, pen hydd*
> *pen grugiar fraith o fynydd*
> *pen pysg o Raedr Derwenydd'*

'When your father went to the hills,
    he would bring back a roe-buck,
        a wild boar, a stag,
    A speckled grouse from the hills,
        a fish from the waterfalls of the
                                Derwent'

(adapted from the original translation of Jarman[5])

The Derwent is, of course, a major south bank tributary of the Tyne, and this makes *Y Gododdin* the first poetic mention of any part of the River Tyne. In passing it is worth noting that the same lyrical *Cymraeg* in which *Y Gododdin* was composed also gave us the name of the Tyne itself, since 'Tyne' is nothing more than an anglicisation of an Old Welsh adjective meaning 'twin'. The name 'Tyne' therefore means 'Twin River', and it presumably alludes to the striking manner in which the main channel of the river is formed by the confluence of two tributaries of roughly equal size (the North Tyne and the South Tyne) at Warden, just west of Hexham.

If we follow the North Tyne upstream from Warden, we soon enter the heart of the Anglo-Scottish borderlands, an upland area of stark beauty with a history to match. It is in this area that the second flowering of poetic allusions to the Tyne have their origins. For most of its existence the Anglo-Scottish Border has been the plaything of the national authorities either side of the somewhat contrived frontier line. For the locals, the Border has never been a sacred dividing line, for family ties have always straddled the frontier. Spend a few hours in Berwick-upon-Tweed sometime and you will soon learn that this remains the case today. In the late Middle Ages the Borderers were not slow to spot the opportunities arising from the fact that the distant officials in London and Edinburgh regarded the Border as inviolable. If one could not be pursued across the border by law enforcers in one direction or the other, yet had family on both sides, the opportunities to make crime pay were enormous. Those Border families who exploited these opportunities became known as the Border Reivers[6], infamous cattle rustlers who, in the words of an exasperated legal official in the sixteenth century, 'are Englishmen when it suits them, and Scotsmen at will'. For all their wicked ways, the reivers had a great propensity for recording their adventure stories in the form of lengthy ballads, usually with four rhyming lines to the verse, and as many as sixty verses per ballad. Many examples of these 'Border Ballads' have been preserved[6], in no small part thanks to the efforts of Sir Walter Scott in the early decades of the nineteenth century.

While the action of many of the ballads undoubtedly takes place in and around the Tyne valley, such as the eerie happenings at Carterhaugh and Bateinghope in upper Redesdale which are recorded in the ballads 'Tam Lin' and 'The Death of Parcy Reed' respectively, relatively few of the ballads make direct reference to the River Tyne. A glorious exception is the 'Ballad of Jock o' the Syde'. In thirty-seven verses, this ballad tells of the aftermath of an inauspicious raid into England by a gang of Liddesdale reivers, which is thought to have taken place sometime in the last two decades of the sixteenth century. The raid did not go according to plan, for one of the reivers was killed, and another, one John or 'Jock' Armstrong of the Syde, was taken prisoner to Newcastle. On the day before he was due to be executed, a party of three Armstrong adherents were despatched to rescue Jock. The rescue party comprised another Jock Armstrong ('the Laird's Jock'), Walter Armstrong ('the Laird's Wat'), and an Englishman, Hobbie Noble, who'd been banished in perpetuity to Scotland under pain of death for bad behaviour. Having successfully entered Newcastle by stealth and violence, the three reivers freed Jock o' the Syde. Jock was so heavily fettered that his rescuers had to carry him bodily out of the jail and set him on a horse to ride side-saddle. Despite his lack of choice in the matter, his rough companions did not hesitate to tease him for riding in the feminine manner. The four reivers then made haste westwards following the line of Hadrian's Wall, but their hasty retreat to Liddesdale was suddenly halted when they reached Chollerford, where they found the Tyne in spate[3]:

' ... The night, tho' wet, they did na mind, but hied them on fu' merrilie,
Until they came to Cholerford brae, where the water ran like mountains hie.

But when they cam' to Cholerford, there they met wi' an auld man:
Says – "Honest man, will the water ride? Tell us in haste if that ye can".

"I wat weel no", quo' the gude auld man. "I hae lived here thretty years and three,
and I ne'er yet saw the Tyne sae big, nor running ance sae like a sea".

Then out and spake the Laird's saft Wat, the greatest coward in the companie —
"Now halt, now halt! We need na try't; the day is come we a maun die".

"Puir faint-hearted thief!" cried the Laird's ain Jock, "there'll nae man die but him that's fey;
I'll guide ye a' right safely thro'; lift ye the prisoner on ahint me".

Wi' that the water they hae tae'en, by ane's and twa's they a' swam thro',
"Here are we a' safe," quo' the Laird's Jock, "and puir faint Wat, what think ye noo?" ...'

No sooner had the rescue party finished the nerve-wracking traverse of the raging waters of the North Tyne than the troop of soldiers who had been pursuing them from Newcastle arrived on the bank they'd just left behind. Discretion being the wiser part of valour, and with less to lose than the capital convicts Hobbie Noble and Jock o' the Syde, the Newcastle men declined to follow the Armstrongs across the Tyne.

The antics of the Border reivers have captured the imaginations of successive generations on both sides of the border, and their memory has now been romanticised to some degree. Most notable amongst the romantics was Sir Walter Scott, whose 'Minstrelsy of the Scottish Border' remains a crucial text for all those interested in the lyrical traditions of the region (real or imagined). For besides recording genuine, ancient ballads (which he assiduously collected from the locals on both sides of the border) Scott also created new ballads, working either from fragments of otherwise lost songs, or simply from local stories which were current on the Scottish side of the border. The famous English poet Algernon Charles Swinburne (1837–1909), whose paternal grandfather hailed from Capheaton in Northumberland, took it upon himself to perform a similar service to the Northumbrian tradition. He produced edited versions of a number of ancient ballads and wrote a number of new ballads in similar style. His full collection of such ballads was only published posthumously, under the title 'Ballads of the English Border'[7]. Swinburne prepared a very attractive edited version of 'Tam Lin', under the title 'The Young Tamlane', and also produced an imitative elegy entitled 'The Tyneside Widow'. Also amongst his imitative ballads is 'The Bride's Tragedy', which describes how a man of Tynedale, delayed by the wild weather of North Tynedale, arrives too late to prevent his fiancée being forced to marry a 'fause faint lord of the south seaboard'. The unhappy bride agrees to abscond with her erstwhile lover, and the two of them ride off up the North Tyne valley until, like Jock o' the Syde before them, they are halted by the Tyne in spate at Chollerford. Again, the only alternative to death at the hands of their pursuers is to risk a dangerous wade of the river. This time, however, the outcome is less felicitous:

'... The first ae step they strode therein it smote them foot and knee,
But ere they wan to the mid water the spate was as the sea.
In, in, out and in, blaws the wind and whirls the whin.

But when they wan to the mid water, it smote them hand and head:
And nae man knows but the wave that flows where they lie drowned and dead ...'

The Tyne is further mentioned in the refrain of one of Swinburne's modern ballads, 'The Sea-Swallows', but it is only in 'A Jacobite's Exile' that it is praised profusely:

'... O lordly flow the Loire and Seine, and loud the dark Durance:
But bonnier shine the braes of Tyne than a' the fields of France ...

... On Kielder-side the wind blaws wide; there sounds nae hunting horn
that rings sae sweet as the winds that beat round banks where Tyne is born ...'

This last excerpt represents Swinburne's own contribution to the romanticisation of the Jacobite rebellions of 1689 to 1745. The fame of Bonny Prince Charlie and his army of highlanders in the last of the uprisings (1745) has been so widely commemorated in Scottish songs that many people have gained the impression that the Jacobites were a purely Scottish phenomenon. This impression is so strong that the Jacobite movement has for long been a *cause celebre* for Scottish nationalists. As with many such *causes celebres* the tendency has been not to allow the truth to get in the way of a good story; hence the prominence of Northumbrian Jacobites in the uprising of 1715[8] has been largely overlooked north of the Border. However, like their Scottish cousins thirty years later, the ignominious defeat of the Northumbrian Jacobites has been romanticised in music and song. Pipe tunes such as 'Fenwick o' Bywell' and 'Sir John Fenwick's the Flower Amang Them All'[2(a)] celebrate one of the Northumbrian Jacobite luminaries. In song, it is James Radcliffe, Earl of Derwentwater, who has received the accolades. Derwentwater was lord of Dilston Hall, near Corbridge, at the confluence of the 'Deil's' or Devil's Water (which gives its name to Deil'ston (Dilston)) and the Tyne. Leaving aside Swinburne's compositions, two well-known traditional songs concerning Derwentwater have come down to us[3], and these make it clear that his preferential mention in verse is explicable for reasons familiar to us today: he was the best-looking of the local Jacobites[3]:

> '... Oh Derwentwater's a bonny lord, and golden is his hair,
> and glintin' is his hawkin' e'e, wi' kind love dwellin' there ...'

Thus when one local lady watches her husband ride off to war with Derwentwater:

> '... for every sigh for her gude lord, for Derwent there were three ...'[3]

As with all of the Jacobite uprisings, the 1715 rebellion ended in failure, and Derwentwater himself was beheaded on Tower Hill on 24th February 1716. An elegy purporting to have been written by Derwentwater himself (though actually thought to have been penned by James Hogg, the 'Ettrick Shepherd') began circulating some time afterwards, and this song, 'Derwentwater's Farewell', is still sung today in the North East. It is mentioned here mainly because of its haunting allusions to the River Tyne[3]:

> '... Nae mair alang the banks o' Tyne I'll rove in autumn gray.
> Nae mair I'll hear at early dawn the laverock wake the day.
> And who shall deck the hawthorn bower
> where my fond childhood strayed?
> And who when Spring shall bid it flower
> shall rest beneath its shade?
>
> And although here in London Tower it is my fate to die,
> Oh carry me to Northumberland in my father's grave to lie,
> And chant my solemn requiem 'neath Hexham's holy towers,
> and let six maids of fair Tynedale scatter my grave with flowers ...'

With the eschewal of nineteenth century romanticism in the mid-twentieth century, the somewhat 'gritty' popular image of the North East appears to have militated against further outpourings of praise for the Tyne by famous poets. One brief exception may be cited in the person of W.H. Auden, who had a lifelong devotion to the stark landscape of the North Pennines[9], in which the River South Tyne rises. In his 'New Year Letter' of 1940, Auden wrote:

> '... Always my boy of wish returns
> to those peat-stained deserted burns
> that feed the Wear and Tyne and Tees ...'

Although the imagery of water is never far from his mind, the bulk of Auden's praise is reserved for the lead mining remains of the region:

> '... Tramlines and slagheaps, pieces of machinery,

> That was, and still is, my ideal scenery ...'
> ('Letter to Lord Byron', 1937)[9]

Evidently Auden, for one, had no trouble with the industrial aspects of the northern landscape.

A renewal of aesthetic appreciation of the Tyne in verse is long overdue, but a good start was made in the late twentieth century by the celebrated dialect poet Fred Reed[10]. In 'Abeun Chollorford' Reed heaps praise on that same spot where Jock o' the Syde and the tragic bride of Swinburne's ballad played out their dramas[10]:

> '... An' theer ye'll see whaat words cud not define,
>   the beauty o' the tree-waaed Northern Tyne,
>   nee mair reddened wi' claymore and sword,
>   glintin' i' the sun, frum Chollorford ...'

Besides the heroic balladry and the formal poetry, the Tyne has also been widely used as a backdrop for numerous 'standard' romantic songs, which have mostly come down to us by oral tradition and presumably have their roots in the 1600s or earlier. These songs are perhaps a little unusual in being expressions of a love-sick **woman**, whereas most old songs express the often less genteel sentiments of men. Perhaps the best-known of these songs is the 'The Water of Tyne', in which the damsel in distress complains[3]:

> '... I cannot get to my love if I would dee,
>   the water of Tyne runs between him and me;
>   and here I must stand with a tear in my e'e,
>   both sighing and sickly my sweetheart to see ...'

The first line of this song has often been misinterpreted (when sung in a bowdlerised accent) as ending in the word 'die', rather than in the less dramatic (and more sensible) 'do', which most dialect speakers agree is the intended meaning in this context. In two more verses the singer pleads for a boatman to carry her to her loved one. The late Sid Chaplin has quipped that "the lass in the song who called for a boatman to get to her true love must have lived well up above Blaydon"[11], for boatmen with an eye for a bonny lass were never hard to come by downstream of Blaydon coal drops between about 1600 and 1970. However, as the Tyne was readily fordable (except when in spate) at many points upstream of Blaydon, an alternative deduction is that 'The Water of Tyne' is indeed a very old song relating to the unfordable tidal reaches of the river.

Three more poignant songs in the female voice deal with different types of danger which beset the trade of the keelman. The first ('My Bonny Lad') concerns the great fear of all keelmen, that they would be swept out of the river into the open sea, there to be drowned:

> 'Ha' ye seen owt o' my bonny lad,

an' are ye sure he's weel, O?
he's gone ower land with his stick in his hand,
he's gone to un-moor the keel, O!'

'Aye, now I've seen your bonny lad,
upon the sea I spied him,
his grave is green but not wi' grass
an' you'll never lie aside him'[12].

The second two songs both deal with the grief caused by abductions of keelmen by the naval press-gangs, who preyed upon the sea-worthy Tyne boatmen in the late eighteenth and early nineteenth centuries. Firstly there's the 'Sandgate Lassie's Lament'[13], a song which was originally written (by Henry Robson, 1775–1850) to the metre of the somewhat too cheerful 'Bonny Pit Laddie'. It is now more commonly sung to the Scots Jacobite tune 'Ower the Watter to Chairlie':

'... They've prest my dear Johnny, se sprightly and bonny -
Alack! I shall ne'er mair d' weel, O!
The kidnapping squad laid hold of my lad
As he was unmooring the keel, O!

Chorus: O, my sweet laddie, my canny keel laddie,
Se hansum, se canty, and free O!
Had he staid on the Tyne, ere now he'd been mine,
But, oh! He's far ower the sea, O!   ...'

Two more verses record the hope that the lad may survive the war and return to marry her.

The song 'Captain Bover' concerns the same risk to keelmen, but the ending is less tragic, for the worst that happens to the girl's lover is that he is late home, having kept to the water to avoid marauding press gangs[3]:

'... 'Where hes ti' been, maw canny hinny!
Where hes ti' been, maw winsome man?'
... 'Aw've been ti' the norrard, cruisin' back and forrard,
but daurna come ashore for Bover and his gang' ...'

Further songs deal with the press gangs in much the same terms (e.g. 'The Weary Cutters', 'Here's the Tender Coming').

In a similar vein (i.e. girl pines for keelman), but far more cheerful in outlook, is 'The Keel Row', one of Tyneside's best known songs. In this song, a male narrator's voice introduces the rest of the song[3]:

'... As I came thro' Sandgate, thro' Sandgate, thro' Sandgate,
As I came thro' Sandgate I heard a lassie sing:
"Weel may the keel row, the keel row, the keel row,

weel may the keel row, that my laddie's in" ...'

The song then continues in the female voice, once again that of the love-struck damsel hankering for her keel lad, though this time she prefers not to think about the perils which might beset him (other than generally expressing the wish that his keel 'may row well'). Many versions of the subsequent verses are known, but in my experience the truly popular ones are:

'... He wears a blue bonnet, blue bonnet, blue bonnet
he wears a blue bonnet, a dimple in his chin

Oh whe's like my Johnny, sae leish, sae blithe, sae bonny?
he's foremost 'mang the mony keel-lads o' Coaly Tyne! ...''

To which I and a few others invariably add the following (apparently unpublished) verse:

'... His keel boat is laden, it's up the Tyne to Blaydon,
the neet he'll get paid 'n he spends it aall on me! ...'

The Keel Row has enduring appeal, and was adapted for satirical purposes in 1982 to criticise perceived shortcomings of the local public transport system:

'... As I came thro' Monument, thro' Monument, thro' Monument,
As I came thro' Monument I heard me lassie sing:
"Oh where the hell's the Met-ro, the Metro, the Metro,
where the hell's the Metro that my laddie's in?" ...'[14]

One example of a love song rendered completely in the male voice can be offered: 'The Banks of Tyne'[15]:

'As I walked out one summer's day to view the fields so green,
the bushes they were in full bloom so lovely to be seen,
when posey bushes was adorned so brightly they did shine,
there I met my lovely Nancy down by the banks of Tyne'.

And so it goes on, an altogether more formulaic love song than the four preceding examples, rehearsing the well-worn story-line of: 'girl loves sailor, sailor goes to sea, girl is faithful, sailor returns, they are married and live happily ever after'.

Another example of a formulaic song is the 'Tyne Exile's Lament', which is remarkable only in that it mentions the Tyne, all the sentiments within it being common to any homesick traveller:

'... But all is in vain the fond wish to restrain,
I wish I were again on the Banks of the Tyne ...'[16]

The same theme was picked up with far greater success in the 1980s by a singer-songwriter who went by the name of 'Busker', whose muse was to express the homesickness of so many unemployed Geordies, stuck in London during the Thatcher era:

'... It's cold up there in summer, like sittin' inside a fridge,
still Aa wish Aa was on the Quayside, lookin' at the owld Tyne Bridge ...
... Aa'm comin' home, Newcastle, ye can keep ya London wine,
Aa'd waalk the streets aal day an' aal neet for a bottle of the River Tyne ...'[17]

'COALY TYNE': INDUSTRIAL SONGS AND POEMS

'... The may, who care to yell, keep boozy Blaydon Races for Tyneside's national anthem;
the discerning know it is that tremendous criss-cross of steel over water that sings the true song of Tyne ...'[11]

Thus wrote the region's literary champion Sid Chaplin in 1967, praising the dramatic 'congeries of bridges' which span the Tyne gorge at Newcastle (Chapter 14). Though a genius of the written word, Sid Chaplin was not noted for his singing, and hence may not be regarded as the best person to consult over what constitutes the 'true song of Tyne'. However, in identifying the industrial and engineering feats of Tyneside as the deepest fount of local inspiration, he was definitely right. For, well before the present Tyne Bridge was constructed in the 1920s, the bustle of industry along the Tyne was already inspiring the greatest flowering of local song-writing. The mood of celebration is well represented in the following anthem, 'Coaly Tyne'[13]:

'... Tyne River, running rough or smooth, makes bread for me and mine,
of all the rivers, north or south, there's none like coaly Tyne!

Chorus: So here's to coaly Tyne, my lads, success to coaly Tyne;
of all the rivers, north or south, there's none like coaly Tyne

Long has Tyne's swelling bosom borne great riches from the mine,
All by her hardy sons uptorn, the wealth of coaly Tyne
Our keelmen brave, with laden keels, go sailing down in line,
And with them load the fleet at Shields that sails from coaly Tyne ...'

'Coaly Tyne' is sung to the same tune as 'Auld Lang Syne' (a tune which, despite its indelibly Scottish associations, was actually written in Gateshead).

The 'keelmen brave' have already been mentioned in the context of love songs. For two hundred years or more, the keelmen dominated the workforce of the River Tyne[18]. Their final demise around 1890 was due to the extension of navigability throughout the tidal reaches of the Tyne by extensive dredging, so that steam-powered collier boats could load directly from the various coal staithes (Chapter 12). Until their departure from the Tyneside scene, the keelmen were the subject of many Tyneside songs, the editorial content of which varies from unalloyed praise to outright slander. But love them or hate them, it seems no-one could ignore the 'keel lads o' coaly Tyne' in their heyday. So who were these larger-than-life Tynesiders?

The keelmen were a crucial link in the coal trade[18,19]. In their small boats ('keels') , each of which was built to carry **precisely** 21.2 tons of coal, the keelmen would transport coal from the river bank depots to the large 'collier brigs' (or just simply 'colliers', i.e. the sailing ships which took the coal to London or even further afield[19]). The colliers were moored in the navigable waters of the Tyne estuary. When a keel arrived alongside, hatches on the brig would be opened and the coal shovelled in by the keelmen. The operation was usually timed to coincide with the tidal cycle, with the downstream current of a falling tide aiding the shipping of coal to the waiting colliers, and the rising tide aiding the weary journey back up river. The keel boats were little more than floating coal hoppers, with short decks to fore and aft. They typically had a small cabin (or 'huddock') sunk into the after deck, and a sail which could be raised when winds were favourable to save on rowing and punting efforts. The crew of a keel numbered four[18]: three adults, namely the 'skipper' and two 'keel bullies', and a young lad to act as a look-out and general helper. This young lad, invariably referred to as 'P.D.' (or 'peedee') is either the hero or butt of many keel songs. As far as I can ascertain, P.D. was an abbreviation of *per diem*, referring to the day-by-day manner in which the youngsters were hired.

The arduous nature of the keelmen's work can readily be imagined, and the success with which these strong men discharged their duties spawned a prickly pride and an appetite for self-celebration, both of which are clearly evident in the song lyrics of the period. It is perhaps not stretching things too far to note that the same attitudes are detectable today in the behaviour of many Geordies, whom Austin Mitchell MP has memorably described as having 'a built-in sense of superiority based on a clamorous inferiority complex'[20]. In preparing their self-congratulatory songs, the keelmen and their sympathisers used the convenient poetic device of putting the words of praise in the mouths of swooning women. The 'Keel Row' is a case in point. As a further example consider 'The Sandgate Lass on the Ropery Banks'[13]:

'... hearty Aw heard this lass singin' -
" Maw bonny keel lad shall be mine"

Chorus: O wad the keel come doon the river
that Aw my dear laddie could see;
he whistles he dances se cliver,
maw bonny keel laddie for me'

That mornin' forget Aw will niver,
when first Aw saw him on the kee,
the 'Keel Row' he whissel'd se cliver

> he wun my affections frae me;
> his drawers on his doup luik'd se canny,
> his keel hat was cock'd on his heed,
> an if Aw'd not gettin' my Jimmy,
> Faith, by this time Aw wad been deed ...'

This song, which was written by R Nunn (1808–1853), amply demonstrates that the swashbuckling image of the keelmen was fully fledged by the early nineteenth century. Other groups of workers in the region were not slow to adopt the same image. As Robert Colls has noted[21], the outcome was that the dashing keelman and the hardy pitman became readily interchangeable as stereotypes of the local hero very early in the nineteenth century. Nowhere more clearly is this seen than in the following parallel songs, both printed for the first time in 1812[22]:

My bonnie pit laddie,   My bonnie keel laddie,
My canny pit laddie   my canny keel laddie
My bonnie pit laddie for me, O!   My bonnie keel laddie for me, O!
He sits on his cracket and hews in his jacket   He sits in his keel, as
                                                             black as the de'il
And brings the bright siller to me, O! And brings the white money to
                                                             me, O!

However, the image of the keelman was by no means unblemished, for he often drank at least as hard as he worked, and displayed the kind of boorish behaviour still associated with certain present-day Geordie celebrities. Hence we have the 'Sandgate Lass's Lament'[16]:

> '... I was a young maiden truly and lived in Sandgate Street,
> I thought to marry a good man to keep me warm at neet,
> Sum good-like body, sum bonny body, to be with me at noon,
> But last I married a keelman and my good days are done.
>
> *Chorus:* He's an ugly body, a bubbly body, an ill-far'd hideous loon,
>   and I have married a keelman and my good days are done.
>
> I thought to marry a parson to hear me say my prayers,
> but I have married a keelman and he kicks me down the stairs,
> I thought to marry a joiner to make me chair and stool,
> but I have married a keelman and he's a perfect fool   ...'

Nothing too complimentary there, then! Insults to the keelmen were by no means the sole province of embittered wives. While no-one doubted the physical strength of the keelmen, and few would be likely to mock them to their face for any shortcomings, many songs of the period make fun of their perceived lack of navigational skills. Certainly, from the point of view of a true seafarer, the voyage up and down the Tyne in a keel could hardly be considered demanding in terms of route-finding. The keelmen may be partly to blame for fostering the image of poor navigators, for they often gave vent to their fears of strong currents carrying their keels over Shields Bar, the submerged sandbank which hindered shipping around the mouth of the Tyne, and into the open sea. Of course it was not the navigational aspects of the open sea that bothered them, but the thought of what ocean waves might do to a low-slung open keel boat. Nevertheless, it is for a lack of realism about the geography of the oceans that they are chiefly mocked in song.

Songs mocking the supposed navigational ineptitude of the keelmen appear to have become ever more extravagant in their absurdity over time. One early song, 'The Skipper in the Mist'[13] is quite moderate in its scorn. When a thick fog descends on the Tyne, the crew of a keel boat begin to argue over their whereabouts. The skipper, who was evidently a pessimist, swears they have crossed Shields Bar and are in open sea. He is enraged when one of the crew argues that, as his oar just touched the bottom, they are still well up the river, 'between King's Meadows and Newcassel Brig':

> '... The skipper, enraged, then declared he kenn'd better,
> for at the same time he had smelt the salt wetter;
> "And there's Marsden Rock, just within a styen thraw,
> Aw can see't throo the mist, aw'll swear by my reet paw".

> "The anchor let's drop till the weather it clears,
> for fear we be nabb'd by the French privateers!"
> The anchor was dropt; when the weather clear'd up,
> they fund the keel moored at th' awd Javil Group.

> The skipper was vex'd and he curs'd and he swore
> That his nose had ne'er led him se far wrang before;
> But what most of all did surprise these four people
> Was Marsden Rock chang'd into Gateshead Church Steeple! ...'

By 1826, when the 'The Skipper's Mistake' was published, two keelmen adrift in Jarrow slake on a misty day are depicted making latitudinal calculations which persuade them they are crossing the North Sea[13]:

> 'We're ower the bar, there's nowt left for us,
> but either Holland or France, man!'

When the mist finally lifts and land is sighted, they are relieved to find themselves alongside St Paul's Church in Jarrow. The hyperbole goes one step further in a second song published the same year, in which a keel crew get benighted in a stiff gale, and fail to find a solid purchase for their anchor. After a night of prayer and fasting, all squeezed together in the huddock, the gale drops at sunrise. The skipper looks out and concludes they've crossed not merely the North Sea but the Atlantic:

> '... see the high cliffs of Virgini',
> where they grow all the green tea and baccy.
> Aye, as sure as I'm living, my hinny,
> the folks aw believe are all wild.
> An' sure they will some of us fry,
> but now we're all meekness and mild
> we needn't mind how seun we die ...'

The crew of a passing steamer soon disabuse them of their delusions — the cliffs are none other than those of Tynemouth.

The keelmen were not immune from less focused scorn. One piece of slapstick, related in 'Tars and Skippers', has two keel skippers keeping vigil over the grave of a friend at the height of the Burke and Hare grave-robbing scandal. Four sailors are nearby doing the same. Both groups become jumpy on spying the others and end up in a shooting match before they realise that neither party are grave robbers. In 'The Amphitrite'[13,16] a crew of half-drunken keelmen find they cannot remember the correct name of the collier ship (i.e. Amphitrite) to which they have been hired to make their delivery of coal. 'Empty Kite' and 'Appetite' are both tried before they eventually chance upon the right ship. The heights of absurdity are reached in 'A Floatin' Grunstan'[13], in which a keel crew make strenuous efforts to retrieve what they take to be a valuable grindstone floating in the Tyne. Grindstones, of course, do not float. In reality, the object in question was a wooden hoop with iron ochre scum floating inside, but the mistake was not discovered before one of the crew had been soaked to the skin.

Clearly the scriptural exhortations relating to millstones around necks would have been lost on the heroes of 'A Floatin' Grunstan'. Indeed, in the songs which have come down to us the religiosity of the keelmen leaves much to be desired. In 'Hydrophobie'[13,16] (by Robert Emery, 1794–1871) a keel bullie who happens to have been bitten by a dog pretends to have contracted rabies in order to frighten a Quaker preacher who has accepted a lift onboard. The keel bullie's interpretation of the symptoms of rabies is not too convincing to modern eyes, but it convinces not only the Quaker but the skipper as well, and both dive into the Tyne and swim for their lives:

> 'To howl an' bark he wasn't slack, the Quaker owerboard in a crack,
> with the fat skipper on his back, for fear of Hydrophobie!'

A more considered cynicism towards organised religion is displayed by the chief protagonist of the song 'The keelman's reason for attending church'. After listening to his colleague describe how the sermon had moved him to fear for his soul in view of his many sins, our keelman calmly explains his own motivations:

> 'To tell the truth, what meyks me gan, wor Maister's torn'd religious,
> he'll think aw's sec a godly man and mevvies raise me wages'[16].

A lack of serious religious commitment was apparently accompanied in the keelmen's psyche (as in many similarly irreligious people to this day) by a *penchant* for superstition and fear of the occult. A number of songs have them cowering in their keel huddocks in fright at devils or ghosts. In two such songs, the 'De'il' turns out to be a bearded, clove-footed goat. In another tale, a skipper ineptly crashes his keel into Hebburn Quayside, at a point where a recently-deceased landlady called Lizzie Mudie had kept a pub. The crew at once hear a mocking call of 'hoo, hoo' from the shore, and assume it is the ghost of Lizzie. The intrepid skipper leaps ashore to confront the mocker, armed 'wiv a coal in each hand'. He returns soon afterwards to report that the source of the ghostly 'hoo, hoo' was 'nee ghost at all, but — an au'd Jenny Howlet!' — in other words a female owl[13,16]. Only one song, 'Sandgate Pant'[13] (another Robert Emery song), records a 'true' haunting of keelmen: this concerns the ghost of Jean Jamieson, a fruit seller who was hanged on the Town Moor in 1829 for murdering her mother. The ghost confronts Skipper Johnson at 2 a.m. as he heads towards his keel after a heavy session of drinking. The ghost demands the Skipper bring her lover, Billy Ellison, to meet her on the bridge without delay. He promises to bring him along at the next tide, at which the ghost leaves him to his hangover. The song continues:

> '... She waits for her lover, each night at this station,
>   and calls her ripe fruit with a voice loud and clear,
>   the keel bullies listen in great consternation,
>   tho' snug in their huddocks they tremble with fear ...'.

So much for the antics of the grown men of the keels — now for a few words on 'little peedee', the 10 to 14-year-old keel lad. Overall, 'peedee' receives sympathetic commentary in the keel songs. Two rather similar songs, both set near the confluence of the Skinner Burn with the Tyne, relate instances of bullying. In 'The Flay Craw'[13], the crew become short-tempered when the wind drops and leaves them benighted with two miles to punt home. They take their anger out on the hapless peedee, nipping and kicking him. The peedee is then given a keel hook (a kind of punting pole) and begins to help the keelmen drive the boat upriver. His pole soon jams in the river bed, and the peedee is pulled from the boat to cling for dear life to the pole through the night. When dawn breaks, he is eventually saved by a passing huntsman, who had at first tried to shoot him thinking he was a bedraggled crow. In the second of these two songs, 'The Half-Drowned Skipper'[13], the peedee is knocked overboard by the bad-tempered skipper. After the keel bullies retrieve the frightened boy, the skipper himself ends up in the water:

> '... Noo the keelmen bein tired of thor skipper se brave,
>   Not one e'er attempted his life for te save.
>   They hoisted thor sail - and we saw no more
>   But the half-drowned skipper wes swimmin ashore ...'

The peedee's finest hour is recorded in one of the earliest known dialect songs, 'The Little P.D.'[13,16], which was published as early as 1805 and was certainly popular before then.

'... Twas between Hebbron an' Jarrow, there cam' on a varry strang gale,
the skipper luik'd out o' the huddock, crying "Smash, man! Lower the sail!
.... Or else to the bottom we'll go!" ...'

(Incidentally, the spelling 'Hebbron' used in this song is not an error; three generations ago, this was precisely how the name of the town now labelled 'Hebburn' was pronounced locally). Back to the drama: While the peedee is trying to drop the anchor the keel bangs into the quay, and the other three occupants jump out. Following yelled instructions from the shore the peedee manages to steer the keel close enough that he can fling a rope to the skipper on the shore. His adroit handiwork having saved the day, the peedee is joined onboard by the crew once more, who begin to fry up a celebratory meal. Any pride that the peedee might have been feeling at his precocious boatmanship is soon overshadwoed by an act of clumsiness:

'... the skipper roored out for a drink, P.D. ran to bring him th' can,
But odsmash! Mun, what d'ye think! He coup'd a' the flesh out o' the' pan! ...'

Before leaving the keelmen, mention must be made of one of the most popular of all Tyneside songs, 'Cushy Butterfield', in which the narrator describes himself as 'a broken-hearted keel lad an' Aw's ower-heels in luv'. The chorus is very widely known[23]:

'... She's a big lass and a bonny lass and she likes hor beer,
an' the call hor Cushy Butterfield an' Aw wish she was here! ...'

What is less widely known is that this song is a parody of a somewhat more genteel London song of the period, 'Pretty Polly Perkins of Paddington Green', the heroine of which did not include a proclivity for beer swilling amongst her alluring charms! The final verse of Cushy Butterfield, as originally written, includes an interesting competition between a keelman and a pitman for the affections of Cushy:

'They say she's got another lad an' he hews at Shipcote,
if Aa thowt she'd deceive us, why Aa'd sure slit me throat!
So Aa'll sail doon the river, an' sing "Aa'm afloat!
An' adieu to Cushy Butterfield an' hor chep from Shipcote!"

Besides the coal trade and the keelmen, Tyneside in its heyday could boast many allied industries (Chapter 13), just a few of which are listed in R.O. Heslop's song 'Howdon for Jarrow'[13], which describes the sights to be seen when travelling down river from Newcastle in the 1870s:

'... There's chemicals, copper, coals, clarts, coke an' stone,
iron ships, wooden tugs, salt, an' sawdust, an' bone,
manure, steam ingins, bar iron an' vit'rol,
grunstans an' puddlers (Aa like to be litt'ral) ...'

All of which were served by a myriad of trades, from sailors through shipwrights to soda ash makers. Of these trades, none can boast a canon of songs to compare with that of the keelmen. Although the sailors and fishermen were prolific songsters, the Tyne was merely a harbour to most of them, and they expended little energy in praising it. However a few of their songs make specific reference to the Tyne. 'Till the Tide Cums In'[13] describes the drunken proceedings on Newcastle quayside whilst waiting for a favourable tide:

'... While strolling down sweet Sandgate street, a man-o'-war's blade I chanc'd
to meet
to the sign of 'The Ship' I hauled him in, to drink a good glass till the tide
came in ...'

Despite its suggestive title, the song entitled 'The Sailors are all at the Bar'[3] is **not** a drinking song, but rather expresses the frustration of sailors arriving back at the mouth of the Tyne only to find that the tides and currents prevent them crossing Shields Bar and getting into port. 'Liberty for the Sailors'[3] is a North Shields song which describes the general delight in the town when the sailors return *en masse* to spend some time at home, and more to the point, to spend their pay.

One of the enduring mysteries of the Tyneside folk music scene is the seemingly total absence of songs from the shipyard workers' community. I hope someone will read this and prove me wrong, but coming from a musical shipyard family myself, I'm fairly sure of my facts: for some reason the shipyard workers were not subject to the same muse as their neighbours, the keelmen and pitmen. Which is not to say that the shipyard workers weren't musical. Woodwind instruments were particularly popular amongst the Hebburn shipyard workers, for instance. One of their number, the late, great John Doonan, won the 'Champion Flute of All Ireland' in the 1950s, and continued to inspire generations of young musicians in his native district right up to his death in 2002. Several Hebburn shipyard men of my father's generation are skilled makers of the Northumbrian and Irish bagpipes, turning the instruments out on lathes installed in their garages and garden sheds. Singing was a popular pastime too. So why are there no shipyard songs of note? My guess at an explanation invokes the fact that the majority of Tyneside shipyard workers were of either Scottish or Irish ancestry, and while I can vouch that they took up the existing Geordie songs with great gusto, they did not, in their first century or so in the Tyneside melting pot, get round to composing dialect lyrics themselves. However, if we turn to verse rather than song, the story is different. Humorous doggerel was always circulating in the Hebburn and Wallsend shipyards, passing freely across the river via the Mid-Tyne Ferries. I remember my Dad coming home from

Hawthorn Leslie's with scruffy scraps of paper bearing hand-written ditties. Most of the satirical efforts produced in this way were never written to be preserved for posterity. Thankfully, there is one exception to this generality, in the work of Jack Davitt, whose *nom de plume* was Ripyard Cuddling, or as the men of the Hebburn Yard adapted it 'Shipyard Codling'. Jack Davitt's poems were featured for a while on BBC Radio Newcastle in the late 1970s, and subsequently appeared in published form, as books[24] and cassettes. The poems are wide-ranging in subject and devastatingly funny. One of the best-known of the poems is 'The Truth aboot the waall', which is a hilarious re-writing of the construction of Hadrian's Wall:

> '... The' started the waall on the banks o' the Tyne,
>   an' the' tried varry hard for te keep a strite line.
> There wiz thoosands o' Geordies wi' shovels an' picks,
>   An' the rate for the job was eleven and six.
>
> Noo the stones for the waall came by bogey an' barra,
>   The cut them in quarries in Hebburn an' Jarra',
>   The floated them ower the Tyne on a raft,
> Them aad-fashioned Geordies could certainly graft! ...'

I'm not going to spoil the pleasures of the full poem by recounting the punch line here! Most of Davitt's poems relate directly to his experience in the Wallsend shipyards, though the stories he tells are almost all comical exaggerations. 'The Million Ton Tanker' is widely remembered. The fantastic vessel slowly takes shape in a giant shipyard formed by the amalgamation of neighbouring yards:

> '... The journey to the after-peak,
>   on foot took half a working week,
>   and though the workers had to hike,
>   each gaffer got a motorbike ...
> ... and up among the beams and struts,
>   two helicopters checked the butts ...'

When the tanker is finally complete the crunch comes - the ship cannot be launched at Wallsend for it turns out to be two feet wider than the Tyne! The crisis meeting comes up with a solution:

> '... we'll turn the berth the other way,
>   and launch the ship at Whitley Bay ...'

This has the minor complication of several towns in the path of the ship. However, the deed is accomplished, albeit:

> '... No architect could ever cure
> the damage done to Shiremoor ...'

Scarcely less outrageous is the fanciful tale of 'The Swan and Hunter Robot'. A welder to trade, Davitt made fun of the withdrawal of productivity incentives for welders which was introduced when management agreed to an invidious demand by the other trades in the boilermakers union:

> '... When piece-work was abolished and the welders went on time,
> production in the fab. sheds began a downward climb ...'

('fab' standing for 'fabrication'). To solve this problem the management decide to go all out for automation, and they buy a prototype robot welder. Working its first night shift, it is an instant success, achieving in two hours what seven human welders might achieve in a week. As such, it quickly outstrips the supply of work, and the foreman decides to switch it off:

> '... but the robot wasn't programmed to be destitute of work.
> When they tried to switch the juice off, that is when it went berserk ...'

After running amok in the shipyard, welding everything in sight, it welds the yard gates shut behind it and heads up the bank into Wallsend town centre, where it welds together buses and metro trains. It then shatters two tankers in the Wallsend dock before turning its attention to the other bank of the river:

> '... As the sun began to rise just like a ripe red cherry,
> the robot left the stricken town and headed for the ferry.
> Now its sights were set on Jarrow, that town of song and wine,
> but it stumbled on the landing stage and plunged into the Tyne.
> The Swan and Hunter Robot was never seen again:
> from the landing stage that morning it took the count of ten ...'

The management decide to discontinue automation experiments; thereafter each job would be welded by hand!

'CHAMPIONS O' THE TYNE': SPORTING SONGS

One of the most vigorous living traditions of singing on Tyneside (albeit by far the most profane also) is that associated with the 'Toon Army', i.e. the supporters of Newcastle United Football Club. Provided one can tolerate the vulgarities, a deeply appealing wry wit may be found in many of the songs which are chanted on the terraces of St James' Park during every home game. However, virtually no reference is made to the River Tyne in these songs. Furthermore, the contemporary chants of the Newcastle fans are only the latest flowering of an entire tradition of sporting songs peculiar to Tyneside, a tradition which reached its zenith between 1840 and 1880, when the sport in question was rowing[25] (Chapter 11).

The professional oarsman of the River Tyne were the Alan Shearers of their era, and like Shearer they were cherished not only for their sporting prowess, but also as symbols of regional pride. Accordingly, their enthusiastic followers composed numerous songs in their honour, which not only documented their numerous victories, but celebrated them as vindicators of the pride of Tynesiders in the face of their arch-rivals, the Cockneys, who were represented by the Thames boatsmen. That intense feelings of rivalry should have developed between the Tyne and the Thames is understandable. London was the principal port of call for the collier brigs which left the Tyne on virtually every tide, and the 'Coal-whippers' of the River Thames (i.e. the local counterparts of the Tyne keelmen, who unloaded, or 'jumped' the coals from the boats and took them ashore[19]) no doubt boasted of their physical prowess in much the same way as their northern cousins. Add to that the jealousy felt by the inhabitants of Newcastle, self-styled capital of the North, towards London, the undisputed capital of England, and the roots of antipathy are not far to seek. Geordie pride had been badly wounded by the successive defeats of the Tyne oarsmen at the hands of Robert Coombes of Vauxhall in 1842 and 1844. Revenge, when it eventually commenced in 1845, was not only complete but sustained. Henry ('Harry') Clasper, who was subsequently nicknamed 'Hadaway Harry' by his ecstatic followers, wrested the championship away from the cockneys at the London Regatta that year, and it was to return but rarely to southern hands in the following three decades. Besides Clasper, the roll-call of Tyneside rowing heroes includes Robert ('Honest Bob') Chambers, James Renforth, and finally in the mid-1870s, Messrs Boyd and Elliot.

Great as the successes of the sportsmen were, their historian Harvey Taylor has commented[25] that 'even more essential to the promotion of local pride were the balladeers who sang [their] praises'. Foremost amongst these balladeers was Joe Wilson, one of Tyneside's greatest-ever singer-songwriters, whose prodigious output of dialect lyrics amounts to some 250 pieces, fortunately published in a single volume[26] following his untimely death in 1875 at the early age of 33. Best remembered today for the classic comic song 'Keep yor feet still Geordie, hinny!', Wilson was a great enthusiast for the 'Champions o' the Tyne', whose praises he sang in not less than 21 separate songs! He not only celebrated their victories, but also expressed undying support when they lost crucial competitions (a familiar sentiment to this day amongst Newcastle United fans!), as in the song 'A Welcum'[26], addressed to the recently-defeated Bob Chambers:

'... Yor welcum back agyen, Bob, yor welcum te the Tyne,
where ye've displayed yor manly skill, so dinnet ye repine.
An' man yor high amang the best that ivvor pull'd an oar
We'll not forget, - tho beat the day, the wundors deun afore ...'

So generalised did the support for the rowing heroes become that Wilson felt comfortable penning a stylised romantic song concerning them ('Me Bonny Brave Boat Rower'), in which a young maiden strolling on Newcastle Quayside is heard to sing the praises of her young lover, a Tyneside oarsmen away in training for competition against the London squads:

'... For he pulls se clivor on the coally river, he's myed the Cocknies glower,
   An' he says that he'll be champion yit, maw bonny brave boat rower ...'

Nor did the sentimental outpourings stop there, for when James Renforth died suddenly in 1871, actually in the middle of a race in Canada, the upsurge of popular sentiment which saw 150,000 Tynesiders take to the streets to pay their last respects[25] was captured by Wilson in a funeral lament ('Champein ov all Champeins') which was sung (no doubt with great pathos) to the tune 'Babylon is Falling'.

Wilson was by no means alone in capturing the popularity of the rowing heroes in song: two such songs are recorded from the repertoire of Ned Corvan (a former keelman himself), one from Geordie Ridley (better known as author of 'The Blaydon Races' and 'Cushy Butterfield'), one each from John Taylor of Dunston and Richard Heslop (the author of the first and greatest dictionary of the Northumbrian dialect), and a further song about Chambers which was evidently very popular, but which remains anonymous[13]. The impression which this combined lyrical output conveys, more than 125 years later, is of a Tyneside alive with passion, with all eyes focused on the sportsmen who enlivened what was then an extremely busy working river. Despite the association of the river with toil, therefore, it is clear that people were still attracted to its banks in their leisure time in great numbers.

A TYNESIDE MISCELLANY

Not even the foregoing categories of music, lyric and verse fully exhaust the supply of memorable tunes and songs concerning the Tyne. While the oarsman of the eighteenth and nineteenth centuries are the Tyneside personalities most celebrated in song, more famous internationally is the Venerable Bede, Doctor of the Church, and author of the first history of the English people. The name 'Bede' is still a relatively common Christian name in Jarrow, particularly amongst the Catholic population. The same population also celebrates St Bede with a hymn which is not only sung in Church once a year, but is also to be heard in more profane surroundings, often immediately after that other portable piece of piety, 'Hail Glorious St Patrick'. The hymn to Bede recounts the death of the Saint on May 25th 735 A.D. The hymn opens with a tranquil image of the Tyne in this simpler age:

'... From Jarrow's tower, the vesper bell tolls solemnly across the Tyne.
   Resting his oar the mariner stays listening to its sacred chime ...'

The following verses describe how the monks of St Paul's Monastery rush from vespers to gather round the bed of the dying master, and the chorus prays:

'... Glorious St Bede, pray that we may praise God for all eternity ...'

The monastery at Jarrow overlooks Jarrow Slake, or 'Slacks', which was the setting for a much more macabre death scene in August 1832. This was the gibbeting in an iron cage of William Jobling, a pitman widely believed to have been framed for the murder of a local magistrate. The barbaric ritual of displaying tarred-and-feathered corpses of executed convicts in this manner had been discontinued almost a century before. The reintroduction of the practice for the case of Jobling betrayed the motives of his judicial murderers: to intimidate the local miners, who were in the midst of a major strike which sought to destroy the feudal 'bond' system, under which miners were treated as little more than casual possessions of the mine owners. Several songs have been written about the cruel treatment of Will Jobling. The late Jock Purdon, celebrated miner and songwriter of Chester-le-Street, wrote a ballad, 'Farewell Jobling', recounting the incident and its significance for the mining community[27]. Less detailed, but perhaps more moving, is the song 'Whe knaas where Bill Jobling lies?', which was originally written by David Bell of South Shields. Never previously published, the verses below are transcribed from the arrangement of the song made by the late Pete Elliott of Birtley:

' ...*Chorus:*   Whe knaas where Bill Jobling lies? He'll not be seen again.
But Aa knaa where he'll always be: in the hearts of workin' men.

They used Bill Jobling aall his life, t' hew an' toil an' sweat,
An' noo they've put him oot t' hang, they'll use poor Billy yet.

Thiv left poor Billy oot t' rot, as a warnin' to his kind,
That they can kill when they do not imprison, flog or fine.

Bill Jobling was nee wicked lad, nor yet was he a fool,
But what else can a poor lad dee, when they myek aall the rules?

But late one neet his marras came an took poor Billy back
From the iron cage where he'd been hung on lonely Jarra Slacks...'

A tragedy of a different nature which occurred some 22 years later, up the river at the Newcastle and Gateshead quays, is recorded in Ned Corvan's song 'The Fire on the Kee':

'It was a fearful crash, old buildings they went smash, 'twas never so before;
the haunts of 'Auld lang syne' burnt doon on coaly Tyne, laying waste the desolate shore ...
For, Oh! The flames Vesuvius-like, they spread oe'r land and sea,
Laying desolate waste the spot where once had been Newcastle Kee ...'

The problem lay in an explosion in a Gateshead chemical works which was so violent that balls of flame crossed the river and ignited warehouses and timber dwellings on the Newcastle side.

The same site had been the setting for an event of the opposite extreme some forty years previously, in the winter of 1813–1814, when the Tyne froze over for three weeks. The local residents cheerfully took advantage of the circumstances and held an impromptu, but extensive, fair on the ice. William Mitford recorded the event in song, in 'The Tyne Fair':

> '... There were some rowley-powley, tetum, dice-box,
>   while others, for liquor, were fighting game cocks,
>   when Neddy the Bellman - his bell tinkled on
>   said a Cuddy Race started exactly at one ...'

How the cuddies (horses) coped with racing on ice we are not told, but ice-skating races were certainly successful, with one 'Mall Trollop' winning the ladies' event ahead of her rival, 'Bow-Legged Nan'.

A light-hearted tale of an excursion gone wrong is the subject of the archaic song 'Jemmy Johnson's Whurry', which was written by one Thomas Thompson. The excursion was a boat trip from Newcastle to Shields, and it featured singing and dancing on board. All went well until the boat approached Hebburn, where (as in 'The Little P.D.') a gale suddenly blew up and rendered the passengers sea-sick. They nevertheless survived the voyage as far as Shields, whence they made their way to Tynemouth beach, only to fall head over heels in the surf:

> '... Amang the rest Aw cowp'd me creels, Eh Gox! 'twas funny varry,
>   an' so Aw end me voyage to Shiels iv Jemmy Johnson's Whurry ...'

Ironically, having survived the ordeal by water recounted in this song, the author met an untimely death from exhaustion on January 9th 1816 after battling to save his property from the Tyne floods of December 1815[13].

As the case of Thomas Thompson illustrates, flooding on the Tyne is rarely a laughing matter. Nevertheless, flooding in November 1875 on one of the river's lower-reach tributaries (the Causey Burn, which feeds water to the Tyne via the River Team) was commemorated with mirth in 'The Sheel Raa Flud', a comic song of the great Tommy Armstrong of Tanfield Lea (1848–1920)[28]. The song uses humorous exaggeration to describe how two married couples (the Johnsons and the Clarkes) woke to find their homes under considerable depths of water. When Mrs Johnson wakes and asks her husband to find her clothes, she gets this response:

> '... 'Thi claithes' he says 'the've gyen wi' mine,
>   like Boyd and Elliot doon the Tyne!' ...'

(Boyd and Elliot being contemporary rowing heroes). Meanwhile, in the Clarke household, Mrs Sally Clarke steps out of bed into deep water and cries out in fright. On hearing her, her husband Bob leaps from bed to aid her, but both end up in bother:

' ... he went wherivver he hord hor squaal,
      but the watter wuz aalwis shiftin' Sal, that nasty Sunda' mornin' - O!
At last the watter brok' oppen the door, an' weshed away byeth Bob an' hor,
      at Timmith they wor weshed ashore, that nasty Sunda' mornin' - O!'

'Timmith' (Tynemouth) is a very long downstream swim from Shield Row,
County Durham!

Two major river engineering works on the Tyne have been commemorated
by popular songs written a full 120 years apart. The first, 'The High Level an'
the Aud Bridge' (written by Ned Corvan in 1862)[13] is a comic imaginary
argument between the new and old bridges over the Tyne. The second is far
more recent, dating from the 1980s, and concerns the construction of the Kielder
Dam. At the time of its construction, Kielder Dam was highly controversial.
Most criticism centred upon claims that the reservoir was far too large for any
conceivable demand. Such criticisms have fallen away in recent years as Kielder
Water has time and again kept the North East well-watered through droughts
that have severely stressed water resource systems further south. One relic of
criticism remains from the time of dam construction, however, in the popular
song 'Hawkhope Hill' by Terry Conway[29]. This song does not criticise the
reservoir *per se*, but rather satirises the County Council's re-housing exercise
for people displaced from the flooded area:

'... When first the planners back a while, decided to put on some style,
      and keep the Tyne in one big pile to save the waste and spill,
They told the folk; 'Good afternoon, we've come to knock your hooses doon,
      We cannot send you to the moon, so we chose Hawkhope Hill ...'

The song goes on to describe the residents' bemusement at the location chosen
for the replacement housing: halfway up a hillside a short distance down valley
from the dam. A number of enjoyable digs are included at the Council officials
and the builders:

'... In clarty holes like ducks at play, the County men cried 'Hip-Hooray!
      It's just like bein' at Whitley Bay!' They howked away like hell.
Then fowerty thoosand builders came, they said "Stand back! We knaa the game".
      But they myed Selwyn Froggat seem like Isambard Brunel ...'

The very latest engineering feat on the Tyne, Gateshead's majestic Millennium
Bridge (which was officially opened by Queen Elizabeth II on 7th May 2002) has
already been celebrated in verse, by none other than that erstwhile troubadour
of the shipyards, Jack Davitt, who has continued to write dialect poetry
throughout his retirement[30]. His verses beautifully capture the universal esteem
in which this new landmark is held locally; for once, Davitt keeps his satirical
muse at bay, and heaps wholehearted praise on the elegant structure. (This is
more respect than he accords that other recently-erected landmark, the 'Angel
of the North', of which Davitt remarks that, if that is what angels really look

like, he doesn't want to go to heaven!).

'THE VOICE OF TYNE': TYNESIDE SONG AND VERSE TODAY

Jack Davitt's sustained output is a major contribution to the ever-growing canon of poetic and lyrical output concerning the Tyne. His comments on the present-day quietness of the river, in comparison to the bustling river he knew in his prime, are poignant and moving[24]:

> '... I stood in Wallsend shipyard and looked across the Tyne,
>   the river of my homeland, more famous than the Rhine.
>
> The yard of Hawthorn Leslies lay spread before my gaze,
> The birthplace of the 'Kelly' in those distant wartime days
>
> The berths were still and empty, the cranes stood stark and still;
>   I admit my heart was heavy and my eyes began to fill ...'

Jack Davitt is not alone in expressing the pain of industrial decline. In a local anthology of amateur verse published in 1995[31], no less than seven of the poems dealt directly with the decline of the river as a port and shipbuilding centre. The titles of some of these poems capture the general atmosphere: 'Death of the River Tyne', 'Death of a River', 'They've gone and closed the shipyards down'. The same wistfulness is to be found in more subtle form in the lyrics of Wallsend-born Sting, who reflects obliquely on the hardships endured by his Tyneside forebears in the title song of his 1991 album 'The Soul Cages'. Jimmy Nail has written an altogether more stirring and direct song traversing the same emotional territory, a song which benefits from having a rousing chorus very much in keeping with mainstream Geordie tradition. In 'Big River' (released on the album of the same name in 1995), Nail recalls childhood days when the shipyards were in full production, and contrasts them with the recent years of decline:

> ' ... 'Cause that was when coal was King, the river was a living thing
>   and I was just a boy but it was mine, the coaly Tyne
> This was a big river, I want you all to know that I was proud
>
> This was a big river, but that was long ago, that's not now, that's not now ...'

And despite all the doom and gloom of shipyard closure, Nail cannot suppress the desire to end on an optimistic note:

> 'This is a big, big river, and in my heart I know it will rise again,
>   the river will rise again'.

Other currently-famous sons of Tyneside have felt moved to refer to their native river in their work. There is no Geordie who is unfamiliar with that modern-day, light-hearted anthem of the 1970s which proclaims that 'The fog on the Tyne is all mine'. Having proclaimed as much, the authors of the song (the late, great Alan Hull and his band Lindisfarne) give the rest of the song up to comic verses, and make no further reference to the river! Mark Knopfler's lyrics for the band Dire Straits are more serious in nature, but no less fleeting in their references to the Tyne (e.g. 'Southbound again, rolling over the River Tyne').

A more substantial poetic reflection on the post-industrial riverscape of Tyneside has flowed from the pen of Katrina Porteous, who interrogates the 'Team Gut' (the lowermost reach of the River Team, immediately above its confluence with the Tyne in post-industrial Dunston) in twenty-one stanzas[32]. The interrogation covers the geographical nature of the river (what the waters experience on their contemporary journey seawards), the history of its valley (what scenes the Team has witnessed over the centuries), and finally its modest contribution to those generic values which bind us all:

> ' ... *Then what can you know of the grief of men*
> *And women trapped in time?*
> Only their bodies are water, mostly,
> Moving, like mine ....'

With such a substantial canon of music, song and verse from which to draw, contemporary Tyneside folk performers are never short of a verse or two about their native river. Singers who are today in full voice on the life and times of the Tyne include the music hall revivalist, Billy Fane, and myriad enthusiasts for traditional song who gather in the many singaround and 'folk club' sessions in the region. If you would really appreciate the River Tyne in music, song and verse, it is to these people that you must turn. There is, after all, something sad about reading lusty lyrics in print, divorced from the melodies to which they appertain. As an old man of the Hebrides remarked to the Gaelic scholar Alexander Carmichael, after reciting for him a traditional song: "Proud, indeed, shall I be if it give pleasure to yourself, but I should not like cold eyes to read it in a book"[33]. So, if you possibly can, get along to a singalong on Tyneside. My personal favourite sessions are:

○ The Birtley Folk Club, the well-known singaround session organised by the Elliott family, four generations of whom have made major contributions to traditional Geordie song[34]

○ The Ryton Folk Club, which is home to many wonderful singers, including Alan Fitzsimmons[35], who delivers gems of dialect song in his wonderfully rich bass voice.

If you cannot get to hear the music live, then settle for second best and listen to recordings, of which there are many excellent examples, including those of the Elliotts[34] and Alan Fitzsimmons[35] already mentioned. The list could be endless, but amongst my personal favourites I have to mention Johnny Handle,

Bob Fox, and Brian Watson[36]. As a closing personal wish, I hope you find the full, live versions of the songs and poems discussed in this chapter as inspiring as I always have, and that you'll harmonise with the sentiments of the following, final verse of a contemporary Tyneside song:

'... Now as we stand by our river, and our lives float on down to the sea,
they key of the Voice of Tyne changes, now it's singin' for you and for me,
now it's our turn to listen in silence to the eternal songs it might bring,
and it's our turn to capture the motion, and make sure our children can sing,
with the Voice of Tyne, always singin', but always changin' its key,
the Voice of Tyne, still ringin', ringin' the changes,
across the ages, for all its bairns, you and me ...'[37]

DEDICATION

This chapter is affectionately dedicated to the memory of the late Peter Elliott of Birtley (1925–2000)[34]: Marra, mentor, singer, controversialist, and the finest of standard-bearers for Geordie culture. Pete's personal copy of *Allan's Tyneside Songs*[13] (which he gifted to my wife and me in December 1991, as we set off for voluntary work abroad) is amongst my most treasured possessions, and was ever open at my side as I wrote this chapter.

REFERENCES

1. King, A. and Clifford, S. (editors), (2000) *The River's Voice. An Anthology of Poetry.* Common Ground / Green Books, Totnes. 221pp.
2. (a) Charlton, F., Hall, J. and Ross, C. (editors), (1970) *Northumbrian Pipers' Tunebook.* Northumbrian Pipers' Society, Newcastle Upon Tyne. (ISBN 902510 00 2). 52pp. (b) Butler, R. and Hume, B. (1981) *Northumbrian Pipers' Second Tune Book.* Northumbrian Pipers' Society, Newcastle Upon Tyne. (ISBN 0 902510 08 8). 78pp.
3. Collingwood Bruce, J. and Stokoe, J. (editors), (1882) *Northumbrian Minstrelsy. A Collection of the Ballads, Melodies and Small-Pipe Tunes of Northumbria.* Society of Antiquaries of Newcastle upon Tyne, Newcastle Upon Tyne. (Facsimile reprint 1998, Llanerch Publishers, Felinfach; ISBN 1 86143 039 6). 192pp.
4. Dixon, G. (editor), (1987) *The Lads Like Beer. The Fiddle Music of James Hill.* Random Publications, Pathhead (Scotland). (ISBN 0-9511572-05). 52pp.
5. Aneirin, c. 600 AD, *Y Gododdin.* Transcribed and translated into English by A.O.H. Jarman, (1988) *Y Gododdin. Britain's Oldest Heroic Poem.* The Welsh Classics vol. 3. Gomer Press, Llandysul (Dyfed, Wales). (ISBN 0 86383 354 3). 205pp.

6. For the history of the reivers, see: (a) MacDonald Fraser, G. (1971) *The Steel Bonnets. The Story of the Anglo-Scottish Border Reivers.* Barrie and Jenkins, London. (ISBN 0 214 65308 0). 404pp. (b) Watson, G. (1974) *The Border Reivers.* Sandhill Press, Cramlington. (ISBN 0 946098 01 8). 208pp. For their songs, see (*inter alia*) Marsden, J. and Barlow, N. (1991) *The Illustrated Border Ballads : The Anglo-Scottish Frontier.* University of Texas Press. (ISBN 0292738633).

7. Swinburne, A.C. (1925) *Ballads of the English Border.* Heinemann, London.

8. Dickinson, F. (1996) *The Reluctant Rebel - A Northumbrian Legacy of Jacobite Times.* Cresset Books, Newcastle. 108pp.

9. Myers, A. and Forsythe, R. (1999) *W.H. Auden - Pennine Poet.* North Pennines Heritage Trust, Nenthead. (ISBN 0 9513535 78). 60pp.

10. Reed, F. (1999) *The Northumborman. The Dialect Poetry of Fred Reed.* (Foreword by Melvyn Bragg). Iron Press, North Shields. (ISBN 0 906228 71 9). 104pp.

11. Chaplin, S. (1971) *The Smell of Sunday Dinner.* Frank Graham, Newcastle Upon Tyne. 128pp.

12. Learned aurally, from the singing of Doreen Henderson (née Elliott) of Birtley, Co Durham. (See also note 34).

13. Allan, T. (editor), (1891) *Allan's Illustrated Edition of Tyneside Songs and Readings. With Lives, Portraits and Autographs of the Writers, and Notes on the Songs.* (Revised Edition; First Edition was 1862). Thomas and George Allan, Newcastle Upon Tyne. (Reprinted 1972 in facsimile edition, with a new introduction by David Harker, by Frank Graham Publishers, Newcastle Upon Tyne; ISBN 902833 75 8). 578pp.

14. from 'The Metro Song', written by P L Younger in 1982.

15. Polwarth, G.M. (1966) *Folk songs of Northumberland.* Oriel Press Ltd, Newcastle. 47pp.

16. Crawhall, J. (1888) *A Beuk o' Newcassel Sangs.* Published privately, Newcastle Upon Tyne. (Facsimile edition published 1965 by Harold Hill, Newcastle Upon Tyne). 129pp.

17. From memory of original recording.

18. Forster, E. (1970) *The Keelmen.* Frank Graham, Newcastle Upon Tyne. (ISBN 902833 000 6). 31pp.

19. Keys, D. and Smith, K. (1998) *Black Diamonds by Sea. North East Sailing Colliers 1780 – 1880.* Newcastle Libraries and Information Service, Newcastle Upon Tyne. (ISBN 1 85795 019 4). 48pp.

20. Mitchell, A. (1986) *The North East. In* Critchley, J. (editor), *Britain: a view from Westminster.* Blandford Press, Poole.

21. Colls, R. (1977) *The Collier's Rant: Song and culture in the industrial village.* Croom Helm, London. 216pp.

22. Bell, J. (editor), (1812) *Rhymes of Northern Bards. Being a curious collection of old and new songs and poems, peculiar to the Counties of Newcastle Upon Tyne, Northumberland and Durham.* Angus and Son, Newcastle Upon Tyne. (Reprinted 1970 in facsimile edition, with a new introduction by David Harker, by Frank Graham Publishers, Newcastle Upon Tyne).

23. Harker, D. (1973) *George Ridley. Gateshead Poet and Vocalist.* Frank Graham, Newcastle Upon Tyne. (ISBN 902833 81 2). 48pp.

24. Davitt, J. (1993) *Shipyard Muddling and More Muddling by Ripyard Cuddling. (The Poems of Tyneside Shipyard Worker Jack Davitt).* North Tyneside Libraries, North Shields. (ISBN 0 906529 13 1). 75pp.

25. Taylor, H. (1992) *Sporting Heroes. In* Colls, R. and Lancaster, B. *Geordies - Roots of Regionalism.* Edinburgh University Press, Edinburgh. pp. 113 - 130.

26. Wilson, J. (1890) *Tyneside Songs and Drolleries.* Collected and edited by Thomas Allan. T & G Allan Publishers, Newcastle Upon Tyne. 472pp.

27. Purdon, J. (1998) *'The Echo of Pit Boots'. Pitwork, Politics and Poetry - The Collected Songs and Poems of Jock Purdon.* The Common Trust, North Shields. 166pp.

28. For the lyrics of Armstrong's many songs, see: (a) Armstrong, W.H. (editor), (1930) *Song book containing 25 popular songs of the late Thomas Armstrong compiled by his son W H Armstrong.* Noel Wilson Publishers, Chester-le-Street. 42pp. (b) Forbes, R. (editor), (1987) *Polisses and Candymen. The Complete Works of Tommy Armstrong, the Pitman Poet.* Tommy Armstrong Trust, Stanley. 75pp. (The latter work also includes melody lines and a biography of Armstrong).

29. Manuscript copy in the possession of the author; this song has already entered the traditional canon and is widely sung in local folk clubs.

30. Davitt, J. (2001*) Geordie Muddling by Ripyard Cuddling.* The People's History, Seaham. (ISBN 1902527763). 128pp.

31. Goodall, S. (editor), (1995) *North East Poets.* Arrival Press, Peterborough. (ISBN 1 85786 370 4).

32. This poem is reproduced in the book 'The River's Voice' (see ref. 1 above).

33. De Waal, E. (editor), (1988) *The Celtic Vision. Selections from the Carmina Gadelica, orally collected in the Highlands and Islands of Scotland by Alexander Carmichael.* Darton, Longman and Todd, London. (ISBN 0-232-51811-4). 263pp.

34. For some appreciation of the centrality of the Elliott family of Birtley to the preservation and development of North Eastern traditional music, see the following references: (a) Watson, I. (1983) *Song and democratic culture in Britain. An approach to popular culture in social movements.* Croom Helm, London. (ISBN 0-7099-2770-3). (see especially pages 37 - 38 and 42). (b) Lloyd, A.L. (editor), (1978) *'Come all ye bold miners'. Ballads and songs of the coalfields.* Lawrence and Wishart, London. (ISBN 85315 537 2). 384pp. (c) Bean, D. (1963) The singing miners. *Coal Quarterly,* Spring 1963, pp 7 - 9. The following classic recordings should also not be missed: (i) *The Elliotts of Birtley - a musical portrait of a Durham Mining Family.* Recorded by Ewan MacColl and Peggy Seeger (1969, Transatlantic Records, Cat. No. XTRA 1091). (ii) *Jack Elliott of Birtley - songs and stories of a Durham miner.* (1969, Trailer Records / Leader Sound, Halifax / London, Cat. No. LEA 4001).

35. Alan Fitzsimmons' singing can be heard on the CD album: *Old Wood is Best.* Alan Fitzsimmons (1998, Keel Music, Cat. No. FITZ014).

36. The fine traditional singing of Brian Watson can be heard on the CD album: *'Where Ivvor heh thi gone?' Songs of the Northern Bards.* Brian Watson (2001, Old and New Tradition, Cat. No. ONTCD2004).

37. 'Voice of Tyne', written in 1986 by P L Younger, on the occasion of the Tyne Tall Ships Race.

GENERAL INDEX

Figures in **bold** refer to illustrations; **'P'** refers to colour plates.

95% flow, 12, 13

abstraction licence, 2
acid streamflow, 41, 72, 85, 106, 107
Acts of Parliament
  Control of Pollution Act
  1974, 115
  Environment Act 1995, 55
  Electricity Act 1989, 153
  General Highways Act 1555,
  212
  Municipal Corporations
  Reform Act 1835, 180
  Public Health Act 1846, 113
  Reservoirs Act 1975, 16
  River Prevention of
  Pollution Act 1951, 114
  Rivers Pollution Prevention
  Act 1876, 110, 114
  Rivers Prevention of Pollution
  Act 1961, 114, 115
  Salmon Fisheries Act 1861,
  80
  Statute of Bridges 1531, 212
  Town and Country
  Planning Act 1990, 46
  Town and Country
  Planning Act 1947, 45
  Tyne Fisheries Act 1842, 80
  Tyne Improvement Act
  1850, 185
  Water Act 1973, 110, 113,
  143
  Water Act 1989, 106, 152
  Water Resources Act 1963,
  139
Adamsez Works, **197**
afforestation, 12, 14, 15, 40-41, 85
Agenda 21, 2
aggradation, 37
alevin, **78**
algae, 63, 86
Alhusen's Chemical Wks., **197**
alien invaders, xi, 69-72
alkali manufacture, 76, 117, 196,
197
ammonia, 82, **83**, 106, 115, 117,
118, 133, 198
angling, 73, 75, 76, 90-104, 226
armouring, 40, 154
Armstrong Works, 187, 203, 223
Auden, W.H., 240

ballads, 236-244
ballast, 175, 177, 185, 194
ballast industries, 195-198
Baltic Centre, xii, 123, 136, 199
base level, 30,31

benzole, 195
Bewick, Thomas, xiii, 75, 226-233
biochemical oxygen demand, 106,
110, 114, 115, 117, 119, 133
biodiversity, xi, 72
Birtley Folk Club, 260
Blackett Beaumont WB Lead, 202
'Blaydon Races', 255
Blue Flag Award, 135
boat building (rowing), 161-162
braided river, 36, 37, 39
breweries, **117**
bridges
  Allensford, 213,
  Alston, 213
  Armstrong, 223
  Bellingham, 211, 217
  Blackhall Mill, 216
  Blaydon A1 Bypass, 31, 224
  bridgescape, ix, **P1, P2**
  Burnstones Viaduct, 221
  Byker, 223, 224
  Bywell, 212, 221
  Causey Arch, 218
  Chollerford, 210, 213
  Corbridge, 207, 210, 211, 213,
  214
  Dilston, 211, 213
  East Woodburn, **P24**
  Erring, 213
  Falstone, 221
  Featherstone, 213
  Gateshead Millennium, xii,
  123, 136, 225, 258, **P2**
  Gosforth, 213
  Haltwhistle viaduct, 221
  Haydon Bridge, 210, 213
  Hexham A69, 53
    Blackett/Gott's, 52, 215
    Border Counties Rail, 53,
    221
    Smeaton's, 215, 216
    Mylne, 53, 54, 79, 93, 98,
    216, **P11, P12**
  Kielder Viaduct, 221
  Lambley Viaduct, 62, 221
  Linnels, 213
  Little Shotley, 213
  Newburn, 213, 223
  Newcastle High level, 161,
    219, 222, 223, 224, 258
    King Edward, 224
    Mylne's Tyne Bridge, 181,
    186, 212, 219, 223, 258
    Newcastle Old Tyne Bridge,
    172, 191, 210-212, 219
    Newcastle Swing Bridge,
    161, 186, **188**, 203, 212,

    222, 223, 224
    Newcastle Tyne Bridge
    (1928), 224, 225, 241
    Redheugh, 218-221, 221-224
    Tyne Metro Bridge
  Ouseburn, 219
  Ovingham, 54, 223
  Prudhoe Castle, 211
  Ridley Hall, 207, 214
  Roman, 209, 211
  Sandyford, 213
  Scotswood, 161, **197**, 218,
  219, 224
  stone-arch, xii, 207, 208
  suspension, xii, 216-218
  Warden, **217**, 219
  West Wylam, 221, **P25**
  Whitfield, 217
  Willington, 219, **220**
  Wylam, 56, 207
British Canoe Union, 167
British Steel Corp., 147
brown trout, 84, 86, 92, 93, 100,
115
brown trout flies and lures, 100
buried valley, 31
Burston, U., 144
Bye Report, 20, 21

caddis fly, 63
Calvert Trust, **166**
canals, 175-176, 213
canoeing, xii, 154, 157, 160, 166-
169, **P23**
Canoeing Access Agreement, 169
caravans, 20-22
Carmichael, J.W., xiii
carp, 70
catchment, 29-30
Chambers, Bob, 158, 159, 254
Chaplin, Sid, 241, 244
Chaytor, A.H., 91, 101, **102**
chemical industries, xii, 190, 196-
198, 251, 256
cholera, xi, 106, 112, 140
Cholera Commission 1854, 111,
112, 115
chub, 93
Clasper, Harry, 158, 159, 162, 236,
254
climate, 3, 5, 6
climate change, 29, 36
coal chutes, **176**
coal drops, 110, **179**, 186
coal gasworks, 117
coal trade, xii, 109, 173-175, 188,
190-195
'Coaly Tyne', xiii, 243-253

coarse fish, 61, 73, 74, 84, 93, 95
cobles, 81
coke trade, 195
coke works, 76, 77, 79, 82, 117
collier brig, **176**, **179**, 191, 193, 194, 244, 245
collier, screw, 185, 187
colliery railways, 192
compensation flow, 12, 85, 149, 154
consents to discharge, 2, 114, 115
conveyance, 55
cormorants, 86, 93
corn mills, 190, 198, 199
Corvan, Ned, 255, 256
country dance music, 234-236
coypu, 69
crayfish, 66, **67**, 68
Crowley Ironworks, 199
cumecs, 1, 8
current meter, 2
'Cushy Butterfield', 250, 255
Custom House, 183
cyanide, 106, 117, 118, 121
cycle of erosion, 29, 30
cycling routes, 170

dace, 74, 88, 93
dams, 10-12
data, 1, 2, 10
data management, 2
Davitt, Jack, 252, 258, 259
deforestation, 35
deltas, 32
demand forecasting, 138, 146-148
Derwent Sailing Club, **165,** 169, **P22**
Derwentwater, Earl of, 239
development control, 22-23
direct supply reservoir, 10
discharge, 1
dissolved oxygen, 12, 61, 82, **83**, 106, 124
domestic water demand, **146**
Dove Marine Lab., 124
dredging, 24, 33, 45, 52, 56, **57**, 113, 134, 184, 186, 203, 244
drift, 60
drift nets, 77, 80-82, 89
drought, 10, 12, 36, 60, 61, 101, 149, 151, 155, 165
dynamic equilibrium, 33

Earth Summit, 2
Easter Floods 1998, 16, 20
ecological diversity, 55, 56
ecology, x, 10, 12, 34, 40, 41, 52, 55, 59-72, 138
elbow of capture, 32
electricity supply, 205
Elliot, Pete, 256, 261
Emery, Robert, 248-249
Environment Agency, 2, 16-17, 19-23, 26-27, 46, 55, 86-88, 93, 97, 98, 118, 121, 133, 134, 143, 152, 153

eskers, 32
estuarine barrages, 143
estuarine muds, 84, 119, 120, 134
EU Bathing Waters Directive, 132, 135, 136
EU Water Framework Directive, 16, 41
EU Urban Wastewater Directive, 134, 136
European Capital of Culture, 136
evapotranspiration, 6, 10
Fane, Billy, 260

ferries, 209, **210**, 217, 223, 232
filter beds, 114
fish counter, 88, 95, **96**
fish kills, 82, 83, 98, 100, 121
fish microtags, 92, 97
fish passes, 54, 56, 80, 84, 87, 88
fish spawning, 61
fish traps, 74, 75
fisheries, xi, 73-89
'fisherman's mantra', 14
fishing beats, 92, 98, 99
fishing clubs, 94-95
fishing licences, 81, 88, 90, 94
fishing season, 95
fishing tackle, 99-100
'Fitters', 191-192
floods and flooding, 16-28
flash floods, 8
flood losses, 16
flood breach, 18, 19, **P6**
Flood control room, 16, 18
flood defence, xiv, 17, 45, 55
flood embankment, 17-19, 22-25
flood forecasting, 2, 7, 8, 25-27
flood history, 16-17, 24
flood insurance, 16
Flood of 1771, 52, 212-215
Flood of 1955, 50, 53, 54
flood risk, 155
flood storage, 22-24
flood travel time, 26
flood warning, 2, 16, 18, 22, 25-28
flood wave, **7**, 8, 25, 26, **27**
Floodline, 28
floodplain, xiv, 8, 18, 23, 24, 29, 30, 55, 108
flow duration curve, 12, **13**
flow regime, 1, 10, 59, 69
flow variability, 14, 40, 41
fluoride, 63, 142
fords
    Crossgate, 51, 55
    Haltwhistle, 208
    Hexham, 209
Forestry Commission, 51
Frostbite Challenge, 167
fungi, 63, 66

gas industry, 205
Gateshead Garden Festival, 132, 189

gauging station, 1, 2, **4**, 17, 25, 50, **P3**
geology, 30, 107
geomorphology, 29-43
glaciation, 30, 32. 35
glass industries, xii, 190, 196
global warming, 36, 84
goosanders, 86, 93
graded river, 31
gravel bed rivers, 44, 60
gravel extraction, 24, 39-40, 44-58, 72, 76, 79, 86, 88, 98, 115
grayling, 93
greenhouse gases, 36
grilse, **78**, 97
groundwater, 6, 12
groynes, 54, 74, 75

Himalayan balsam, 71, **P13**
'Hands off flow', 150
heavy metals, 59, 106, 119, 133
helliborine, 64
Hemy, B.B., xiii
Heslop, R.O., 250, 255
Hexham Canoe Club, 169
Hexham Rowing Club, 163
hogweed (giant), 70, **P13**
hornpipe, 235
'Hostmen', 174, 191, 192
Hurricane Charlie, 21
hushing, 38, 108, 201
hydraulic modelling, 6, 55
hydrograph, 6, 14
hydrological cycle, 6
hydrological personality, 1
hydrological regime, 1, 6, 36, 40. 107
hydropower, 10, 40, 139, 153

Ice Age, 30, 36, 73, 79
ice cores, 36
Indicative floodplain maps, 22
industrial water demand, 146
instars, 60, 68
Irish famine, 111

Jacobite rebellions, 239-240
Japanese knotweed, 70, **P14**
jet skis, 167, **168**, 170
Jobling, Will, 256
'John Bowes', 185, 194, 195

kames, 32
'Keel row', 242-243, 245
keels and keelmen, 172, **176**-178, 182, 186, 192, 199, 202, 241-251, 255
kelts, 74, 87, 102
Kielder Dam, 40, 84, 85, 101, 138, 258, **P20**
Kielder Fish Hatchery, 82, 84, 92, 101, **166**
Kielder Forest, 3, 14, 40, 69, 72, 85, 144

Kielder Inquiry, 13, 84, 86, 139, 144-146, 148, 149, 150, 152, 155, 165
Kielder Objections, 144-145, 147-148
Kielder Operating Agreement, 152
Kielder releases, 13, 82, 83, 93, 97, 119, 120, 143, 152, 153, **154**, **P20**
Kielder Scheme, xi, 2, 12, 13, 14, 138-156, 205
Kielder transfers, **148**, 150-151, 155
Kielder tunnel, 120, 130
Kielder Water, xii, 18, 23-24, 51, 72, 84, 85, **116**, 165-167, **P19**, **P21**
Kielder Water Order, 144-145, 153
Kielder Water Sailing Club, 166
Kielder Yacht Club, 166
knickpoint, 31, 32

'Laws of Newcastle', xii, 172
lead industries, 201-202
lead mills, 190
lead mining, 38, 62, 63, 76, 77, 107, **108**, 119, 201, 240
Leblanc process, 196
lichens, 38, 62
lifeboats, 204
limpet, 62-63
Lindisfarne, 260
Little Ice Age, 37, 74, 226, 227
longitudinal profile, 30, **31**
low flow, 12-14
Lyonnaise des Eaux, 143

Maling's, 195
marina villages, 189
Mauretania, **204**
mayfly, 63
meander, 29, 30, 35, **P9**
meltwater channels, 32
Met Office, 25
metal tolerant plants, 38, 63-64, 108
microhabitats, 60, 62
microtagging, 85
middens, 114, 115
midges, 68, 166
mine pumping engines, 192
minewater, 141
minewater drainage, 86, 108, **109**, 110
minimum maintained flow, 149-150
mink, 69, 86
minnows, 93
monkey flower, 71
moorland drainage, 12, 14, 15, 41, 85
Mosaic Law, 110-111
mosses, 61, 62
Mougeotia, 64, 109

Nail, Jimmy, 259
National Flood Warning Centre, 27
National Rivers Authority, 16-18, 133, 143, 152, 153

navigation, 55, 56, 172-189
netties, 114
Newcastle and Gateshead Water Co., 112, 141, 143
Newcastle Corporation, 174, 180-184, 212
Newcastle Fire Office, 112, 139
Newcastle Subscription Water Co., 140
Newcastle Univ. Rowing Club, 163
nightsoil, 114
noctule bat, 92
Non fossil fuel obligation, 153
North East Water, 113, 143, 152
North Pennine Orefield, 201
North Shields Water Co., 141
North Tyne Preservation Soc., 144
Northumberland County Council, 45, 50, 53, 54
Northumberland Dock, 128, 131, 185
Northumbria Univ. Rowing Club, 163
Northumbrian River Authority, 13, 16, 45, 84, 86, 139, 144, 147, 165
Northumbrian smallpipes, 234-235, 251
Northumbrian Water, 8, 13, 16, 17, 113, 133, 134, 143, 152, 153
Nunn, R., 246
nutrient levels, 59

OFWAT, 137
oil tankers, 203
otters, 62, 92, 103
outriggers, 162

paint manufacture, 190
palaeo channels, 39
Palmers shipyard, 194, 203
paper mills, 190, 199-200
Paradise, ix-xiv
parr, **78**, 82, 84, 85, 86
pearl mussel, 62, 64, **65, 66**
peedee, 245, 249, 250
peneplain, 29
penny-cress, 64
perch, 93
pesticides, 106
piers, 180, 187
pike, 86
pipe and fiddle tunes, xiii, 234-236
planning authority, 20, 22
poaching, 76, 82, 88
pollutant spills, 2, 12
pollution, 61, 105-122, 123-137
pollution – definition, 105-106
pollution, domestic, 110-115
pollution, industrial, 115-118
pollution, thermal, 118
polycyclic landscape, 30, 31
port, 172-189
Port of Tyne Authority, 169, 189
Porteous, Katrina, 260

pottery industries, 190, 195
power boating, 157, 167
predators (of fish), 76
privatisation, 2, 17, 127, 143, 152, 153
privies, 111
put-and-take fisheries, 93

Quaternary Era, 30, 32

rabbits, 17-20, 69
radar rainfall, 18, 25
railway companies, 47, 180, 181, 186, 187
rainbow trout, 70
rainfall, 1, 3, 6, **7**, 10, 27, 85
rainfall map, **5**
raingauge, 3, **5**, 18, 25, **P4**
rant, 235
roach, 74
rating curve, 2
Reed, Fred, 241
regatta, 158, 163, 165
regulating reservoir, 10, 144
reivers, 237
Renforth, James, 158, 159, **160**, 254, 255
reservoir yield, 144, 149, 150
return period, 22, 23
Richardson, T.M., xiii
Ridley, Geordie, 255
riffle and pool, 35, 40, 54, 55, 56, 60, 90
River Boards, 45, 55, 56, 81
river borne diseases, 106, 111-113
river capture, 32
river channel, 29-43
river landforms, 29-30
river processes, 24, 33-35
river regulation, 40
river restoration, 34, 41
river terraces, 39, 49
River Tyne Recreational Users Group, 169
Rivercall, 97
roe deer, 92
Roman waterworks, 141, **142**
romantic songs, 236-244
ropemaking, xii, 190, 203-205, **220**
rowing, xii, 54, 157-164, 253
rowing, amateur, 162-164
rowing, origins, 157
rowing, world championships, 158, 159, 164
Royal Commission 1972, 115,
Royal Commission on Sewage Disposal, 114
Royal Quays, 136
Ryton Folk Club, 260

SACs, 64
Sage Music Centre, 123, 136
sailing, xii, 157, 164, 167, **P22**
sailmaking, 203
salmon, xi, 73-89

salmon colonisation, 73
salmon disease (UDN), 101
salmon flies and lures, 99-100
salmon life cycle, **78**
salmon migration, 75, 77, 80, 82, 84, 88, 89, 110, 115, 119, 120, 134, 136
salmon nets, 74, 75
salmon, 75, 101-103, **102**
salmon rod catches, **79, 83**
salmon sea net fishery, 77, 80-82, 86
salmon spawning, 40, 45, 55, 84-86, 154
salmon stocking, 82, 85
salt, 202
sanitation, 111, 113
Scott, Sir Walter, 238
scour, 52
sculling, 158, 159, 161
sea level, 30, 31, 36
sea net fishery, 77, 80-82
sea trout, 75, 77, 81, 92, 95, 97, 98, 100, 103
sea outfalls, 128, 133
seals, 92
seasonal flow, 6, 8, **9**, 10
sediment movement, 29, 30, 33
sediment erosion, 45, 53-54
sewage disposal, 113, 127
sewage treatment
    definition, 114
    preliminary, 114, 127
    primary, 127
    secondary, 114, 119, 127, 135
shipbuilding, xii, 187, 190, 203-**204**
slaughterhouses, 112, 115, 116
sludge, 127, 128, 134
Smeaton, John, 208, 212, 214-216
Smith, T. Dan, 41
smolts, 77, **78**, 82, 84, 86, 110
snow cover, 17
snow pillow, 3
snow water equivalent, 6
snowberry, 71
snowmelt, 1, 3, 6

Solvay process, 198
source, 30, **P7**
South Shields Sailing Club, 167, **168**
spates, 14
spills, accidental, 120-121
sporting songs, 253-255
'springers', 95, **96**, 97
SSSIs, 64
St Bede, 255
stage, 2
staiths, **176**-178, 181, 186, 187, 192, 193
statutory minimum flow, 2, 11, **12**
Stephenson's birthplace, 56
stillwater fisheries, 93
Sting, 259
stonefly, 63
stream power, 32
Sunderland and South Shields Water Co., 141, 142, 143, 148, 164
sustainability, xiii, 41, 154
Sustrans, 170
Swinburne A C., 238, 241

Tall Ships Race, 135, 189, **P18**
tanneries, 112, 115, **116**
telemetry, 2, 3, 18
Tertiary Era, 32, 36
tidal flow, 112, 118-119
tidal limit, 31, 55, 56
timescale, 29, 34
tourism,155, 167, **P21**
Trinity House, 180, 190
'Turbinia', 203
Turner, J.M., xiii
turnpike trusts, 213-216
Tuxedo Royale, 135
Tyne Angler's Code of Practice, 101
Tyne Head Race, 163
Tyne Improvement Commission, xii, 56, 185-187, 193, 221, 223, 224
Tyne Rowing Club, 162, 163, **168**

Tyne Tour (canoeing), 169
Tyne tug, 193
Tyne Valley Canoe Club, 169
Tyne zoning policy, 169
Tynemouth Corporation, 141
Tynemouth Rowing Club, 163, **168**
Tynemouth Sailing Club, 167, **168**
Tyneside Environmental Concern, 148
Tyneside Interceptor Sewer, 101, 119, 129-131, **130**, 133
Tyneside Joint Sewerage Board, 126, 128
Tyneside Sewerage Scheme, ix, 82, **130,** 123-137

waggonways, 176, 192, 193, 218
Walker Alkali Works, 196
washlands, 24, 45
water crowfoot, 62
'Water of Tyne', 241
water powered industries, 198-201
Water Resources Board, 143
water resources planning, 143-148
water skiing, 157, 167, 170
water temperature, 12, 84
watersports, 157-170
weirs, 74, 87
wet dock, 185
wherries, 157
Whittle Dean Water Co, 140
Wilson, Joe, 234, 254, 255
windsurfing, 157, 166
woody debris, 60-62
wool trade, 173-174
woollen mills, 190, 200-201
wrack, 60-62

Younger Dryas, 36, 73
zinc mining, 62, 63, 107, 109, 114
zinc pollution, 63-64

PLACENAMES INDEX

Note: References to Tyne, North Tyne, South Tyne and Newcastle omitted, being too numerous.

Figures in **bold** refer to illustrations; **'P'** refers to colour plates.

Acomb, 51,110
Albert Edward Dock, 185, 188
Alnwick, 151
Alston, 7, 8, **9**, 26, **27**, 30, 64, 170, 213, 219
Amble, 180
Arthur's Hill, 140
Bardon Mill, 198, 200
Barrasford, 147
Bellingham, 25, 96, 169, 170, 235
Bellister, **47**, 48, 51, 54
Benwell, 172, 173
Bishop Auckland, 151
Black Burn, 36
Blackhall Mill, 84
Blagill, **39**, 64
Blanchland, 201
Blaydon, 56, 77, 131, 186, 187, 195, 202, 241, 243
Blyth, 177
Briardene, 133
Broomhaugh, 98
Broomhouse, 36
Bywell, 7, 8, **9**, 10, 12, **13**, 24, 26, **27**, 35, **47**, 48, 49, 75, 86, **87**, 94, 95, 200, 239
Cambois, 147
Capheaton, 238
Catton, 87
Causey Burn, 257
Cherryburn, 226-228, 232
Chesters, 95, 96, 99, 100
Chipchase Castle, 95, 96
Chirdon Burn, 40
Chollerford, 88, 95, 169, 238, 239, 241
Chopwell, 199
Coalburn, 14, 41
Cockshaw Burn, 115
Consett, 12, 117
Consett Iron Works, 84, 187, 188
Corbridge, 18, 19, 24, 25, 75, 94, 200, 226
Countesspark, 96, 100
Cow Green, 3
Coxlodge, 112, 139
Crawcrook, 227
Cross Fell, 3, 97
Derwenthaugh, 117-118, 131, 132, 170, 195
Derwenthaugh Coke Works, 12, 78, 84
Derwenthaugh Staiths, 187
Devils Water, 32, 87, 202, 239
Dilston, 239

Dowgang Hush, 108
Dunston, 49, 118, 128, 129, 131, 164, 170, 206
Dunston Staiths, 187, 189
Eals, 36, 97
East Dipton, 32
Ebchester, 32
Eddys Bridge, **11**
Elsdon, 170
Elsdon Burn, 65
Elswick, 112, 113, 117, 141, 163, 173, 187, 189, 203, 205, 223
Eltringham, 226, 228, 232
Erick Burn, 113
Erring Burn, 68
Falstone, 51
Featherstone, 17, 26, **27**, 36
Felling, 115, 135, 199
Fourstones, 24, 40, **47**, 48, 51, 54, 55, 199, 200
Gateshead, xii, 35, 111, 112, 123, 128, 131, 141, 160, 173, 196, **197**, 200, 236
Gibside, 199
Glenwelt, 213
Greenlee Lough, 164
Haltwhistle, 17, 18, 24, 25, **47**, 48, 51, 54, 88, 170, 198, 199, 200, 201, 219, **P5**
Hartlepool, 143
Haughton Castle, 199
Hauxley, 73
Haydon Bridge, 3, 7, 8, **9**, 17, 24, 26, **27**, **47**, 48, 51, 88, 94, 97, 169
Hebburn, 135, 141, 249-252, 257
Hedwin Streams, 56
Hesleyside, 62
Hexham, 3, 24, 37, **47**, 48, 50, 51, 53, 78, 88, 94, 95, 115, 163, 164, 169, 175, 237
Houxty Burn, 87
Howdon, xi, 82, 83, 89, 119, 128, 131, 134, 185, **P17**
Jarrow, 125, 128, 130, 131, 141, 172, 188, 194, 200, 247, 250, 253, 255, 256
Jarrow Slake, 188
Kibblesworth, 110
Kielder Burn, 8, **9**, 72
Kings Meadows Island, 56, 158, 186, 247
Knar Burn, 36
Knarsdale, 36
Lambley, 36, 64
Lemington, 158, 186, 196, 225

Lintzford, 199
Lipwood, 97
Longtown, 51
Lort Burn, 113
Melkridge, 97
Merryshields, 49, 50, 51, 94
Mickley, ix, 46, 226, 227
Mickley Junction, **47**, 48, 49, **50**, 54
Middlesbrough, 180
Mosswood T.W., 10, 142, 151
Nenthead, 108
Newburn, 56, 119, 120, 134, 141, 163, 164, 170, 175, 200
Ninebanks, 64
North Pennine Orefield, 63
North Shields, 81, 141, 173, 174, 183, 184, 187, 202, 218, 251
North Shields Fish Quay, 187
Norwood, 78
Nunwick, 96
Otterburn, 24
Otterstone, 144
Ouseburn, **9**, 41, 195, 199, 201
Ovingham, 24, **47**, 48, 49, 70, 74, 75, 94, 114, 141, 226, 228, 232, **P13**
Ovington, ix, 35
Pandon Burn, 113
Pandon Dene, 195
Parkend, 96
Priors Haven, 163
Prudhoe, 18, 24, 37, 74, 114, 118, 119, 132, 169, 170, 198, 200
Reaverhill, 8, **9**, 10, 13
Red Burn, 99, 110
Redebridge, 2, **9**, **P3**
Redesdale, 237
Redesmouth, 32, 65
Redheugh, 117, 205, 219
Reivers Well, 93
Reservoirs
   Balderhead, 144
   Burnhope, 142
   Catcleugh, **140**, 141
   Colt Crag, **140**, 141
   Cow Green, 144
   Derwent, xii, 10, 12, 84, 142, 151, 164
   East Hallington, 47, **140**, 141
   Font, 141
   Little Swinburn, **140**, 141
   Scaling, 164
   Selset, 144, 151
   Tunstall, 151
   West Hallington, **140**, 141

Riding Mill, 13, 88, 92, 95, 98, 138
Ridley Hall, 97, 169
Rivers
  Allen, 169
  Blyth, 32, 33, 68
  Cocker, 44
  Coquet, 94, 144, 151
  Derwent, 10, 11, 12, 64, 84, 86,
    93, 95, **108**, 117, 120, 121, 138,
    150, 151, 198, 201, 236
  Don, 115, 130
  East Allen, 63, 87, 202
  Eden, 14
  Irthing, 14, 41, 144, 150
  Nent, 39, 63, 64, 107, **108**
  Pont, 68, 141
  Rede, 2, 3, 24, **31**, 32, **33**, 65, 85,
    86, 93, 94, 96, 97, 141
  Severn, 8, 26
  Team, 32, **33**, 34, 41, 110, 117,
    257, 260
  Tees, 17, 107, 138, 150, 151
  Trent, 26, 30, 93, 114
  Tweed, 17, 30, 76, 82, 99
  Wansbeck, 32, 141
  Warwickshire Avon, 21
  Wear, 14, 17, 32, **33**, 107, 138,
    150, 186

West Allen, 63, 64, 107, **108**, 202
  Yorkshire Ouse, 24, 26
Rowley Burn, 32
Ryal, 141
Ryton, 32, **47**, 56, 70, 108, 125, 131,
  132, 163, 164, 224
Sandgate, 111, 139, 245, 251
Scotswood, 163, 173, 187, 196, **197**,
  228
Shotley Bridge, 200
South Shields, 81, 120, 141, 172,
  173, 180, 181, 183, 184, 186, 196,
  199, 202, 204, 218
Spechells, 118
St Anthonys, 195
St Peter's Marina, 167
Stanley Burn, 75
Stella, 118, 186, 206
Stella Power Station, 77
Stocksfield, 46, 200
Swalwell, 199, 200
Tanfield, 218, 257
Tarset Burn, 40, 87
Team Valley, 200
Team Valley Trading Est., 49, 131
Thinhope Burn, 37
Town Moor, 173

Tyne Dock, 186, 187, 188
Tynemouth, 75, 80, 133, 135, 141,
  172, 173, 189, 190, 248, 258
Walker, 117, 118, 196
Wallsend, 125, 172, 251, 252, 259
Warden, 24, **47**, 48, 51, 237
Warden Gorge, 31, 169
Wark, 69, 169
Warks Burn, 32, **33**, 68
Warkworth T.W., 151
Waters meet, 65, 99
West Hartlepool, 180
West Woodburn, 24, 32, 86
Westerhope, 173
Wharnley, 64
Whichkham, 131, 173
Whickhope, **166**
Whitehill Point, 180, 188
Whitley Bay, 128, 133, 135
Whittle Burn, 49
Whittonstall, 32
Williamston, 36, 64
Willimontswick, 97, 99
Willington, 199
Winlaton Mill, 84, 86
Wylam, **47**, 48, 49, 56, 88, 94, 95,
  97, 98, 141, 195, 228, **P14**